GW00775691

ANALYSIS,
DESIGN
AND
APPLICATIONS
OF
FIN LINES

The Artech House Microwave Library

Introduction to Microwaves by Fred E. Gardiol

Microwaves Made Simple: Principles and Applications by W. Stephen Cheung and Frederic H. Levien

Microwave Tubes by A. S. Gilmour, Jr.

Electric Filters by Martin Hasler and Jacques Neirynck

Nonlinear Circuits by Martin Hasler and Jacques Neirynck

Microwave Technology by Erich Pehl

Receiving Systems Design by Stephen J. Erst

Microwave Mixers by Stephen A. Maas

Feedback Maximization by B.J. Lurie

Applications of GaAs MESFETs by Robert Soares, et al.

GaAs Processing Techniques by Ralph E. Williams

GaAs FET Principles and Technology by James V. DiLorenzo and Deen D. Khandelwal

Dielectric Resonators, Darko Kajfez and Pierre Guillon, eds.

Modern Spectrum Analyzer Theory and Applications by Morris Engelson

Design Tables for Discrete Time Normalized Lowpass Filters by Arild Lacroix and Karl-Heinz Witte

Microwave Materials and Fabrication Techniques by Thomas S. Laverghetta

Handbook of Microwave Testing by Thomas S. Laverghetta

Microwave Measurements and Techniques by Thomas S. Laverghetta

Principles of Electromagnetic Compatibility by Bernhard E. Keiser

Linear Active Circuits: Design and Analysis by William Rynone, Jr.

The Design of Impedance-Matching Networks for Radio-Frequency and Microwave Amplifiers by Pieter L.D. Abrie

Microwave Filters, Impedance Matching Networks, and Coupling Structures by G.L. Matthaei, Leo Young, and E.M.T. Jones

Analysis, Design, and Applications of Fin Lines by Bharathi Bhat and Shiban Koul

Microwave Engineer's Handbook, 2 vol., Theodore Saad, ed.

Handbook of Microwave Integrated Circuits by R.K. Hoffmann

Microwave Integrated Circuits, Jeffrey Frey and Kul Bhasin, eds.

Computer-Aided Design of Microwave Circuits by K.C. Gupta, Ramesh Garg, and Rakesh Chadha

Microstrip Lines and Slotlines by K.C. Gupta, R. Garg, and I.J. Bahl

Advanced Mathematics for Practicing Engineers by Kurt Arbenz and Alfred Wohlhauser

Microstrip Antennas by I.J. Bahl and P. Bhartia

Antenna Design Using Personal Computers by David M. Pozar

Microwave Circuit Design Using Programmable Calculators by J. Lamar Allen and Max Medley, Jr.

Stripline Circuit Design by Harlan Howe, Jr.

Microwave Transmission Line Filters by J.A.G. Malherbe

Electrical Characteristics of Transmission Lines by W. Hilberg

Microwave Diode Control Devices by Robert V. Garver

Tables for Active Filter Design by Mario Biey and Amedeo Premoli

Active Filter Design by Arthur B. Williams

Laser Applications by W.V. Smith

Ferrite Control Components, 2 vol., Lawrence Whicker, ed.

Microwave Remote Sensing, 3 vol., by F.T. Ulaby, R.K. Moore, and A.K. Fung

ANALYSIS, DESIGN AND APPLICATIONS OF FIN LINES

Bharathi
Bhat

Shiban K.
Koul

Artech House

Library of Congress Cataloging-in-Publication Data

Bhat, Bharathi.
   Analysis, design, and applications of fin lines.

   Bibliography: p.
   Includes index.
   1. Microwave integrated circuits.   2. Microwave
transmission lines.   I. Koul, Shiban K.   II. Title.
TK7876.B498 1987   621.381'73   86-71905
ISBN 0-89006-195-5

Copyright © 1987

ARTECH HOUSE, INC.
685 Canton Street
Norwood, MA 02062

International Standard Book Number: 0-89006-195-5
Library of Congress Catalog Card Number: 86-71905

10 9 8 7 6 5 4 3 2 1

Dedicated to Our Parents

Contents

Preface

The *fin line* was introduced as a viable transmission line for millimeter-wave applications in the early 1970s. Since then, significant advances have taken place in fin-line techniques as well as component technology. With its many advantages compared with the microstrip line—namely, low-loss performance, less stringent tolerance requirements, compatibility with waveguides, and ease of E-plane integration with other forms of transmission lines—the fin line has been recognized as an important transmission medium for millimeter-wave integrated circuits. Fin-line techniques are now fairly well established, as is evident from the numerous recent publications reporting the development of fin-line and other E-plane components to operate in the frequency range of 30 to 140 GHz and, in special cases, even up to 170 GHz.

The bulk of the literature on the fin line has emerged during the mid-1970s to mid-1980s, and is mostly comprised of papers published in various technical journals and symposia digests. While the foundation for fin-line techniques in millimeter-wave circuits has been well laid, their potential applications in diverse fields such as radar, communication, and radiometry continue to grow. The authors believe that the time is ripe for consolidating the information published thus far in the form of a book, which can serve as a single reference for further research and development in this fast growing technology. Another motivation for writing this book has been the authors' involvement in teaching a special graduate-level course on millimeter-wave integrated circuits at the Indian Institute of Technology, New Delhi, India. The efforts applied to the preparation of the course material on fin-line techniques, which formed more than half the course, were utilized to orient the manuscript toward a textbook style.

The book begins with a general review of millimeter waves and various types of transmission lines proposed thus far for microwave and millimeter-wave circuit applications. Chapters 2 through 5 provide a systematic presentation of the basic principles, analyses, design formulas, and characteristics of various practical fin-line configurations. Starting from the basic field equations, analytical steps are carried through in detail to facilitate better understanding of the various techniques and their applicability to different structures. We summarize rigorous formulas as well as approximate closed-form expressions, which can be readily programmed to generate design data for any structure. A large number of design data graphs are nevertheless included in Ch. 4 and 5.

Theory and design of the basic building blocks that constitute fin-line circuits—namely, resonators, discontinuities, and transitions—are covered exhaustively in Ch. 6 to 8. The final chapter is devoted to a review of the state of the art for the various fin-line components. An exhaustive list of references is included at the end of each chapter.

In the nine chapters, the authors have tried to include almost all aspects of fin lines reported thus far. The various analytical techniques covered in the text should provide graduate students and researchers with a solid analytical base that can be used for solving new structures. For research and development engineers, this book offers ready-to-use design formulas, graphical illustrations showing the characteristics of different types of fin lines, and design techniques for various circuit elements and components. Therefore, with all the up-to-date information on fin lines, the book should serve as a handy reference to all workers active in the field.

The authors wish to thank Mr. R.P. Kapoor for drawing all the figures with great patience and precision. The authors also owe their thanks to the Directorate of Training and Sponsored Research of the Defence Research Development Organisation (India) for sponsoring a project in the area of millimeter-wave integrated circuits, which has greatly helped to intensify the research interests of the authors in this area.

Bharathi Bhat
Shiban K. Koul

Chapter 1
Introduction to Millimeter-Wave Circuits

1.1 MILLIMETER WAVES AND THEIR APPLICATIONS

The *millimeter-wave* region, which typically spans from 30 to 300 GHz, represents a vast spectrum resource with enormous potential applications. This frequency band lies between the microwave region at the lower end, and the infrared and optical regions on the higher side. In the microwave and optical regions, the techniques and technologies are well developed, leading to a multitude of applications in radar, communication, and other commmercial sectors. The microwave area, in particular, has undergone a significant change during the 1970s and 1980s. The advent of microwave solid-state devices and microwave integrated circuit technology has resulted in the miniaturization of microwave components and systems. The use of planar transmission lines as the basic transmission medium has enhanced the performance of circuits through the reduction of parasitics and elimination of superfluous interfaces.

The congestion of the microwave spectrum in recent years has brought about an increasing demand for use of the millimeter-wave frequencies. Because of the smaller wavelengths, millimeter waves offer several advantages over microwaves. Practical utilization of millimeter waves, however, should take account of the fact that they interact rather strongly with the atmospheric constituents. In this section, we present a brief review of the essential characteristics of millimeter waves, their relative merits and demerits as compared to microwaves, and their applications.

Propagation Characteristics [1–7]

In the millimeter-wave region, the electromagnetic energy interacts with the atmospheric constituents—namely, gases, particulate matter, and hydrometeors—considerably more than in the microwave region. These interactions occur through three primary mechanisms: absorption, scattering, and refraction. The primary gases that affect millimeter waves are oxygen and water vapor. The resonances of these gases cause frequency-selective absorption and scattering. Figure 1.1 shows the curves of average atmospheric absorption of millimeter waves, reproduced from Rosenblum [1]. Absorption peaks caused by resonances in oxygen molecules are in the vicinity of 60 and 120 GHz, and those caused by resonances in water vapor molecules are in the vicinity of 22 and 183 GHz. There are, however, atmospheric windows within which the attenuation is reasonably low. These windows are centered at 35, 94, 140, and 220 GHz, each having a bandwidth of about 20%.

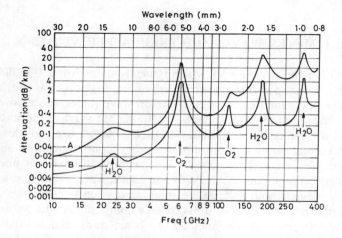

Fig. 1.1   Average atmospheric absorption of millimeter waves:

A = Sea level B = 4 km
T = 20°C T = 0°C
P = 760 mm ρ_{H2O} = 1g/m^3
ρ_{H2O} = 7.5 g/m^3

The particulate materials that affect millimeter waves are dust, smog, and smoke particles. Because these particulates have dielectric constants that are much smaller than the dielectric constant of water droplets, their attenuation cross section is very small. Thus, particulate matter has a negligible effect on millimeter waves, whereas the loss can be prohibitive at optical frequencies.

The hydrometeors that generally affect millimeter waves are rain, cloud droplets, fog, and snow. Among these, the dominant factor contributing to the attenuation is rain. Attenuation due to rain is a function of rain-fall rate, droplet size, temperature, frequency, and path length. For a typical rain-fall rate of 5 mm/hr, the attenuation at 10 GHz is 0.1 dB/km, and at 100 GHz it is 4 dB/km.

Advantages and Limitations of Millimeter Waves [2–9]

In view of the smaller wavelengths of millimeter waves as compared with microwaves, smaller antenna diameters are required to achieve the same gain and beamwidth. Alternatively, for the same antenna diameter, higher angular resolution is obtained in radars, thereby leading to higher target-to-clutter ratio, increased tracking accuracy, and reduced susceptibility to jamming. Smaller beamwidths offer increased immunity to friendly interference (electromagnetic, EMI) as well as hostile interference (electronic countermeasures, ECM).

Millimeter waves offer greater bandwidth than do microwaves. Greater bandwidth allows more information to be transmitted per unit time in a communication system, greater range resolution in a radar, and greater sensitivity in a radiometer. With greater bandwidth, there is a reduction of the mutual interference between the users of the spectrum. The larger Doppler frequency shift possible in the millimeter-wave region can provide a more accurate measurement of relative velocity than that attainable at microwave frequencies.

In general, the propagation losses in the millimeter-wave region are high compared with those in the microwave region, thus making it less attractive for "all-weather" operation. For reasonably low values of attenuation, a millimeter-wave system must operate within one of the atmospheric windows. The frequency-selective absorption of millimeter waves can also be utilized to advantage for remote sensing of atmospheric constituents and for secure communications. For example, the 60 GHz frequency range, corresponding to oxygen absorption, provides approximately 15 dB of attenuation per kilometer and is particularly suitable for short-range secure communication.

It is pertinent to point out that optical systems offer basically the same advantages as millimeter-wave systems. Millimeter waves, however, have a clear advantage over optical frequencies in view of their ability to penetrate clouds, smoke, fog, and haze. For tactical military applications, millimeter-wave systems offer the advantages of rapid deployment and lower vulnerability as compared with optical systems.

Applications [5–10]

A comparison of millimeter waves with microwaves and optical waves shows that a microwave system is clearly better for a large volume search, even in adverse weather, while an optical system is superior in high-resolution applications in clear weather conditions. The main attractive features of a millimeter-wave system are its small size compared with a microwave system and its ability to penetrate clouds, smoke, and fog in contrast with an optical system. These features enable millimeter waves to offer several distinct advantages in a variety of military and civilian applications. The main applications of millimeter waves can be classified under radar, communication, radiometry, and instrumentation.

Radar.   The narrow beamwidth offered by millimeter waves as compared with microwaves is advantageously utilized in several radar applications. Some of the military applications are in low-angle tracking, high-resolution radar, secure military radar, interference-free radar, missile guidance, and imaging radar. Millimeter-wave radars are also suitable for several civilian applications. The viability of such applications, however, is dependent on the availability of low-cost components and sources. Some of the civilian applications include security systems, such as intrusion alarms; systems for the determination of distance, velocity, and acceleration in railways; and vehicle radars for collision avoidance and in industrial operation. Another distinct advantage of millimeter-wave systems is their small size due to the shorter wavelength. This property has been utilized in special military applications, such as in active fuses and seekers in small-sized projectiles, terminal guidance of rockets, and hand-held radars. Some of the civilian gadgets include traffic aids, hand-held communicators, and obstacle sensors for the blind.

Communication.   The narrow beamwidth of millimeter-wave antennas makes communication links difficult to intercept. Thus, *low probability of intercept* (LPI) communication links can operate at the resonant peaks of oxygen or water vapor absorption, where the atmospheric attenuation limits the range of detectability. For example, a 60 GHz millimeter-wave system can be used for satellite-to-satellite communication above the earth's atmosphere, without any interference or detection from the atmosphere. LPI communication links are also useful for short-range ship-to-ship communication and battlefield communication. Millimeter waves are ideal for high-capacity trunk lines because of the large available bandwidth. For example, a millimeter waveguide link can transmit about 500,000 voice channels per link as compared with 6000 voice channels per link for a microwave radio link.

Radiometry. The radiometer achieves passive detection by measuring the noise temperature as viewed by the antenna. Because the undesired background radiation interferes with the target radiation, it is desirable to have an antenna with a narrow beam in order to achieve a large target-to-background contrast. Radiometer sensitivity is also proportional to the square root of the predetection bandwidth. Millimeter waves, therefore, are attractive for radiometers because wide bandwidths are available and narrow beams can be achieved with small antennas. Millimeter-wave radiometry applications include remote sensing of the environment, radio astronomy, the detection of missiles, ships, and ground targets, and weather monitoring.

Instrumentation. Millimeter waves offer unique advantages in instrumentation because of the interaction with scattering objects that are dependent on wavelength. Millimeter-wave systems can be used as measurement instruments in plasma diagnostics, spectroscopy and rocket exhaust plume measurements, and radar cross section measurements.

1.2 BASICS OF MICROWAVE CIRCUIT INTEGRATION [11–19]

It is logical to extend the integrated circuit techniques that are well developed at microwave frequencies to the lower end of the millimeter-wave band. In order to understand the extent to which these techniques can be adapted, we shall first review the basic elements of microwave circuit integration.

Circuit integration of microwave frequencies is based on the use of (1) *planar transmission lines* as the transmission medium, (2) *distributed* circuit elements or *lumped* elements in planar form, (3) *microwave solid-state devices* compatible with the planar transmission lines, and (4) *hybrid technology,* particularly thin-film techniques, for fabrication. With these features, *microwave integrated circuits* (MICs) offer several advantages over waveguide and coaxial circuits—namely, reduction in size and weight, ease of mass production with improved reproducibility, and potentially lower cost. Microwave integrated circuit technology offers the further advantage of combining multicircuit functions without any interconnecting wires, thus permitting compact integrated modules with highly reliable performance.

Among the various planar transmission lines, the most extensively used for microwave integrated circuits is the *microstrip*. It is a versatile transmission line for the incorporation of devices and the integration of several circuit forms. A variety of other transmission lines, such as the *suspended stripline, inverted microstrip, slotline,* and *coplanar line,* have also been found to be useful in practice. Each of these transmission lines offers certain advantageous features with respect to other lines. The circuit designer can choose a combination of two or more of these transmission lines to achieve the desired circuit performance. Salient features of the aforementioned transmission lines are summarized in Sec. 1.3.

Passive microwave integrated circuits are generally comprised of distributed elements. These elements consist of one or more transmission line segments on the order of a wavelength or more. Examples are resonating transmission line segments of length equal to a half-wavelength or integral multiples of half-wavelengths. At lower microwave frequencies, these circuits also incorporate lumped elements—namely, inductors, capacitors, and resistors—in planar form. The lumped element concept is based on the use of circuit elements that are electrically small so that the current distribution in the element is essentially uniform. This criterion is satisfied if the element size does not exceed one-tenth of a wavelength. A short transmission line segment of very narrow width results in inductance, and one of broad width results in capacitance. Larger inductance values are achieved by printing the line in the form of a meander line or a spiral, and larger capacitances can be achieved by means of interdigital capacitors. Resistors are realized by the vacuum deposition of thin films of nickel-chromium, or by sputtering tantalum directly on the substrate carrying the circuit pattern. Discrete chip resistors are used for biasing and as line terminations. These lumped elements offer considerable size reduction at lower microwave frequencies.

Active components, which perform a variety of functions such as power generation, amplification, switching, and mixing, incorporate suitable microwave semiconductor diodes and transistors. These include the IMPATT diode, *pin* diode, Schottky-barrier diode, gallium arsenide (GaAs) FET, and silicon (Si) bipolar transistors.

The fabrication of MICs can make use of either hybrid technology or *monolithic technology*. Hybrid technology involves the realization of passive circuit patterns on dielectric substrates using the *thin-film* or *thick-film* techniques and the mounting of solid-state devices by soldering or bonding. The substrates used for hybrid MICs should possess a well controlled dielectric constant, low loss tangent, and good surface finish. Table 1.1 summarizes the properties of some of the substrate materials. The most commonly used substrate materials are fiberglass-reinforced Teflon™ (trade name RT-duroid™) for stripline and high purity alumina for microstrip, slotline, and their modified versions. Despite their high cost, fused quartz substrates are recommended for use at millimeter-wave frequencies, especially in suspended stripline configuration. The main features overriding the cost considerations are its high degree of surface finish (≈ 0.006 μm) and availability in sufficiently small thicknesses, as low as 0.002 inches. Polycrystalline beryllium oxide (BeO), with its high thermal conductivity

Table 1.1

PROPERTIES OF SUBSTRATES USED IN HYBRID MICs

Material	Relative dielectric constant ϵ_r	Dielectric loss tangent $\tan \delta \times 10^4$ at 10 GHz	rms surface roughness (μm)	Thermal conductivity K(W/cm/°C)	Remarks/MIC applications
RT-duroid™ 5880	2.16–2.24	5–15	{0.75–1.0*, 4.25–8.75**}	0.0026	• Cu-plating, flexible/stripline
RT-duroid™ 6010	10.2–10.7	10–60	{0.75–1.0*, 4.25–8.75***}	0.0041	• Cu-plating, flexible/microstrip, stripline at L band***
Epsilam-10™	10–13	20	—	0.0037	
Alumina (99.5%)	9.6–10.4	0.5–3.0	0.05–0.25	0.37	• Cr-Au plating/microstrip, slotline and their variants
Cuflon™	2.1	4.5	—	—	• Flexible/microstrip at millimeter-wave frequencies
Fused quartz (99.9%)	3.75	1	0.006–0.025	0.01	• Cr-Au plating, optical finish/microstrip-like transmission lines
Beryllia	6.6	1	0.05–1.25	2.5	• High conductivity/compound substrates
Ferrite, Garnet	13–16	2	0.25	0.03	• Porous/nonreciprocal devices in microstrip, slotline, and coplanar line
Sapphire (single crystal)	$\epsilon_{r\perp} = 9.4$, $\epsilon_{r\parallel} = 11.6$	0.4–0.7	0.005	0.4	• Well defined and repeatable electrical properties, anisotropic/microstrip, suspended microstrip
Pyrolytic boron nitride	$\epsilon_{r\perp} = 3.4$, $\epsilon_{r\parallel} = 5.12$	—	—	—	• Anisotropic/microstrip, suspended microstrip

* Average peak to valley difference in height (rolled copper).
** Average peak to valley difference in height (electrodeposited copper).
*** Not limited to L-Band.

coefficient, is used for devices in which high dissipation rates are encountered. Ferrites or garnets are used essentially in the fabrication of nonreciprocal components. Sapphire and pyrolytic boron nitride are
anisotropic materials with equivalent dielectric constants close to those of
alumina and quartz, respectively. Sapphire substrates have some advantages over alumina, which include optical grade surface finish, well defined
and repeatable electrical properties, and higher thermal conductivity. Sapphire has become an attractive medium for MICs that require a high level
of reproducibility.

In thin-film technology, the substrate is first metalized using either the
vacuum evaporation or RF/dc sputtering. The deposited metal film should
adhere well to the substrate, while having good conductivity at operating
frequencies. This is achieved by means of a composite metal system such
as Cr-Au, Cr-Cu, Cr-Cu-Au, Ti-Au, or Ti-Pd-Au. The process of deposition, in the case of Cr-Au, for example, involves providing a thin flash
of chrome approximately 100–200 Å thick, followed by a deposited layer
of Au having similar thickness in the same vacuum run. The gold layer is
then increased in thickness to a few "skin depths" by electroplating. The
circuit pattern is formed by using photolithographic techniques. A pho-
toresist mask of the desired circuit pattern is produced at the metalized
surface and the undesired metalization is etched away by means of a wet
chemical process, called *wet etching*.

Thick-film circuits are generally formed on high purity alumina substrates, and the technology is based on the screen printing process. This
process involves printing certain kinds of inks or pastes onto the substrates,
then melting, sintering, or reacting them into continuous layers to form
conductors, resistors, and capacitors. The inks or pastes used for conducting patterns are suspended in an organic vehicle of finely powdered
metals such as Ag, Au, Pd-Au, and Ag-Pd with a glass frit or binder.
Insulator materials are similarly constituted, but they have no metallic
component. Resistor pastes generally have complex compositions of metals
and compounds.

In comparison with thin-film technology, the thick-film process is simpler
and less expensive. However, the pattern definition that can be achieved
is inferior, and the dc resistance of the fired conductor is higher than that
of evaporated thin films. In view of these limitations, thick-film technology
is used for fabricating MICs at lower microwave frequencies.

MICs with a much higher degree of miniaturization and integration can
be achieved through the use of monolithic technology, whereby active
devices are grown *in situ* on semiconducting substrates and passive circuitry
is either deposited on the substrate or grown in it. The base materials
generally used in monolithic microwave integrated circuits (MMICs) are

high-resistivity Si and semi-insulating GaAs. The fabrication involves highly reproducible device technology using epitaxial or ion implantation, multilevel metalization, and a composite process involving photolithography and electron-beam lithography.

Of the two technologies, hybrid techniques are more prevalent because of their advantages in terms of simplicity of fabrication and low cost of manufacture. Monolithic technology, by contrast, is capital intensive, and hence can be cost-effective only in the case of large volume system requirements as in phased array radars and direct broadcast satellite (DBS) television receivers.

1.3 PROPERTIES OF PLANAR TRANSMISSION LINES

Planar transmission lines form the basic transmission medium for microwave integrated circuits, whether the circuits are fabricated in hybrid or monolithic form. Figure 1.2 shows cross-sectional views of the three basic forms of planar transmission line—namely, the stripline, the microstrip line, and the slotline. Several variants of these basic lines have evolved over the years, each offering certain different advantages. Some of the configurations found to be useful in practical circuits are illustrated by Fig. 1.3. A number of coupled-conductor configurations arising from these basic types also find a variety of applications. In the following, we shall briefly outline the essential characteristics of the most commonly used structures, shown in Figs. 1.2 and 1.3, and their special advantages.

Strip Transmission Line [20–24]

The concept of a homogeneous strip transmission line was first proposed by Barrett [20] as early as 1952. (See Fig. 1.2(a).) The basic structure consists of a flat strip conductor situated symmetrically between two large ground planes. The dominant mode of propagation is the TEM mode. The electric and magnetic fields are concentrated around the strip conductor, and away from the strip the fields decay rapidly with distance. The characteristic impedance Z and the guide wavelength λ of the homogeneous stripline are given by

$$Z = \frac{Z_0}{\sqrt{\epsilon_r}} \tag{1.1a}$$

$$\lambda = \frac{\lambda_0}{\sqrt{\epsilon_r}} \tag{1.1b}$$

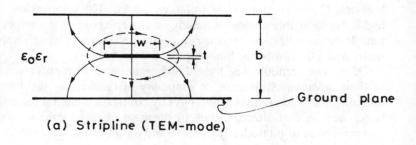

(a) Stripline (TEM-mode)

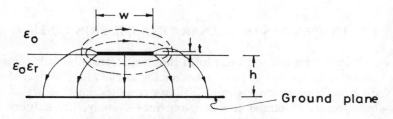

(b) Microstrip line (quasi-TEM mode)

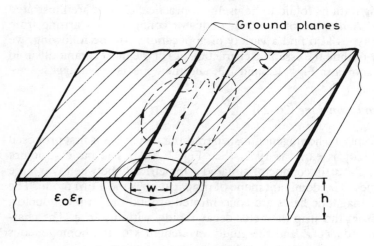

(c) Slotline (non-TEM mode)

Fig. 1.2   Basic planar transmission lines:
——— $\vec{E}$ field lines, – – – $\vec{H}$ field lines

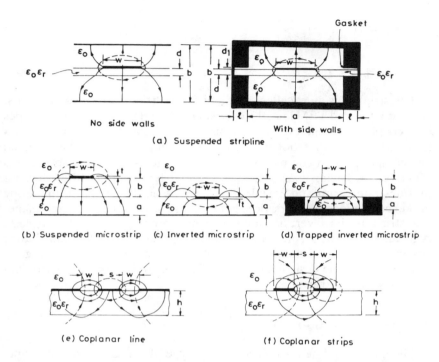

Fig. 1.3 Some variants of: stripline (a), microstrip line (b, c, d), and slot line (e, f), and their quasi-TEM mode field distributions

($\underrightarrow{\quad\quad}$ $\overrightarrow{E}$ lines, $\underrightarrow{\text{-----}}$ $\overrightarrow{H}$ lines).

where ϵ_r is the relative dielectric constant of the dielectric medium, Z_0 is the characteristic impedance of the stripline with air as the dielectric, and λ_0 is the free-space wavelength. An exact analysis of the homogeneous stripline using the conformal transformation method has been reported by Cohn [21].

In practice, the dimensions of the stripline are chosen so as to operate in the TEM mode, while keeping the losses to a minimum. As shown by Cohn [21], the attenuation in the stripline decreases with a decrease in the characteristic impedance for a constant ground plane spacing, and also with an increase in the ground plane spacing for a constant characteristic impedance. The maximum ground plane spacing, however, is governed by the onset of TE or TM mode. The cut-off wavelengths of the lowest order TE and TM modes, denoted as λ_{ce} and λ_{cm}, respectively, are approximately given by [22]:

$$\lambda_{ce} = \sqrt{\epsilon_r} \left(2w + \frac{\pi b}{2} \right) \tag{1.2a}$$

$$\lambda_{cm} = 2\sqrt{\epsilon_r} b \tag{1.2b}$$

The stripline is an excellent medium for realizing passive components. As in any coupled TEM line, the even-mode and odd-mode phase velocities in a coupled stripline are equal. This property enables high directivities to be achieved in directional couplers and high isolation in other coupled line components. A commonly used substrate for stripline construction is RT-duroid®, having an $\epsilon_r = 2.22$ and loss tangent $\tan \delta_d \approx 10^{-3}$. Because the substrate is soft and flexible, holes can be easily drilled for mounting packaged semiconductor devices between the strip and the ground plane. The structure, however, is not convenient for incorporating chip devices. A detailed account of single and coupled strip transmission lines, including design data and applications, is available in Howe [23]. Gunston [24] gives formulas and some design data on striplines, as well as for microstrip lines and a few other structures.

Microstrip Line [14, 24–31]

The microstrip line is the second basic type of planar transmission line, proposed [25] immediately after the stripline. (See Fig. 1.2(b).) Unlike the stripline, the microstrip line is an inhomogeneous structure with quasi-TEM as the dominant mode of propagation. The electric and magnetic field lines are concentrated predominantly in the dielectric substrate beneath the strip conductor and somewhat less so in the air region above. The larger the relative dielectric constant ϵ_r of the substrate, the greater would be the concentration of energy in the substrate region. The propagating medium can be approximated by an effective dielectric constant (relative) ϵ_f, the value of which lies in the range $(1 + \epsilon_r)/2 < \epsilon_f < \epsilon_r$, depending on the value of w/h. The characteristic impedance Z and the guide wavelength λ can be expressed in terms of ϵ_f as [26]:

$$Z = \frac{Z_0}{\sqrt{\epsilon_f}} \tag{1.3a}$$

$$\lambda = \frac{\lambda_0}{\sqrt{\epsilon_f}} \tag{1.3b}$$

Strictly speaking, the effective dielectric constant ϵ_f is a function of frequency. Its value remains fairly constant within the quasistatic limits, and then increases asymptotically with frequency, approaching the substrate permittivity ϵ_r as the frequency tends toward infinity [27, 28]. In practical circuits, the frequency limit is set by the onset of the TM surface-wave mode, which couples easily to the quasi-TEM mode. For narrow microstrip lines, the cut-off frequency of the TM mode is given approximately by [29]:

$$f_{C,TM} = \frac{v_0 \tan^{-1}(\epsilon_r)}{\sqrt{2}\pi h \sqrt{\epsilon_r - 1}} \tag{1.4}$$

where v_0 is the velocity of electromagnetic waves in free space. The frequency for strong coupling to the lowest order TE surface wave mode is larger than the frequency for TM surface wave coupling, and is given by

$$f_{C,TE} = \frac{v_0}{4h\sqrt{\epsilon_r - 1}} \tag{1.5}$$

Wide microstrip lines (or, equivalently, low impedance lines) are known to couple to surface waves at higher frequencies because of their lower phase velocity. For such cases, the frequency at which the lowest order TM surface wave mode couples to the microstrip line is given by the same expression as (1.5). Another effect that can set the frequency limit prior to the onset of the lowest order TM surface wave mode in the case of wider strips is the lowest order transverse resonance TE mode. This resonance occurs when the cut-off half-wavelength of this resonance mode becomes equal to $w + 2d$, where d accounts for the fringing capacitance and is on the order of $0.2h$. The cut-off frequency of this mode is given by [29]:

$$f_{CT} = \frac{v_0}{2\sqrt{\epsilon_r}(w + 0.4h)} \tag{1.6}$$

Figure 1.4 demonstrates the TM surface wave limits and the useful operating region of a microstrip line in terms of achievable Q-factor as a function of substrate thickness for different values of ϵ_r and operating frequencies. For example, the cross-hatched area corresponds to the operating region for an arbitrary choice of minimum $Q = 100$ with substrate thickness ranging from 0.001 mm to 50 mm. The graph reveals two interesting observations: (1) lower dielectric constant allows higher achievable Q as well as higher operating frequency; and (2) thinner substrates permit higher frequencies to be used, but at the expense of degradation in Q-factor, especially at lower frequencies. Figure 1.5 shows a comparison between the attenuation characteristic of a microstrip line and that of a symmetrical homogeneous stripline having a ground plane spacing b, which is equal to twice the height h of the microstrip substrate. As indicated by the shaded area in the figure, coupling of quasi-TEM to TM surface wave mode in a microstrip line and coupling of TEM to TE mode in the case of symmetrical stripline occur for very high dielectric constants and low impedance levels. For negligible coupling to higher order modes, the line parameters must be on the right-hand side of the shaded area in the figure. For a fixed impedance level, substrate thickness, and frequency within the permissible operating range, microstrip line possesses lower attenuation (in units of dB/λ) or higher Q than stripline. For sufficiently small values of dielectric constant of the substrate, the maximum Q in a microstrip line can be limited due to increased radiation losses.

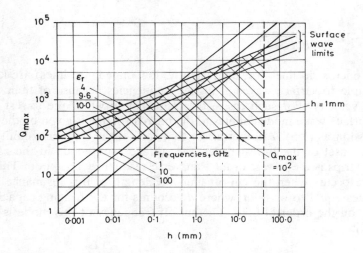

Fig. 1.4   Microstrip line maximum Q *versus* substrate thickness, showing limitation due to TM surface wave excitation.

(From Vendelin [29], reprinted with permission of *Microwave Journal*, Copyright © 1970 Horizon House-Microwave, Inc:)

Among the three basic lines shown in Fig. 1.2, the microstrip line is the most versatile, and hence it has received considerable attention from the viewpoints of theoretical investigations and practical implementation. A consolidated review of the various analytical techniques applied to microstrip line has been published by Mittra and Itoh [30]. The books by Edwards [14] and Gupta *et al*. [31] together provide a comprehensive account of the analyses of single and coupled microstrip lines, characterization of discontinuities, plus various other aspects such as losses, dispersive behavior, and circuit applications.

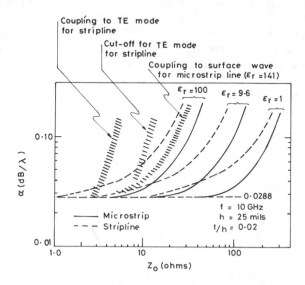

Fig. 1.5 Attenuation per guide wavelength *versus* impedance level for microstrip line (Fig. 1.2(b)) and stripline (Fig. 1.2(a) with b = $2h$).

(From Vendelin [29], reprinted with permission of *Microwave Journal*, Copyright © 1970 Horizon House-Microwave, Inc.)

Slotline [32–34]

The slotline, which was proposed by Cohn [32] in 1969, is the third basic line. (See Fig. 1.2(c).) Structurally, the slotline is complementary to the microstrip. The mode of propagation in the slotline is non-TEM. The electric field is essentially across the slot, while the magnetic field has both transverse and longitudinal components. Compared with the microstrip, the slotline is much more dispersive. The characteristic impedance increases with increased slot width, and hence the line is suitable for obtaining higher impedance values, typically in the range 50 to 200 Ω. Circuits using a slot-microstrip combination can be easily realized by etching slots in the ground plane of the substrate carrying the microstrip (Fig. 1.6). The coupling between the slot and microstrip is maximum when the slot is oriented perpendicular to the microstrip (Fig. 1.6(a)). The interaction reduces as the angle of intersection between the two becomes smaller and reaches a minimum when they are aligned parallel to each other (Fig. 1.6(b)). The slot-microstrip hybrid combination caters to a wide range of impedance levels, from approximately 20 to 200 Ω, and offers considerable flexibility in the circuit design. The slotline is particularly useful for ferrite components [33–34] that require regions of circularly polarized magnetic field or shunt-mounted elements. One disadvantage of the slotline is that its Q-factor is around 100, which is rather low compared with other transmission lines. Chapters 5 and 6 of Gupta *et al.* [31] provide a detailed discussion on slotlines.

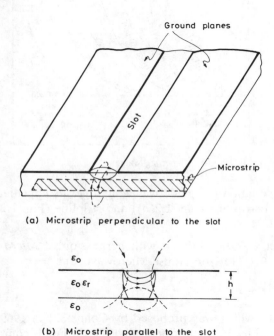

(a) Microstrip perpendicular to the slot

(b) Microstrip parallel to the slot

Fig. 1.6 Microstrip-slot coupling ($\longrightarrow \vec{E}$ field, $----\vec{H}$ field).

Suspended Stripline [35–43]

The suspended stripline is the most useful variant of the stripline. (See Fig. 1.3(a).) Basically, it is an inhomogeneous stripline in which the substrate carrying the strip conductor is placed symmetrically between the two ground planes, thereby leaving an air gap on either side of the substrate. By choosing the substrate to be sufficiently thin, the effective di-

therefore, permits larger circuit dimensions, leading to less stringent mechanical tolerances and increased accuracy of circuit fabrication as compared with the microstrip. The presence of the air gap also reduces the conductor loss in the ground plane because most of the electromagnetic energy becomes concentrated in the dielectric substrate. In edge-coupled suspended microstrip lines, the air gap can be adjusted to equalize the even-mode and odd-mode phase velocities under perfect matching conditions. This feature enables construction of directional couplers with considerably improved directivity [45]. For practical impedance levels, the air gap dimension to be maintained is very small, typically on the order of 1 mm or less. This being a critical design parameter, great care must be taken in the manufacture of the shielding box so that the air gap is uniform throughout the length of the circuit. The top and side conducting plates of the enclosure are kept sufficiently away from the strip conductor so as to have practically no effect on propagation.

Inverted Microstrip [26, 47–48]

The inverted microstrip differs from the suspended microstrip in that the strip conductor is situated on the lower surface of the dielectric substrate facing the ground plane. (See Fig. 1.3(c).) The effective dielectric constant ϵ_f in this case ranges from 1 to $(1 + \epsilon_r)/2$, whereas in a microstrip it lies between $(1 + \epsilon_r)/2$ and ϵ_r. The inverted microstrip retains the advantages of the suspended microstrip in terms of achieving larger strip dimensions and lower dissipative losses. Furthermore, it reduces the radiation loss in contrast to that in an open suspended microstrip. However, two disadvantages are introduced here. First, the strip conductor is not easily accessible for probing the circuit while in operation. Second, because the air gap involved is too small, incorporation of semiconductor devices becomes difficult.

Trapped Inverted Microstrip [48]

The main feature of the trapped inverted microstrip is that the strip conductor is trapped in a narrow rectangular channel, which is cut into the ground plane. (See Fig. 1.3(d).) The fields are largely confined to the channel region, thereby considerably reducing the coupling to free space above the substrate. The channel serves as a shield and also provides for suppression of any higher order modes, which might otherwise propagate if generated at the discontinuities. Short-circuited stubs can be easily realized by contacting a strip conductor from the main line to the edge of the channel because it is simple to adjust the channel width during construction to accommodate for the length of the stub. This is a clear advantage over the microstrip, suspended microstrip, and inverted microstrip, in which shorted stubs are usually simulated by adding an extra quarter-wavelength of open-ended stub. This additional length contributes to conductor loss as well as radiation loss from the open end. Therefore, components involving shorted stubs, such as interdigital and comb-line filters are more easily and efficiently realized in trapped inverted microstrip configuration. Circulators are other components that can be conveniently fabricated by placing a ferrite puck inside the channel, backed by a biasing magnet fitted to the ground plane.

Coplanar Waveguide [31, 49–51]

The slotline, coplanar waveguide (CPW), and coplanar strips (CPS) belong to a class of *coplanar lines*, in which all the conductors are situated on only one surface of the dielectric substrate. The coplanar waveguide (see Fig. 1.3(e)) was first proposed by Wen [49] and is essentially a coupled slotline. Signal is applied to the center strip conductor with respect to the two ground planes on either side. Unlike the slotline, the dominant mode of propagation resembles quasi-TEM. At higher frequencies, however, the field becomes non-TEM because the contribution due to the longitudinal component of the magnetic field is no longer negligible. In fact, the magnetic field in the slots at the air-dielectric interface is elliptically polarized. This property is useful in the design of nonreciprocal ferrite devices. As in the case of the slotline, semiconductor devices can be shunt mounted across the slot without drilling through the substrate. Impedances in the range of 40 to 150 Ω are realizable in the coplanar waveguide. Its Q-factor is low, typically on the order of 100 as compared with a value of about 250 in the microstrip. A detailed discussion of coplanar waveguides as well as coplanar strips is available in Gupta *et al.* [31].

Coplanar Strips [31, 50–51]

The configuration of coplanar strips is complementary to that of the coplanar waveguide. (See Fig. 1.3(f).) It consists of two parallel coupled strip conductors located on the same surface of the dielectric substrate, with one of them serving as ground plane. As in the coplanar waveguide, the dominant mode is a form of quasi-TEM mode. This configuration is suitable for microwave monolithic integrated circuits built on semiconducting substrates. Other transmission structures used in MMICs are the microstrip and the coplanar waveguide. Compared with the microstrip, coplanar strips offer much higher impedance levels, typically in the range of 40 to 250 Ω. The coplanar strip permits mounting active devices in series as well as shunt configurations, whereas the microstrip and its variants are convenient only for series mounting. The loss in this structure, however, is higher than that in a microstrip for the same characteristic impedance.

Strip, Microstrip, and Variant Transmission Lines on Anisotropic Substrates [52–59]

Striplines, microstrip lines, and their variants using anisotropic substrates have found application in a variety of MIC components [52–53]. Sapphire and pyrolytic boron nitride are two materials reported to be useful [52–54], and their properties are listed in Table 1.1. The anisotropic property can be specifically utilized to equalize the even-mode and odd-mode phase velocities in coupled lines, and hence achieve high directivity in directional couplers [52]. The analysis and propagation characteristics of isolated and coupled strip and microstrip-variant transmission lines using anisotropic substrates are reported in several research publications [52–59].

1.4 EXTENSION OF PLANAR TRANSMISSION LINE TECHNIQUES TO MILLIMETER-WAVE FREQUENCIES AND THEIR LIMITATIONS [60–66]

A qualitative comparison of the various planar transmission lines considered above is provided in Table 1.2. The range of impedances and Q-factors given are typical practical values at microwave frequencies. The upper and lower limits of impedances are essentially governed by two factors. First, the accuracy of the photolithographic technique sets tolerances on the minimum strip and slot widths that can be realized in practice. The second limiting factor is the possible excitation of higher order modes when the dimensional parameters approach a quarter-wavelength in the structure considered.

Of the various planar transmission lines available, the microstrip is the most widely used in hybrid MICs as well as for MMICs. It offers a simple geometry, easy fabrication and incorporation of active devices, and the integration of multifunction circuits. Practical microstrip circuits are enclosed in a rectangular metal shield in order to reduce radiation losses and eliminate external electromagnetic interference. Furthermore, the transverse dimensions of the box must be chosen small enough to ensure suppression of higher order modes, which can be generated at the discontinuities.

Table 1.2

QUALITATIVE COMPARISON OF VARIOUS PLANAR TRANSMISSION LINES AT MICROWAVE FREQUENCIES

Configuration	Typical impedance range (Ω)	Unloaded Q-factor (Q_u)	Radiation loss	Dispersion	Other features
• Stripline	20–120	high ($\approx$500)	nil	negligible	• Excellent for passive components, inconvenient for incorporation of chip devices
• Microstrip line	20–100	medium ($\approx$250)	low	small	• Widely used in MICs and MMICs
• Slotline	50–200	low ($\approx$100)	high	large	• Suitable for shunt mounting of chip devices and fabrication of nonreciprocal ferrite components.
• Suspended stripline	40–150	high	nil	small	• Suitable for high-Q passive components; operation can be extended to millimeter-wave frequencies
• Suspended microstrip	40–150	high	low	small	• Useful at higher microwave and millimeter-wave frequencies
• Inverted microstrip	25–130	high	low	small	• Suitable for high-Q passive components, inconvenient for mounting active devices
• Coplanar waveguide	40–150	low	medium	medium	• Easy connection of series and shunt elements, useful for MMICs and nonreciprocal ferrite components
• Coplanar strips	40–250	low	medium	medium	• Easy connection of series and shunt elements, useful for MMICs

The extension of microstrip techniques to millimeter-wave frequencies requires the use of progressively thinner substrates, preferably with a lower dielectric constant, in order to reduce spurious coupling and to ensure propagation in the quasi-TEM mode upon exclusion of unwanted surface-wave modes. The need for a shielding enclosure assumes greater importance because mode control becomes critical, especially for broad-bandwidth circuits. Another factor that plays an important role with increasing operating frequency is the surface roughness of the substrate. The conductor loss increases considerably due to the surface roughness of the metal conductor deposited on the dielectric substrate. By comparing the electrical performance, mechanical properties, and cost of the various substrates, alumina is thus considered suitable for most of the MIC requirements in a microstrip configuration. A variety of integrated circuit components and subsystems up to about 50 GHz have been reported to use thinner alumina substrates (0.2 to 0.3 mm thick) [60–61]. Fused quartz, with its lower dielectric constant ($\epsilon_r = 3.78$), extremely smooth surface finish (≈ 0.006 μm; nearly 10 times smoother than alumina), and availability in sufficiently small thicknesses, enables its operation in microstrip, even up to 100 GHz. By using 0.12 mm thick Z-cut quartz substrates, several microstrip components, such as the up-converter and balanced mixer, have been fabricated and integrated into receiver subsystems operating in the W band (75–100 GHz) [62]. Fused quartz also has the advantage of being thermally compatible with most ferrite materials. This property allows insertion of ferrite disks into the quartz substrate to enable complete integration of circulators with other components on a single substrate. Fused quartz, however, has some undesirable features—namely, it is high in cost, easy to break, and it cannot be drilled easily. There are other low-loss dielectric materials with lower dielectric constant than fused quartz that are useful at millimeter-wave frequencies. They are copper-clad RT-duroid® 5880 ($\epsilon_r = 2.22$) and Cuflon® ($\epsilon_r = 2.1$). Unlike fused quartz, these substrates are flexible, easy to handle, and cost-effective. Compact integrated V-band receivers have been reported to use these substrates in a shielded microstrip configuration [63–64].

Although the use of very thin substrates of low dielectric constant enables the operation of shielded microstrip circuits up to about 100 GHz, the microstrip configuration poses problems due to increased conductor loss and the critical dimensional tolerances at these frequencies. These problems are to a great extent circumvented in the modified versions—namely, the suspended stripline, suspended microstrip, and inverted microstrip. As discussed in Sec. 1.3, introducing an air gap between the dielectric substrate and the ground plane helps to reduce the effective dielectric constant in these structures, and consequently the strip dimensions are nearly two to three times wider than in a microstrip for the same characteristic impedance. This property is illustrated in Fig. 1.7. Therefore, circuit patterns can be realized far more comfortably than in a microstrip. Another advantage of the air gap is that it helps to reduce the conductor loss. A comparison of the loss characteristics (Fig. 1.8) shows that the loss incurred in a microstrip in the 5–10 GHz range for a 50 Ω line is the same as that in a suspended or inverted microstrip at around 60 GHz. The inverted microstrip, theoretically possesses characteristics similar to those of the suspended microstrip. Its practical utility, however, is limited mainly due to the difficulties in incorporating active devices. The suspended microstrip and the suspended stripline, which offer easy accessibility to the strip conductor pattern, have emerged as popular configurations in the realization of millimeter-wave components. For example, by using a 5-mil duroid™ substrate in a suspended stripline configuration, integrated circuit mixers have been realized at W band (75–100 GHz) [65] and even at D band (110–170 GHz) [66].

Coplanar structures—namely, the slotline (Fig. 1.2(c)), coplanar line (Fig. 1.3(e)), and coplanar strips (Fig. 1.3(f)) tend to be excessively lossy at millimeter wave frequencies because of their open configuration. Their

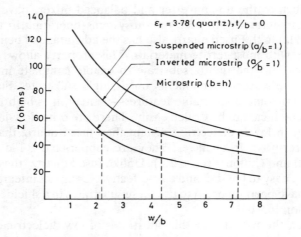

Fig. 1.7 Comparison of impedance characteristics of microstrip, suspended microstrip, and inverted microstrip as a function of normalized strip width.

utility thus far has been limited essentially to microwave frequencies. The problem of radiation can be alleviated by enclosing these transmission lines in a rectangular metal shield. In fact, the shielded versions of slotline and coplanar line, with the substrate mounted in the E-plane of the rectangular waveguide, are known as *unilateral fin line* (Fig. 1.9(a)) and *edge-coupled unilateral fin line* (Fig. 1.10(a)), respectively. The substrate carrying coplanar strips can similarly be mounted in the E-plane of a waveguide as shown in Fig. 1.11(c). All of these belong to a class of E-plane circuits proposed for operation typically in the frequency range of 30 to 120 GHz. The basic properties of these lines are introduced in the next section. Another class of transmission lines, known as *dielectric integrated guides,* and a few other miscellaneous guides suitable for operation exclusively in the millimeter-wave band are also discussed in the subsequent sections.

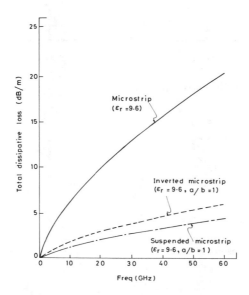

Fig. 1.8 Total dissipative losses as a function of frequency for 50 Ω line in microstrip, suspended microstrip, and inverted microstrip; $t/b = 0$.

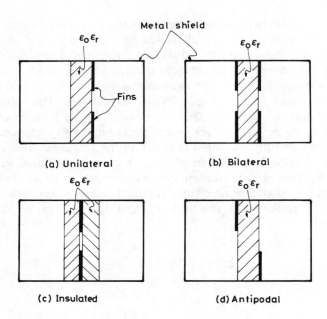

Fig. 1.9   Basic fin-line structures.

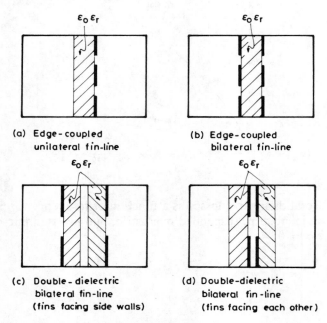

Fig. 1.10   Some coupled fin-line structures.

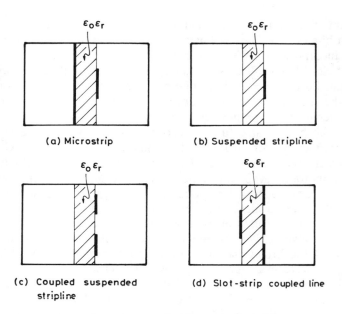

(a) Microstrip   (b) Suspended stripline

(c) Coupled suspended   (d) Slot-strip coupled line
    stripline

Fig. 1.11   E-plane transmission lines other than fin lines.

1.5   FIN-LINE AND E-PLANE INTEGRATED CIRCUIT TECHNIQUES [67–72]

In 1972, Meier [67] proposed a new quasiplanar transmission line called the fin line for millimeter-wave integrated circuits. The structure [68] is basically a slotline inserted in the E-plane of a rectangular metal waveguide (Fig. 1.9(a)). It can also be viewed as a ridged waveguide with thin ridges backed by a dielectric substrate, or as a dielectric slab loaded waveguide with fins. The structure is considered quasiplanar because the entire circuit pattern, including the active devices, is incorporated on the planar surface of a dielectric substrate, while the design of the circuit also takes into account the effect of the waveguide housing. The mode of propagation is clearly not quasi-TEM, but rather a hybrid mode consisting of a combination of TE and TM modes. With a dominating TE term, the mode is designated as HE-mode, and with a dominating TM term it is designated as EH-mode. If the walls are assumed to be perfectly conducting, then at cut-off an HE-mode becomes purely TE and an EH-mode becomes purely TM. The single-mode operating bandwidth in a fin line is greater than the bandwidth of the corresponding hollow waveguide.

Figure 1.9 shows cross-sectional views of the four basic types of fin line used in practice: *unilateral, bilateral, insulated,* and *antipodal.* In a unilateral fin line, the fins are located on one side of the dielectric substrate, and in a bilateral fin line the fins are located on both sides. The insulated fin line incorporates a dielectric gasket to isolate the fin from the waveguide, which thus facilitates dc bias to be applied to active components. Antipodal fin line incorporates one fin asymmetrically located on either side of the substrate. This configuration is used for realizing lower impedance values because the fins can be overlapped.

In all the fin-line structures, the commonly used substrate is copper-clad microfiber-reinforced PTFE (trade name RT-duroid™), having a relative dielectric constant of 2.22. The circuit pattern is defined by using the standard photolithographic techniques, and the substrate is then mounted in a split-block rectangular metal housing with the substrate passing through the broad walls of the guide. The two halves of the housing are then held by nylon or other nonmetallic bolts. In order to maintain RF continuity between the fins and the inner walls of the waveguide, the thickness of the broad wall at the location of the substrate is chosen as equal to a quarter-wavelength (including dielectric loading).

For frequencies in the range of 30 to 100 GHz, the fin line offers a versatile transmission medium. It overcomes the disadvantage of having to maintain tight dimensional tolerances as in a waveguide, and incorporates the advantageous features of planar technology. There are several advantages of fin lines: (1) the dimensions of the circuit in the 30–100 GHz frequency band are compatible with beam-lead and chip devices, thus offering the potential for construction of passive and active integrated circuits; (2) the guide wavelength is longer than in a microstrip, thus permitting less stringent dimensional tolerances; (3) it permits easy transition to a standard rectangular waveguide and operates over the entire bandwidth of the waveguide; and (4) low-loss propagation.

Figure 1.10 shows some of the coupled fin-line structures. The edge-coupled unilateral fin line (Fig. 1.10(a)) is nothing but a shielded coplanar waveguide. In a double-dielectric bilateral finline, the air gap serves as an additional parameter offering flexibility in the design and helping to reduce the insertion loss. Such coupled structures, including the bilateral fin line (Fig. 1.9(b)) and the edge-coupled bilateral fin line (Fig. 1.10(b)), are useful in the design of a number of components, especially filters.

In addition to fin lines, the microstrip line and the suspended stripline can be configured as E-plane transmission lines by mounting the substrate that carries the conductor pattern in the E-plane of a waveguide (Fig. 1.11). The loss in a fin line (expressed in dB/λ) is reported to be nearly three times lower than that in a microstrip using the same dielectric material and waveguide mount. Furthermore, for excitation of a microstrip from a rectangular waveguide, a special transition is required, which can gradually twist the electric field lines of the waveguide by nearly 90°. The suspended stripline as an E-plane transmission line has a larger ground plane spacing than a conventional line operating in the quasi-TEM mode. The determination of propagation parameters for this line requires the use of hybrid-mode analysis [70]. Figure 1.11(d) shows the general configuration of an E-plane transmission line using strip-slot coupling. A spectral domain analysis of this structure, including its propagation characteristics for the quasi-TEM coplanar and slot modes, has been reported by Schmidt *et al.* [71]. A comprehensive review of millimeter-wave E-plane integrated circuits is available in Solbach [72]. Since the rest of the chapters in the present text are devoted to the study of fin lines, further details shall not be given here.

1.6 DIELECTRIC INTEGRATED GUIDES

Beyond about 100 GHz, where suspended striplines and fin lines pose fabricational difficulties because of increasingly stringent dimensional tolerances, dielectric integrated guides offer an alternative approach with the potential for lower losses and relaxed tolerances. Figures 1.12 and 1.13 show the cross-sectional views of some useful dielectric integrated guides. These transmission structures make use of a refractive type of waveguide, which are, in most cases, coupled with planar integration techniques and known to possess a useful operating range spanning from 40 GHz up to about 140 GHz [73–93]. While the principle of wave guiding is the same as in optical dielectric guides, the configuration and fabricational techniques are distinctly different. An optical dielectric guide generally consists of a rectangular core surrounded by one or more dielectric layers of slightly lower dielectric constant. They are formed using such techniques as sputtering, diffusion, and ion implantation. Conversely, millimeter-wave dielectric integrated guides generally make use of rectangular dielectric strips in contact with one or two metallic ground planes. The dielectrics that can be used include a variety of low-loss ceramic materials ($\epsilon_r = 4$ to 15), quartz ($\epsilon_r = 4$), castable resins of various dielectric constants, soft substrates such as Epsilam-10™ ($\epsilon_r = 10$) and RT-duroid™ ($\epsilon_r = 2.2, 10$), hot pressed boron nitride ($\epsilon_r = 4$), and highly resistive semiconductor materials such as Si ($\epsilon_r = 12$) and GaAs ($\epsilon_r = 16$). Various fabrication techniques have been proposed, depending on the type of dielectric material used [94–96]. For example, with ceramic material, circuits can be formed in the green state and then fired in a furnace, whereas soft dielectric substrates can be milled, and quartz and semiconductor materials can be laser cut before being soldered or bonded onto the ground plane. At sufficiently high frequencies, the thickness of the dielectric guide assumes such a small value that the conventional thick-film technique becomes useful [95].

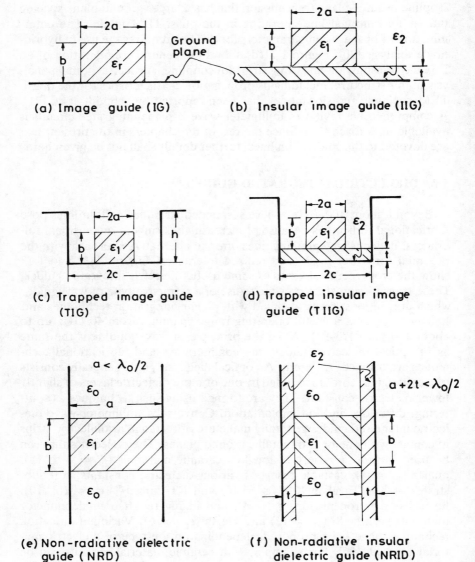

(a) Image guide (IG)

(b) Insular image guide (IIG)

(c) Trapped image guide
    (TIG)

(d) Trapped insular image
    guide (TIIG)

(e) Non-radiative dielectric
    guide (NRD)

(f) Non-radiative insular
    dielectric guide (NRID)

Fig. 1.12 Basic dielectric integrated guides (a, c, e) and their insular
counterparts with $\epsilon_1 > \epsilon_2$ (b, d, f).

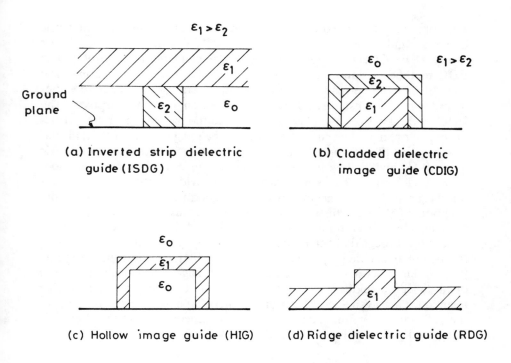

(a) Inverted strip dielectric guide (ISDG)

(b) Cladded dielectric image guide (CDIG)

(c) Hollow image guide (HIG)

(d) Ridge dielectric guide (RDG)

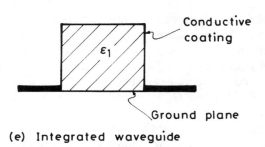

(e) Integrated waveguide technology (INWATE)

Fig. 1.13 Variants of image guide (a–d) and integrated waveguide technology (e).

The commonly employed analytical techniques for the analysis of dielectric integrated guides shown in Figs. 1.12 and 1.13 are the *effective dielectric constant* (EDC) method [76], and the *mode-matching* method [97]. The EDC method is simple, but approximate. Nevertheless, it is a practical method that can be readily used for obtaining sufficiently accurate values of propagation constants, adequate for most engineering purposes. The EDC method has been applied to determine the dispersion characteristics of several open guiding structures, such as the image guide [76–77], insular image guide [78], trapped image guide [85–86], inverted strip dielectric guide [91], and hollow image guide [93]. The mode-matching method, however, is rigorous and complicated, but it provides highly accurate values for the propagation constants of hybrid guided modes as well as the description of the field distributions. Accurate analyses of several guiding structures have been reported to use this method. These include the image guide [79], broadside-coupled image guide [83], insular image guide [84], trapped image guide [87], inverted strip guide [84], and rib dielectric guide [84]. A fine description of the guiding and leakage properties of a class of open dielectric guides and a comparison of the EDC and mode-matching techniques are available in Peng and Oliner [98] and Oliner *et al.* [99]. In the following, we summarize the salient characteristics of the dielectric integrated guides of Figs. 1.12 and 1.13.

Image Guide [73–83]

The image guide, first considered in 1955 [73], is a basic dielectric integrated guide from which a variety of other structures have evolved for millimeter-wave applications. (See Fig. 1.12(a).) The structure supports hybrid modes. They are generally classified as E^y_{mn} and E^x_{mn} modes, where the subscripts m and n indicate the number of extrema of the electric field in the y and x directions, respectively. In the E^y_{mn} modes, the field components E_y, E_z, and H_x are dominant over E_x, H_y, and H_z, whereas the converse is true in the case of E^x_{mn} modes. The dominant mode is E^y_{11} with E_y and H_x as the dominant transverse field components. In the transverse plane, the fields are of the standing wave type inside the dielectric, while outside the guide the fields decay exponentially as shown in Fig. 1.14.

The metal ground plane provides mechanical support to the dielectric strip, and also serves as a heat sink and dc bias ground for active devices. The dominant mode exists down to 0 Hz and, as the operating frequency is increased, there is better confinement of the traveling wave to the dielectric. The lowest frequency of operation of the guide is determined by good guidability and low radiation loss at bends and discontinuities, while the upper frequency is limited by the onset of the next higher order mode.

As the dielectric constant of the strip is increased, the bandwidth of the guide increases in terms of dispersion. The image guide is reported to give an optimum bandwidth from the point of wave guiding properties as well as dispersion for an aspect ratio $a/b = 1$, and a relative dielectric constant $\epsilon_r = 2.5$ [80].

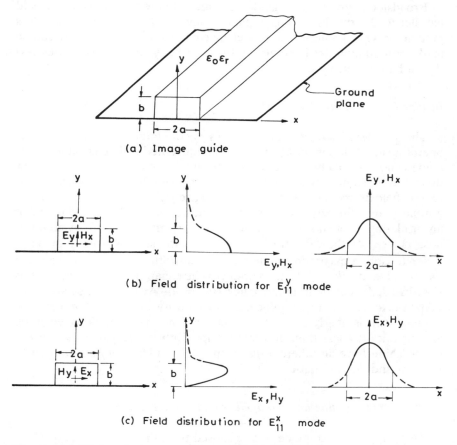

(a) Image guide

(b) Field distribution for E_{11}^{y} mode

(c) Field distribution for E_{11}^{x} mode

Fig. 1.14 Dielectric image guide and field distributions.

The transmission loss in the image guide is essentially due to the conductor loss caused by the large field concentration near the metal image plane and the dielectric loss, which is dependent on the loss tangent of the dielectric. Shindo and Itanami [82] have shown that the conductor loss can be reduced considerably by exciting the guide in the E_{11}^{x} mode, where the principal electric field is parallel to the metal image plane. For example, the total attenuation loss in a guide made of Teflon® strip ($\epsilon_r = 2.0$, tan $\delta = 1.5 \times 10^{-4}$, $2a = 6$ mm, $b = 3$ mm) on a silver-plated image plane at 50 GHz is reported to be 2.26 dB/m for E_{11}^y mode, and 0.99 dB/m for E_{11}^x mode [82]. E_{11}^x, however, is a higher order mode, and spurious modes can occur in curved sections, giving rise to higher radiation loss as compared with that due to the dominant E_{11}^y mode.

Broadside-coupled image guides, excited with the principal electric field parallel to the two metal image planes, have been proposed for low-loss millimeter-wave applications, especially couplers [83]. Such guides can be made nonradiative by keeping the distance between the two plates less than a half-wavelength.

Insular Image Guide [76–77, 84]

The problem of high conductor loss encountered in an image guide operating in the dominant E_{11}^y mode, is circumvented with the insular image guide (Fig. 1.12(b)) by virtue of introducing a thin insulating layer of low dielectric constant between the dielectric strip and the ground plane. Most of the field is concentrated in the dielectric strip, and less so near the ground plane, thereby reducing the conductor loss. The introduction of an insulating layer, however, decreases the E_{11}^x mode cut-off. A compromise choice for the t/b ratio in the 0.015–0.15 range is usually made in order to obtain maximum single-mode bandwidth. For a typical value of $t/b = 0.1$ and $a/b = 0.5$, the conductor attenuation constant in dB/λ is less than half that in an image guide ($t/b = 0$). At frequencies above 60 GHz, the loss in an insular guide using high purity alumina as the dielectric guiding strip is nearly the same as that in a hollow metallic waveguide, and significantly less than in a microstrip. Both image guide and insular image guide have an inherent disadvantage of radiation loss from curved sections and discontinuities.

Trapped Image Guide and Trapped Insular Image Guide [85–87]

The trapped image guide was proposed by Itoh and Adelseck [85] essentially to reduce the radiation loss at curved sections and bends, normally encountered in open dielectric guides. (See Fig. 1.12(c).) In the trapped guide, the energy leaking from the guide in the sideward direction at the bend will be mostly reflected back to the dielectric portion by the metal walls if their height h is sufficiently large. If the guide is operated in a single-mode region, the reflected energy is coupled back to the guided mode. Another effect of the metal side walls is to introduce a low-frequency cut-off for the dominant mode. The conductor loss due to metal side walls is negligible, unless the walls are too close to the dielectric strip. However, the total conductor loss can be considerably reduced by introducing a thin insular film as shown in the trapped insular image guide (Fig. 1.12(d)). The disadvantage of the trapped guide is that it is bulky, and it is thus not convenient for integrating different circuit components.

Nonradiative Guide and Nonradiative Insular Guide [88–90]

The nonradiative dielectric guide proposed by Yoneyama and Nishida [88] consists of a dielectric strip supported between two parallel metal plates. (See Fig. 1.12(e).) The guide is excited with an electric field parallel to the metal plates. The plate separation a is kept less than half a wavelength such that the electromagnetic wave is below cut-off in the air region, but propagates in the dielectric strip. Thus, radiated waves, if any, at the bends and junctions, decay outside the dielectric.

Also, in the insulated nonradiative dielectric guide (Fig. 1.12(f)) the conducting plate separation is less than half a wavelength in order to suppress undesired radiation. The thin insulating layer on either side of the high dielectric constant strip helps to enhance the single-mode operational bandwidth as well as reduce the conductor loss.

Inverted Strip Dielectric Guide [84, 91–92]

The inverted strip dielectric guide consists of a guiding dielectric layer placed on a dielectric strip, which, in turn, is placed on a ground plane. (See Fig. 1.13(a).) With $\epsilon_1 > \epsilon_2$, most of the electromagnetic energy propagates through the top guiding layer, resulting in reduced conductor loss [91]. The supporting dielectric strip can be easily bonded to the ground plane without significantly affecting the loss characteristics. However, the practical utility of this structure is limited by poor guidability at curved sections.

Cladded Dielectric Image Guide [93]

The cladded dielectric image guide [93] is a variant of the image guide, in which the core dielectric guide of high permittivity is cladded by a low permittivity layer (Fig. 1.13(b)). The cladding helps to reduce the bending losses in the image line, and also serves to isolate the power carried by the guide from the environment to some extent.

Hollow Image Guide [93]

The hollow image guide, also known as the pi (π) guide, is another variant of the image line [93]. (See Fig. 1.13(c).) The hollow core offers flexibility in controlling the field distribution outside the dielectric as well as the propagation constant, without altering the exterior dimensions of the dielectric. Furthermore, solid-state devices can be easily mounted in the hollow core, and the core height may be gradually changed to create a smooth transition to an image guide.

Ridge Dielectric Guide [98–99]

The ridge dielectric guide is a variant of the insular image guide with the strip and insulating film formed of the same dielectric material. (See Fig. 1.13(d).) Its main advantage over the insular image guide is the ease of construction, but this is obtained at the expense of increased conductor loss. It has been pointed out [99] that in an image guide all the modes are purely bound, whereas some modes may leak in other open dielectric guides possessing a planar dielectric layer, such as the insular image guide, inverted strip guide, and ridge dielectric guide. Such leakage of energy is especially large at the step discontinuities of the ridge guide.

Integrated Waveguide Technology or INWATE Guide [100]

The INWATE guide proposed by Hinken [100] is basically a dielectric-filled rectangular waveguide, but one that makes use of a low-cost fabrication process, which enables easy integration of circuit components (Fig. 1.13(e)). The process involves, first, forming a dielectric strip to the required shape, then adhering the circuit pattern on a polished metal plate by means of a solvent. The structure is sprayed with a metal film, the thickness of which is increased electrolytically. Because circuits can be fully realized in integrated waveguide technology, tapers to standard waveguide are not needed.

1.7 RECTANGULAR AND CIRCULAR WAVEGUIDES FOR MILLIMETER WAVES

Rectangular Waveguide [22, 101–103]

The characteristics of rectangular waveguides popularly used at microwave frequencies are well known. (See Fig. 1.15(a,b).) For optimum operation in the dominant TE_{10} mode, the width-to-height ratio (a/b) of the guide is usually chosen as 2:1, with the maximum cross-sectional dimension being less than a wavelength. Thus, for frequencies above 100 GHz, the guide cross section assumes minute dimensions, making component fabrication increasingly difficult and expensive. Furthermore, the attenuation of the TE_{10} mode becomes rather excessive (typically 5 to 10 dB/m at 150 GHz). The power handling capability of the guide is also reduced. Oversized guides can be used for reducing the attenuation loss, but at the expense of higher order mode propagation. While mode filters can help to alleviate this problem, the fabrication of cost-effective mode filters at such high frequencies poses a complicated problem.

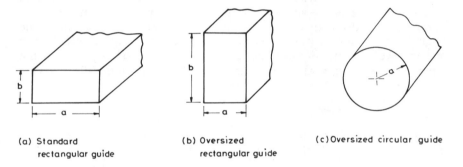

(a) Standard
   rectangular guide

(b) Oversized
   rectangular guide

(c) Oversized circular guide

Fig. 1.15 Rectangular and circular waveguides.

Circular Waveguide [103–106]

Oversized circular waveguides operating in the TE_{01} mode are known to offer extremely low attenuation, on the order of a few dB per kilometer. (See Fig. 1.15(c).) Such guides find utility in long-distance communication at frequencies between 40 and 100 GHz. The TE_{01} mode, however, is not a dominant mode, thus necessitating the incorporation of mode filters. It is also difficult to construct components to fit the circular guide field pattern.

1.8 H-GUIDE STRUCTURES

A class of waveguide media resembling the basic H-guide proposed by Tischer [107] is illustrated in Fig. 1.16. All of these guides have two common features. First, the field is confined sideways between two lateral conducting walls or wire grids. Second, propagation takes place in the form of a slow wave, essentially in the central region, with fields decaying exponentially in the vertical direction—that is, in the upper and lower parallel wall sections.

Basic H-Guide and Double-Strip H-Guide [107–112]

Toward the higher end of the millimeter-wave band, the dielectric integrated guides considered in the preceding section present problems of high attenuation and extremely small size. The H-guide proposed by Tischer [107] has potential applications at frequencies from 100 to 200 GHz (Fig. 1.16(a, b)). The structure resembles the nonradiative dielectric guide, except that the plate separation is larger than a wavelength. The principle of operation is distinctly different from that of the nonradiative guide. The H-guide relies upon surface wave guidance at the dielectric interface in one transverse direction and field confinement by parallel planes in the other. The guide supports a hybrid mode, with both E- and H-lines having

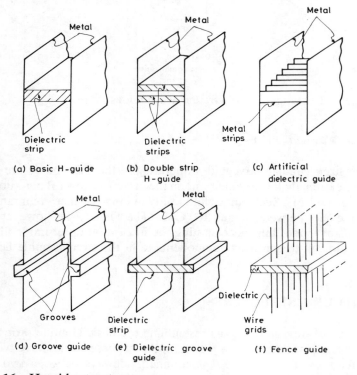

Fig. 1.16 H-guide structures.

a component in the direction of propagation (Fig. 1.17). One interesting feature of the H-guide is that there is no longitudinal current flow on the metal walls because of the absence of a vertical component of the magnetic field at the walls. The electric field lines are essentially parallel to the conducting walls and the magnetic field lines are parallel to the dielectric surface. Therefore, this mode offers low propagation loss, which decreases with an increase in plane separation. However, when the plane separation is several times the wavelength, which is required for convenience of fabrication for operation at frequencies above 200 GHz, multimode propagation can take place in the H-guide.

The double-strip H-guide [109], shown in Fig. 1.16(b), and other multiple strip configurations [110] are variants of the basic H-guide. The air spaces between the dielectric strips help to increase the power-handling capability without increasing the dielectric losses.

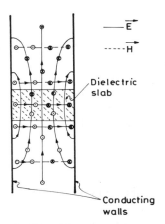

Fig. 1.17 Field configuration in H-guide.

(From Benson and Tischer [10], *IEE Proc.*, Pt. A, 1984, Vol. 131, pp. 429–449, reprinted with permission of IEE.)

Artificial Dielectric Guide [10, 113]

The artificial dielectric guide reported by Tischer [113] is also a form of H-guide, with the dielectric strip replaced by thin vertical metal strips arranged as shown in Fig. 1.16(c). The system of strips acts as a slow-wave structure, with fields decaying exponentially in the upper and lower regions. This guide, however, is not as convenient to fabricate as the basic H-guide.

Groove Guide [10, 111–112, 114–115]

The disadvantage of the H-guide, with respect to the possibility of multimode propagation at frequencies above 200 GHz, is overcome in the groove guide (Fig. 1.16(d)). Despite its relatively larger dimensions, the groove guide offers single-mode operation and low propagation loss. The groove dimensions are not critical and higher order modes generated in the guide, if any, propagate transversely out of the guide and are absorbed. Unlike the H-guide, which supports a hybrid mode, the groove guide supports a TE mode. Figure 1.18 shows the field configuration of the TE_{11} mode in the groove guide. The groove region creates a surface wave effect, and supports slow-wave propagation.

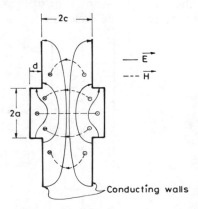

Fig. 1.18   Field distribution of TE_{11} mode in groove guide.

(Reprinted with permission from *J. Infrared Physics,* Vol. 18, Harris *et al.* [112], Low loss single-mode waveguide for submillimetre and millimetre wavelengths, Copyright © 1978, Pergamon Journals Ltd.)

Figure 1.19 shows the attenuation characteristics of the groove guide for various metal plane separations [112]. We can see that for a plane separation of about three wavelengths, the loss is less than 0.1 dB/m at 100 GHz, which is an order of magnitude less than in a TE_{10} mode rectangular waveguide. The similarity of field configuration to the TE_{10} field pattern of a rectangular waveguide should make possible the design of transitions between the two guides. The groove guide dimensions are especially convenient to handle at frequencies of 100 to 300 GHz. With its relatively large dimensions and low-loss property, the groove guide is also suitable for fabricating high-power components.

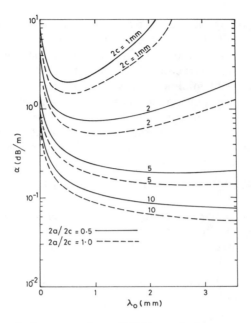

Fig. 1.19   Theoretical attenuation of TE_{11} mode in groove guide.
Groove depth = 1/4 plane separation, $\sigma = 5.8 \times 10^7 \; S_m^{-1}$.

(Reprinted with permission from *J. Infrared Physics*, Vol. 18, Harris *et al.* [112], Low loss single-mode waveguide for submillimetre and millimetre wavelengths, Copyright © 1978, Pergamon Journals Ltd.)

Dielectric Groove Guide [10, 103]

The dielectric groove guide (Fig. 1.16(e)) may be considered as a modified version of the H-guide, in which the dielectric strip extends into grooves cut into metallic side walls. The grooves are effective in suppressing higher order modes, thereby allowing for the wide plane separation required to achieve lower loss. The main limitation of such a guide is that the groove penetration distance is critical to a fraction of a wavelength, thus making it rather unattractive at the upper frequency ranges of the millimeter-wave band.

Fence Guide [10, 116–117]

The properties of the fence guide (Fig. 1.16(f)) are essentially the same as those of the H-guide, except that, structurally, the solid metallic side walls are replaced by wire grids. For waves polarized parallel to the wires, surface wave propagation takes place along the dielectric slab, with the grids on either side serving as effective reflectors. The portion of the dielectric protruding laterally on either side of the fence provides mechanical rigidity to the structure. The fence guide offers a simple approach toward integration of millimeter-wave components on a single dielectric slab. Because current flow on the walls is only along the wires, components made on individual dielectric blocks can also be joined in series to form a system, without the need for connectors and flanges. A useful operating frequency range recommended for fence guide is from 30 to 100 GHz [10].

1.9 COMPARISON OF VARIOUS GUIDE STRUCTURES

As described in the preceding sections, different types of guides are available for application in millimeter-wave circuits. The selection of a particular transmission structure for a given frequency range is based on the following considerations:

1. low loss or high unloaded Q;
2. low radiation loss;
3. low dispersion;
4. maximum achievable bandwidth;
5. ease of bonding solid-state devices in the case of active components;
6. ease of integration;
7. adequate power handling;
8. ease of fabrication and low cost of manufacture.

Based on these broad criteria, the useful frequency ranges of various transmission structures are presented in Fig. 1.20. The dotted lines indicate the possible frequency range over which operation can be extended with increased sophistication in fabrication, but at the expense of higher losses and cost. The lower limit is usually governed by the larger weight and dimensions of the guide, which are within the acceptable limits.

Figure 1.21 shows the attenuation in various guiding structures as a function of frequency [10]. The actual choice of the guide clearly depends on the specific application. For example, in certain ground-based systems, large power-handling capability may be the main requirement, with size and weight assuming secondary importance. Some applications may require a combination of two or more guiding media to yield the desired performance.

Conventional TE_{10} rectangular waveguides, known for their large power-handling capability, are generally used for building high-power transmitting systems at lower millimeter-wave frequencies, even extending up to about 100 GHz. Beyond 100 GHz, the guide assumes minute dimensions, and the problem of dimensional tolerances becomes increasingly acute. The guide suffers from higher losses, and its power-handling capability also becomes limited. A very-low-loss guide that has received wide attention is the TE_{01} circular waveguide, especially for application in long-distance communication at millimeter-wave frequencies. However, the field configuration of the TE_{01} mode is not convenient for component design. The circular guide therefore, is, not preferred for millimeter-wave circuitry.

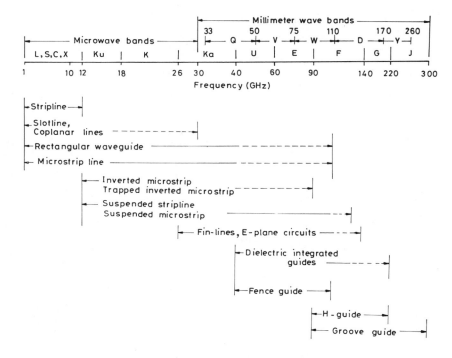

Fig. 1.20 Useful operating ranges of various transmission lines for microwave and millimeter wave circuits.

Of the various planar transmission lines, the *shielded microstrip* is widely used up to about 40 GHz because the structure is simple to fabricate by using standard photolithographic techniques. Furthermore, the circuit pattern is easily accessible for the mounting of active devices. By employing thinner, low-loss, low dielectric constant substrates, and more accurate lithographic techniques, its use has been extended up to about 100 GHz. Alternative transmission media, which offer considerably lower loss and

demand less stringent dimensional tolerances at millimeter-wave frequencies, are the microstrip variants—namely, the inverted microstrip, trapped
inverted microstrip, suspended stripline, and suspended microstrip. In particular, the suspended stripline is the most popular, offering an integrated
circuit approach capability up to about 140 GHz.

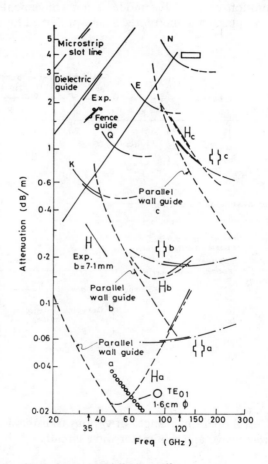

Fig. 1.21   Attenuation of wave guiding media.

	dimension, mm:	wall separation, mm:
K =	10.63×4.30	aKa = 10.63
Q =	4.78×2.39	bQa = 4.78
N =	2.03×1.02	cNa = 2.03

(From Benson and Tischer [10], *IEE Proc.*, Pt. A, 1984, Vol. 131, pp.
429–449, reprinted with permission of IEE.)

All planar transmission lines require proper shielding enclosures at millimeter-wave frequencies in order to prevent radiation and to suppress higher order mode propagation, which might be generated at the bends and discontinuities. Slotlines and coplanar lines, the operation of which is normally confined to microwave frequencies, can be used at millimeter-wave frequencies with proper shielding. A class of fin lines, which are basically shielded versions of slotlines, offer a low-cost integrated circuit capability for operation at frequencies in the range from 30 to 140 GHz. Fin lines allow straightforward transitions to TE_{10} rectangular waveguide. Furthermore, the slot dimensions in the fin line are compatible for the incorporation of solid-state devices.

By using fin lines and other E-plane circuits, a whole range of millimeter-wave components has been realized and integrated into receivers. Fin lines and suspended striplines are two competing circuit media with overlapping ranges of application between 30 and 140 GHz.

The *dielectric integrated guides* form a new class of transmission media, offering convenient size with relaxed fabricational tolerances and the potential for low-cost manufacture in the 40 to 100 GHz frequency range. The basic image guide is the simplest of all the dielectric integrated structures. The insular image guide, which incorporates a thin insulating layer of low dielectric constant between the ground plane and the guiding dielectric strip, offers lower loss than the image guide, but at the expense of reduced bandwidth. Both of these guides have been extensively studied, and the development of a range of millimeter-wave components has been reported.

Another structure which has received considerable attention is the *nonradiative dielectric guide*. The undesirable radiation at bends and other discontinuities, normally encountered in the image guide, insular image guide, and other open dielectric guides, are suppressed in the nonradiative guide. This unique property makes this guide ideally suited for the realization of low-loss millimeter-wave components.

One important feature of most of the dielectric integrated guides is the possibility for integration of high-performance dielectric antennas with the RF front end. Although there has been a growing interest in the development of dielectric integrated guide components, the techniques and technology have not adequately advanced, owing to difficulties involved in the integration of active devices.

An array of H-guide structures has also been under consideration in recent years, of which the basic H-guide and the groove guide have emerged as useful contenders for applications above 100 GHz. The *fence guide,* which is essentially a basic H-guide where side metal walls are replaced by wire grids, has been recommended as a suitable medium for inexpensive mass production of components to operate in the frequency range from 30 to 100 GHz. The most useful feature of the fence guide is the flexibility it offers for adding on different components without the need for connectors and flanges.

The H-guide has the same structural features as the nonradiative guide, except that the plate separation is kept at more than a wavelength and the dielectric slab thickness is much smaller. The H-guide offers convenient dimensions for operation above 100 GHz. However, above 200 GHz, the plate separation must be greater than several wavelengths and multimode propagation is possible. The H-guide is therefore recommended for operation between 100 and 200 GHz.

The modes in the H-guide as well as in the groove guide are modifications of the low-loss mode of a parallel plate guide. As illustrated in Fig. 1.21, these guides offer much lower attenuation than dielectric integrated guides. The groove guide, in particular, holds promise for circuit applications beyond 200 GHz, up to 300 GHz. Properties which make the groove guide unique for this frequency range are low loss, single-mode operation, and convenient dimensions with relaxed tolerances on groove size.

REFERENCES

Millimeter Waves and their Applications
1. E.S. Rosenblum, "Atmospheric Absorption of 10-400 KMCPS Radiation: Summary and Bibliography up to 1961," *Microwave Journal,* Vol. 4, pp. 91–96, March 1961.
2. F.A. Benson (ed.), *Millimeter and Submillimeter Waves,* Iliffe Books, London, 1969.
3. R. Davies, "Millimeter Waves," *Electronics and Power,* pp. 375–378, May 1981.
4. J.C. Wiltse, "History of Millimeter and Submillimeter Waves," *IEEE Trans. Microwave Theory Tech.,* Vol. MTT-32, pp. 1118–1127, Sept. 1984.
5. M.I. Skolnik, "Millimeter and Submillimeter Wave Applications," in *Proc. Symp. on Submillimeter Waves,* Polytechnic Press of Brooklyn Polytechnical Inst., Brooklyn, NY, 1970.
6. J.C. Wiltse, "Millimeter-Wave Technology and Applications," *Microwave Journal,* Vol. 22, pp. 39–42, Aug. 1979.
7. P. Bhartia and I.J. Bahl, *Millimeter Wave Engineering and Applications,* John Wiley and Sons, New York, 1984.
8. S.L. Johnston (ed.), *Millimeter Wave Radar,* Artech House, Dedham, MA, 1980.
9. K.J. Button and J.C. Wiltse (eds.), *Millimeter Systems,* Vol. 4 (series

on Infrared and Millimeter Waves), Academic Press, New York, 1981.

10. F.A. Benson and F.J. Tischer, "Some Guiding Structures for Millimeter Waves," *IEE Proc.*, Vol. 131, Pt. A, No. 7, pp. 429–449, Sept. 1984.

Microwave Integrated Circuits and Planar Transmission Lines

11. L. Young and H. Sobol (eds.), *Advances in Microwaves*, Vol. 8, Academic Press, New York, 1974.

12. K.C. Gupta and A. Singh (eds.), *Microwave Integrated Circuits*, Halsted Press, New York, 1975.

13. J. Frey and K. Bhasin (eds.), *Microwave Integrated Circuits*, 2nd Ed., Artech House, MA, 1985.

14. T.C. Edwards, *Foundations for Microstrip Circuit Design*, John Wiley and Sons, New York, 1981.

15. C.A. Harper (ed.), *Handbook of Thick Film Hybrid Microelectronics*, McGraw-Hill, New York, 1974.

16. J.P. Ramy *et al.*, "Optimization of the Thick and Thin Film Technologies for Microwave Circuits on Alumina and Fused Silica Substrates," *IEEE Trans. Microwave Theory Tech.*, Vol. MTT-26, pp. 814–820, Oct. 1978.

17. R.S. Pengelly, "Hybrid vs. Monolithic Microwave Circuits—A Matter of Cost," *Microwave Systems News*, Vol. 13, pp. 77–114, Jan. 1983.

18. S. Hori *et al.*, "GaAs Monolithic MICs for Direct Broadcast Satellite Receivers," *IEEE Trans. Microwave Theory Tech.*, Vol. MTT-31, pp. 1089–1095, Dec. 1983.

19. A. Chu, W.E. Courtney, and L.J. Mahoney, "Monolithic Circuits for Millimeter Wave Systems," *Microwave Journal*, Vol. 26, pp. 28–46, Feb. 1983.

20. R.M. Barrett, "Etched Sheets Serve as Microwave Components," *Electronics*, Vol. 25, pp. 114–118, June 1952.

21. S.B. Cohn, "Problems in Strip Transmission Lines," *IRE Trans. Microwave Theory Tech.*, Vol. MTT-3, pp. 119–126, March 1955.

22. S. Ramo and J.R. Whinnery, *Fields and Waves in Communication Electronics*, John Wiley and Sons, New York, 1965.

23. H. Howe, *Stripline Circuit Design*, Artech House, MA, 1974.

24. M.A.R. Gunston, *Microwave Transmission Line Impedance Data*, Van Nostrand Reinhold, London, 1972.

25. D.D. Grieg and H.F. Englemann, "Microstrip—A New Transmission Technique for the Kilomegacycle Range," *Proc. IRE,* Vol. 40, pp. 1644–1650, Dec. 1952.

26. M.V. Schneider, "Microstrip Lines for Microwave Integrated Cir-

cuits," *Bell Syst. Tech. J.*, Vol. 48, pp. 1421–1444, May–June 1969.

27. E.J. Denlinger, "A Frequency Dependent Solution for Microstrip Transmission Lines," *IEEE Trans. Microwave Theory Tech.*, Vol. MTT-19, pp. 30–39, Jan. 1971.

28. T. Itoh and R. Mittra, "Spectral Domain Approach for Calculating the Dispersion Characteristics of Microstrip Lines," *IEEE Trans. Microwave Theory Tech.*, Vol. MTT-21, pp. 496–499, July 1973.

29. G.D. Vendelin, "Limitations on Stripline Q," *Microwave Journal*, Vol. 13, pp. 63–69, May 1970.

30. R. Mittra and T. Itoh, "Analysis of Microstrip Transmission Lines," in *Advances in Microwaves*, Vol. 8 (pp. 67–141), Academic Press, New York, 1974.

31. K.C. Gupta, R. Garg, and I.J. Bahl, *Microstrip Lines and Slotlines*, Artech House, MA, 1979.

32. S.B. Cohn, "Slotline on a Dielectric Substrate," *IEEE Trans. Microwave Theory Tech.*, Vol. MTT-17, pp. 768–778, Oct. 1969.

33. G.H. Robinson and J.L. Allen, "Slotline Application to Miniature Ferrite Devices," *IEEE Trans. Microwave Theory Tech.*, Vol. MTT-17, pp. 1097–1101, Dec. 1969.

34. L. Courtois and M. De Vecchis, "A New Class of Non-reciprocal Components using Slotline," *IEEE Trans. Microwave Theory Tech.*, Vol. MTT-23, pp. 511–516, June 1975.

35. M.V. Schneider, "Dielectric Loss in Integrated Microwave Circuits," *Bell Syst. Tech. J.*, Vol. 48, pp. 2325–2332, Sept. 1969.

36. J.I. Smith, "The Even- and Odd-Mode Capacitance Parameters for Coupled Lines on Suspended Substrate," *IEEE Trans. Microwave Theory Tech.*, Vol. MTT-19, pp. 424–431, May 1971.

37. F.E. Gardiol, "Careful MIC Design Prevents Waveguide Modes," *Microwaves*, Vol. 16, pp. 188, 190–191, May 1977.

38. S.B. Cohn and G.D. Osterhues, "A More Accurate Model of the TE_{10} Type Waveguide Mode in Suspended Substrate," *IEEE Trans. Microwave Theory Tech.*, Vol. MTT-30, pp. 293–294, March 1982. See also correction, *IEEE Trans. Microwave Theory Tech.*, Vol. MTT-30, p. 1291, Aug. 1982.

39. I.J. Bahl and P. Bhartia, "Characteristics of Inhomogeneous-Coupled Stripline," *IEEE Trans. Microwave Theory Tech.*, Vol. MTT-28, pp. 529–535, June 1980.

40. J.L. Allen and M.F. Estes, "Broadside-Coupled Strips in a Layered Dielectric Medium," *IEEE Trans. Microwave Theory Tech.*, Vol. MTT-20, pp. 662–669, Oct. 1972. See also correction, *IEEE Trans. Microwave Theory Tech.*, Vol. MTT-23, p. 779, Sept. 1975.

41. B. Bhat and S.K. Koul, "Unified Approach to Solve a Class of Strip and Microstrip-like Transmission Lines," *IEEE Trans. Microwave*

Theory Tech., Vol. MTT-30, pp. 679–685, May 1982. See also correction, *IEEE Trans. Microwave Theory Tech.*, Vol. MTT-30, p. 2067, Nov. 1982.

42. K. Kawano, "Hybrid Mode Analysis of a Broadside-Coupled Microstrip Line," *IEE Proc.*, Vol. 131, Pt. H, No. 1, pp. 21–24, Feb. 1984.

43. S.K. Koul and B. Bhat, "Broadside-Edge Coupled Symmetric Strip Transmission Lines," *IEEE Trans. Microwave Theory Tech.*, Vol. MTT-30, pp. 1874–1880, Nov. 1982.

44. J.E. Dalley, "A Stripline Directional Coupler Utilizing a Nonhomogeneous Dielectric Medium," *IEEE Trans. Microwave Theory Tech.*, Vol. MTT-17, pp. 706–712, Sept. 1969.

45. K. Shibata *et al.*, "Method for Improving Microstrip Coupler Directivity," *Electron. Lett.*, Vol. 17, No. 20, pp. 732–733, Oct. 1981.

46. S.K. Koul and B. Bhat, "Propagation Parameters of Coupled Microstrip-like Transmission Lines for Millimeter Wave Applications," *IEEE Trans. Microwave Theory Tech.*, Vol. MTT-29, pp. 1364–1370, Dec. 1981.

47. S.K. Koul and B. Bhat, "Characteristic Impedance of Microstrip-like Transmission Lines for Millimeter Wave Applications," *Arch. Elek. Ubertragung*, Vol. 35, pp. 253–258, June 1981.

48. B.E. Spielman, "Dissipative Loss Effects in Isolated and Coupled Transmission Lines," *IEEE Trans. Microwave Theory Tech.*, Vol. MTT-25, pp. 648–656, Aug. 1977.

49. C.P. Wen, "Coplanar Waveguide: A Surface Strip Transmission Line Suitable for Nonreciprocal Gyromagnetic Device Application," *IEEE Trans. Microwave Theory Tech.*, Vol. MTT-17, pp. 1087–1090, Dec. 1969.

50. J.B. Knorr and K.D. Kuchler, "Analysis of Coupled Slots and Coplanar Strips on Dielectric Substrate," *IEEE Trans. Microwave Theory Tech.*, Vol. MTT-23, pp. 541–548, July 1975.

51. G. Ghione and C. Naldi, "Analytical Formulas for Coplanar Lines in Hybrid and Monolithic MICs," *Electron. Lett.*, Vol. 20, No. 4, pp. 179–181, Feb. 1984.

52. N.G. Alexopoulos and S.A. Maas, "Characteristics of Microstrip Directional Couplers on Anisotropic Substrates," *IEEE Trans. Microwave Theory Tech.*, Vol. MTT-30, pp. 1267–1270, Aug. 1982.

53. S.K. Koul and B. Bhat, "Generalized Analysis of Microstrip-like Transmission Lines and Coplanar Strips with Anisotropic Substrates for MIC, Electro-optic Modulator, and SAW Applications," *IEEE Trans. Microwave Theory Tech.*, Vol. MTT-31, pp. 1051–1059, Dec. 1983.

54. R.P. Owens, J.E. Aitken, and T.C. Edwards, "Quasistatic Char-

acteristics of Microstrip on an Anisotropic Sapphire Substrate," *IEEE Trans. Microwave Theory Tech.*, Vol. MTT-24, pp. 495–505, Aug. 1976.

55. H. Shibata, S. Minakawa, and R. Terakado, "Analysis of the Shielded Strip Transmission Line with an Anisotropic Medium," *IEEE Trans. Microwave Theory Tech.*, Vol. MTT-30, pp. 1264–1267, Aug. 1982.

56. S.K. Koul and B. Bhat, "Transverse Transmission Line Method for the Analysis of Broadside-Coupled Microstrip Lines with Anisotropic Substrates," *Arch. Elek. Ubertragung*, Vol. 27, pp. 59–64, Jan.-Feb. 1983.

57. S.K. Koul and B. Bhat, "Inverted Microstrip and Suspended Microstrip with Anisotropic Substrates," *Proc. IEEE*, Vol. 70, pp. 1230–1231, Oct. 1982.

58. S.K. Koul and B. Bhat, "Shielded Edge-Coupled Microstrip Structure with Anisotropic Substrates," *Arch. Elek. Ubertragung*, Vol. 37, pp. 269–274, July-Aug. 1983.

59. B. Bhat and S.K. Koul, "A New Approach to Analyse Microstriplike Transmission Lines with Anisotropic Substrates with Tilted Optical Axis," *IEE Proc.*, Vol. 131, Pt. H, No. 3, pp. 191–197, June 1984. See also correction, *IEE Proc.*, Vol. 131, Pt. H, No. 5, p. 289, Oct. 1984.

60. Y. Tokumitsu *et al.*, "50 GHz IC Components using Alumina Substrates," *IEEE Trans. Microwave Theory Tech.*, Vol. MTT-31, pp. 121–128, Feb. 1983.

61. T. Nakagani, H. Yatsuka, and M. Ishizaki, "Millimeter Wave Integrated Circuits using Alumina Substrates," *Fujitsu Sci. and Tech. J.*, Vol. 14, No. 4, pp. 33–43, Dec. 1978.

62. P.L. Lowbridge, C. Burnett, and B. Prime, "W-Band High Reliability Hermetically Sealed Microstrip Receiver," Military Microwave Conf., London, Oct. 1984, *Conf. Digest*, pp. 502–511.

63. M. Dydyk and B.D. Moore, "Shielded Microstrip Aids V-band Receiver Designs," *Microwaves*, Vol. 21, pp. 77–82, March 1982.

64. K. Chang *et al.*, "V-Band Low Noise Integrated Circuit Receiver," *IEEE Trans. Microwave Theory Tech.*, Vol. MTT-31, pp. 146–154, Feb. 1983.

65. R.S. Tahim, G.M. Hayashibara, and K. Chang, "Design and Performance of W-Band Broadband Integrated Circuit Mixers," *IEEE Trans. Microwave Theory Tech.*, Vol. MTT-31, pp. 277–283, March 1983.

66. L.Q. Bui, N. Ton, and D. Ball, "A D-Band Millimeter-Wave Crossbar Mixer," *IEEE MTT-S Int. Microwave Symp. Digest*, 1984, pp. 555–556.

Fin-Line and E-Plane Integrated Circuits
67. P.J. Meier, "Two New Integrated-Circuit Media with Special Advantages at Millimeter Wavelengths," *IEEE MTT-S Int. Microwave Symp. Digest*, 1972, pp. 221–223.
68. P.J. Meier, "Integrated Fin-Line Millimeter Components," *IEEE Trans. Microwave Theory Tech.*, Vol. MTT-22, pp. 1209–1216, Dec. 1974.
69. R.N. Bates, "E-Planes Drop Millimeter Costs," *Microwave Systems News.*, Vol. 10, pp. 74–80, Dec. 1980.
70. J.B. Davies and D. Mirshekar-Syahkal, "Spectral Domain Solution of Arbitrary Coplanar Transmission Line with Multilayer Substrate," *IEEE Trans. Microwave Theory Tech.*, Vol. MTT-25, pp. 143–146, Feb. 1977.
71. L.P. Schmidt, T. Itoh, and H. Hofmann, "Characteristics of Unilateral Fin-Line Structures with Arbitrarily Located Slots," *IEEE Trans. Microwave Theory Tech.*, Vol. MTT-29, pp. 352–355, April 1981.
72. K. Solbach, "The Status of Printed Millimeter Wave E-Plane Circuits," *IEEE Trans. Microwave Theory Tech.*, Vol. MTT-31, pp. 107–121, Feb. 1983.

Dielectric Integrated Guides
73. D.D. King, "Properties of Dielectric Image Lines," *IRE Trans. Microwave Theory Tech.*, Vol. MTT-3, pp. 75–81, March 1955.
74. D.D. King and S.P. Schlesinger, "Losses in Dielectric Image Lines," *IRE Trans. Microwave Theory Tech.*, Vol. MTT-5, pp. 31–35, Jan. 1957.
75. E.A.J. Marcatili, "Dielectric Rectangular Waveguide and Directional Coupler for Integrated Optics," *Bell Syst. Tech. J.*, Vol. 48, pp. 2071–2102, Sept. 1969.
76. R.M. Knox and P.P. Toulios, "Integrated Circuits for the Millimeter through Optical Frequency Range," *Proc. Symp. Submillimeter Waves*, New York, March 31–April 2, 1970.
77. R.M. Knox, "Dielectric Waveguide-Microwave Integrated Circuits—An Overview," *IEEE Trans. Microwave Theory Tech.*, Vol. MTT-24, pp. 806–814, Nov. 1976.
78. W.V. McLevige, T. Itoh, and R. Mittra, "New Waveguide Structures for Millimeter-Wave and Optical Integrated Circuits," *IEEE Trans. Microwave Theory Tech.*, Vol. MTT-23, pp. 788–794, Oct. 1975.
79. K. Solbach and I. Wolff, "The Electromagnetic Fields and Phase Constants of Dielectric Image Lines," *IEEE Trans. Microwave Theory Tech.*, Vol. MTT-26, pp. 266–274, April 1978.
80. R.J. Collier and R.D. Birch, "The Bandwidth of Image Guide,"

IEEE Trans. Microwave Theory Tech., Vol. MTT-28, pp. 932–935, Aug. 1980.

81. N. Deo and R. Mittra, "A Technique for Analyzing Planar Dielectric Waveguides for Millimeter Wave Integrated Circuits," *Arch. Elek. Ubertragung,* Vol. 37, pp. 236–244, July-Aug. 1983.

82. S. Shindo and T. Itanami, "Low-Loss Rectangular Dielectric Image Line for Millimeter Wave Integrated Circuits," *IEEE Trans. Microwave Theory Tech.*, Vol. MTT-26, pp. 747–751, Oct. 1978.

83. B. Bhat and A.K. Tiwari, "Analysis of Low-Loss Broadside Coupled Dielectric Image Guide Using Mode-Matching Technique," *IEEE Trans. Microwave Theory Tech.*, Vol. MTT-32, pp. 711–717, July 1984.

84. U. Crombach, "Analysis of Single and Coupled Rectangular Dielectric Waveguides," *IEEE Trans. Microwave Theory Tech.*, Vol. MTT-29, pp. 870–874, Sept. 1981.

85. T. Itoh and B. Adelseck, "Trapped Image Guide for Millimeter Wave Circuits," *IEEE Trans. Microwave Theory Tech.*, Vol. MTT-28, pp. 1413–1436, Dec. 1980.

86. W.B. Zhou and T. Itoh, "Analysis of Trapped Image Guides Using Effective Dielectric Constant and Surface Impedances," *IEEE Trans. Microwave Theory Tech.*, Vol. MTT-30, pp. 2163–2166, Dec. 1982.

87. A.K. Tiwari and B. Bhat, "Analysis of Trapped Single and Coupled Image Guides Using the Mode-Matching Technique," *Arch. Elek. Ubertragung,* Vol. 38, pp. 181–185, May-June, 1984.

88. T. Yoneyama and S. Nishida, "Nonradiative Dielectric Waveguide for Millimeter Wave Integrated Circuits," *IEEE Trans. Microwave Theory Tech.*, Vol. MTT-29, pp. 1188–1192, Nov. 1981.

89. T. Yoneyama, M. Yamaguchi, and S. Nishida, "Bends in Nonradiative Dielectric Waveguide," *IEEE Trans. Microwave Theory Tech.*, Vol. MTT-30, pp. 2146–2150, Dec. 1982.

90. T. Yoneyama, N. Tozawa, and S. Nishida, "Coupling Characteristics of Nonradiative Dielectric Waveguides," *IEEE Trans. Microwave Theory Tech.*, Vol. MTT-31, pp. 648–654, Aug. 1983.

91. T. Itoh, "Inverted Strip Dielectric Waveguide for Millimeter Wave Integrated Circuits," *IEEE Trans. Microwave Theory Tech.*, Vol. MTT-24, pp. 821–827, Nov. 1976.

92. R. Mittra, Y.L. Hou, and V. Jamnejad, "Analysis of Open Dielectric Waveguides Using Mode-Matching Technique and Variational Methods," *IEEE Trans. Microwave Theory Tech.*, Vol. MTT-28, pp. 36–43, Jan. 1980.

93. J.F. Miao and T. Itoh, "Hollow Image Guide and Overlayed Image Guide Coupler," *IEEE Trans. Microwave Theory Tech.*, Vol. MTT-30, pp. 1826–1831, Nov. 1982.

94. K. Solbach, "The Fabrication of Dielectric Image Lines Using Casting Resins and the Properties of the Lines in the Millimeter Wave Range," *IEEE Trans. Microwave Theory Tech.*, Vol. MTT-24, pp. 879–881, Nov. 1976.
95. M.R. Inggs and N. Williams, "Thick Film Fabrication Techniques for Millimeter Wave Dielectric Waveguide Integrated Circuits," *Electron. Lett.*, Vol. 16, No. 7, pp. 245–247, March 1980.
96. R.V. Gelsthorpe, N. Williams, and N.M. Davey, "Dielectric Waveguide: A Low Cost Technology for Millimeter Wave Integrated Circuits," *The Radio and Electronics Engineer,* Vol. 52, pp. 522–528, Nov.-Dec. 1982.
97. R. Mittra and S.W. Lee, *Analytical Techniques in the Theory of Guided Waves,* Macmillan, New York, 1971.
98. S.T. Peng and A.A. Oliner, "Guidance and Leakage Properties of a Class of Open Dielectric Waveguides: Part I—Mathematical Formulations," *IEEE Trans. Microwave Theory Tech.*, Vol. MTT-29, pp. 843–855, Sept. 1981.
99. A.A. Oliner *et al.*, "Guidance and Leakage Properties of a Class of Open Dielectric Waveguides: Part II—New Physical Effects," *IEEE Trans. Microwave Theory Tech.*, Vol. MTT-29, pp. 855–869, Sept. 1981.
100. J.H. Hinken, "Waveguides Become Integrated Circuits in New Space and Cost Saving Method," *Microwave Systems News,* Vol. 13, pp. 106–118, Nov. 1983.
101. A.F. Harvey, "Optical Technique at Microwave Frequencies," *IEE Proc.*, Vol. 106, Pt. B, pp. 141–157, March 1959.
102. J.W. Griemsmann, "Oversized Waveguide," *Microwaves,* Vol. 2, pp. 20–23, 1963.
103. D.J. Harris, "Waveguiding Difficult at Near Millimeter Waves," *Microwave Systems News,* Vol. 10, pp. 62–72, Dec. 1980.
104. A.E. Karbowiak, *Trunk Waveguide Communications,* Chapman and Hall, London, 1965.
105. S.E. Miller, "Waveguide as a Communication Medium," *Bell Syst. Tech. J.,* Vol. 33, pp. 1209–1265, 1954.
106. J.W. Carlin and P. D'Agostino, "Low-Loss Modes in Dielectric Lined Waveguide," *Bell Syst. Tech. J.,* Vol. 50, pp. 1631–1638, May-June, 1971.

H-Guide Structures
107. F.J. Tischer, "Properties of the H-Guide at Microwave and Millimeter Wave Regions," *IEE Proc.*, Vol. 106B, Suppl. 13, pp. 47–53, Jan. 1959.
108. A. Doswell and D.J. Harris, "Modified H-Guide for Millimeter and

Submillimeter Wavelength," *IEEE Trans. Microwave Theory Tech.,* Vol. MTT-21, pp. 587–589, Sept. 1973.

109. R.F.B. Conlon and F.A. Benson, "Propagation and Attenuation in the Double-Strip H-Guide," *IEE Proc.,* Vol. 113, pp. 1311–1320, Aug. 1966.

110. F.J. Tischer, "H-Guide with Laminated Dielectric Slab," *IEEE Trans. Microwave Theory Tech.,* Vol. MTT-18, pp. 9–15, Jan. 1970.

111. D.J. Harris, K.W. Lee, and J.M. Reeves, "Groove and H-Waveguide Design and Characteristics at Short Millimetric Wavelength," *IEEE Trans. Microwave Theory Tech.,* Vol. MTT-26, pp. 998–1001, Dec. 1978.

112. D.J. Harris, K.W. Lee, and R.J. Batt, "Low-Loss Single-Mode Waveguide for Submillimetre and Millimetre Wavelengths," *J. Infrared Physics,* Vol. 18, pp. 741–747, 1978.

113. F.J. Tischer, "A New Type of H-Guide Structure," *Proc. IEEE,* Vol. 56, pp. 1254–1255, July 1968.

114. D.J. Harris and K.W. Lee, "Theoretical and Experimental Characteristics of Double Groove guide for 100 GHz Operation, *IEE Proc.,* Vol. 128, Pt. H, No. 1, pp. 6–10, Feb. 1981.

115. J. Meissner, "Groove Guide Directional Couplers with Improved Bandwidth," *Electron. Lett.,* Vol. 20, No. 17, pp. 701–703, Aug. 1984.

116. F.J. Tischer, "Fence Guide for Millimeter Waves," *Proc. IEEE,* Vol. 56, pp. 1112–1113, July 1971.

117. F.J. Tischer, "Modified H-Guide," *Int. J. Infrared and Millimeter Waves,* Vol. 3, pp. 309–318, 1982.

Chapter 2
Analysis of Fin Lines: Approximate Methods

2.1 INTRODUCTION

The integrated fin line is a well proven transmission medium for millimeter-wave integrated circuit components. As discussed in Ch. 1, the fin line is particularly useful for the frequency range from 30 to 100 GHz, and with a more careful fabrication its operation can be extended up to about 170 GHz. The attractiveness of fin lines at lower millimeter-wave frequencies is mainly due to a combination of advantageous features—namely, its relatively wide single-mode bandwidth, low-loss characteristics, compatibility with beam-lead devices, and ease of fabrication [1]. The fabrication of fin lines is compatible with the rectangular waveguide, enabling easy transition to the standard waveguide. The main structural aspect of the fin line involves mounting of the dielectric substrate that contains the fin pattern across the broad walls of a split-block rectangular waveguide housing (Fig. 2.1). The realization of the circuit pattern on the dielectric substrate is compatible with planar technology. The fin line thus incorporates the advantages of a planar structure with the waveguide enclosure serving as a metal shield, without any stringent demands upon the fineness of surface finish on its inner walls. Where the substrate passes through the broad walls, the wall thickness is made equal to one quarter-wavelength in the dielectric ($\lambda_d/4$) so as to cause an effective RF short between the fin and the inner wall of the waveguide. The electrical characteristics of the fin line will then be similar to the idealized structure shown in Fig. 2.2(a).

The application potential of fin lines in practical circuits depends on the availability of design information concerning their propagation parameters. Two basic parameters are of prime importance in any circuit design: the guide wavelength and the characteristic impedance. Characterization of discontinuities and resonating elements in fin lines becomes necessary for the design of certain components, such as filters, mixers, and couplers.

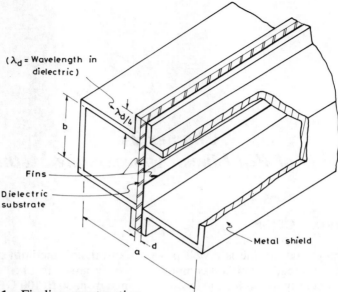

Fig. 2.1 Fin-line construction.

Also, knowledge of the higher order modes and the influence of finite metalization thickness as well as waveguide housing grooves will aid in the accurate design of circuits and better prediction of their performance.

Several analytical techniques have been reported in the literature for studying the behavior of fin-line structures and evaluation of their design parameters. Approximate techniques as well as rigorous methods have been applied by a number of investigators [2–12]. In addition, closed-form expressions for some specific fin-line structures have also been reported in the literature [13–18]. Of particular interest among the approximate techniques is the method originally reported by Cohn for the analysis of the basic slotline [19]. This method is based on the waveguide model, and is known to yield accurate results of guide wavelength and characteristic impedance of slotlines for narrow slot widths. With the same constraint on the slot width, this method can be applied to a number of fin-line configurations possessing certain types of symmetry. The technique, henceforth referred to as *Cohn's method,* is used in this chapter to analyze a variety of fin lines. Except for the antipodal fin line, expressions are derived for the susceptances of other basic fin lines, shown in Fig. 2.2, and some of their variants. The guide wavelength and characteristic impedance are then derived from the susceptance formulas. Other closed-form expressions reported in the literature for specific fin-line structures are also presented in a consolidated manner in this chapter. Within the specified range of validity, these closed-form equations should prove useful in the computer-aided design and optimization of fin-line circuits. Application of rigorous methods and hybrid-mode analyses of symmetrical as well as asymmetrical fin lines are deferred to the next chapter.

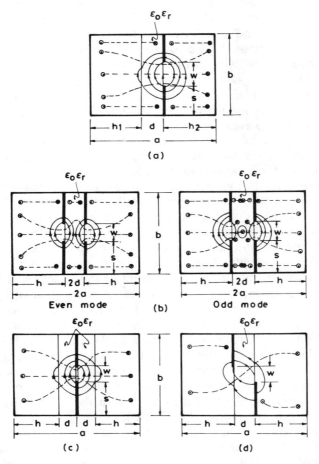

Fig. 2.2 Basic fin-line structures and typical field lines (——— $\vec{E}$, ——— $\vec{H}$):

      (a) unilateral fin line
      (b) bilateral fin line
      (c) insulated fin line
      (d) antipodal fin line

2.2   FIN-LINE STRUCTURES AND FIELD CONFIGURATIONS

Of the fin-line structures proposed to date, the unilateral, bilateral, insulated, and antipodal fin lines may be regarded as *basic* versions, and the rest as their *variants*. These basic structures, and the typical orientation of electric and magnetic field lines in the cross-sectional plane of each structure are shown in Fig. 2.2. Because the fin line is essentially a slotline mounted in the E-plane of a waveguide, for narrow slots, the longitudinal field distribution in the vicinity of the slot resembles that of a slotline. In fact, all slotlines are special cases of fin lines when the housing dimensions are chosen sufficiently large. It is also interesting to note that the unilateral fin line (Fig. 2.2(a)) and the insulated fin line (Fig. 2.2(c)) reduce to the well known ridged waveguide when the dielectric substrate is replaced by air ($\epsilon_r = 1$). The bilateral fin line shown in Fig. 2.2(b) is basically a broadside-coupled slotline with a rectangular shield, which, in principle, can support two fundamental modes, called the even-mode and odd-mode. In the even-mode, the two slots are considered to be excited with voltages that are equal in magnitude and in-phase. For this case, the electric field lines across the two slots become oriented in the same direction. In the case of the odd-mode, the excitations across the two slots are equal in magnitude, but out-of-phase, so that the electric field lines are oppositely directed. At the symmetric E-plane passing through the center of the broad walls of the guide, the normal component of the E-field is zero for the even-mode excitation, whereas the tangential component of the E-field becomes zero for the odd-mode excitation. This plane of symmetry is therefore equivalent to a magnetic wall and an electric wall for the even-mode and odd-mode, respectively. When a bilateral fin line is excited by a rectangular waveguide operating in the TE_{10} mode, as is usually the practice, the fields correspond to the even-mode excitation only. In the antipodal fin line, because the fins are asymmetrically placed, one on either side of the substrate, the field pattern is distinctly different from that in the other three basic versions (Fig. 2.2(d)).

A special feature of the antipodal fin line is that the orientation of the electric field between the two fins can be changed by varying their width. This property is useful in the design of transitions requiring the twisting of E-field lines between one transmission line and another, for example, as in a rectangular waveguide to microstrip transition [20]. Because over-lapping of fins is possible, the antipodal fin line can offer wave impedances starting from a low value of 10 Ω up to about 500 Ω. However, in the unilateral, insulated, and bilateral fin lines, wave impedances are limited to values above 100 Ω because of the restriction on the minimum achievable slot widths.

Figure 2.3 shows the cross-sectional views of the edge-coupled unilateral fin line and the edge-coupled bilateral fin line, as well as the typical field patterns for each of the fundamental modes that these guides can support. For the edge-coupled bilateral fin line, only the electric field lines are shown in order to avoid crowding. The magnetic field lines can be visualized from the magnetic field patterns of the edge-coupled unilateral fin line (Fig. 2.3(a)) and the bilateral fin line (Fig. 2.2(b)). The designations "even-mode" and "odd-mode" follow the same definition as used above for

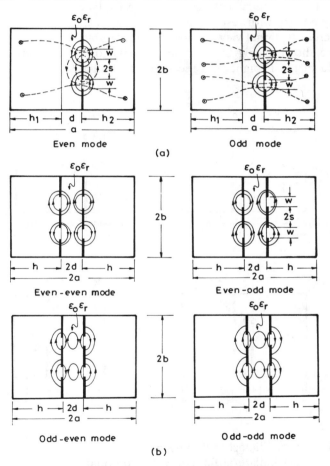

Fig. 2.3 Basic coupled fin-line structures and typical field lines ($\underrightarrow{\quad\quad} \vec{E}$, $\underrightarrow{----} \vec{H}$):

    (a) edge-coupled unilateral fin line

    (b) edge-coupled bilateral fin line

describing the excitation in a bilateral fin line—namely, that the plane of symmetry represents a magnetic wall for the even-mode and an electric wall for the odd-mode. A slight clarification, however, is necessary. In the edge-coupled unilateral fin line, the plane of symmetry coincides with the H-plane of the rectangular guide, and it passes through the center of the two side walls. The edge-coupled bilateral fin line possesses two planes of symmetry. The guide supports four fundamental modes, designated as the even-even, even-odd, odd-even, and odd-odd modes. The first designation refers to the symmetry with respect to the E-plane, and the second refers to the symmetry with respect to the H-plane of the waveguide.

The cross-sectional views of some useful double-dielectric fin-line structures are shown in Fig. 2.4. These make use of two dielectric substrates mounted in the E-plane of a rectangular waveguide, as demonstrated in

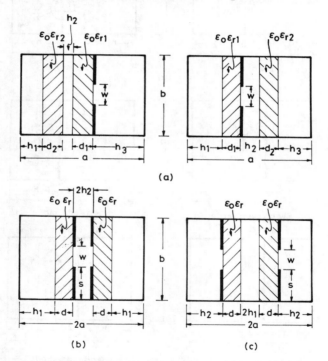

Fig. 2.4 Double-dielectric fin-line structures:
  (a) unilateral fin line with additional dielectric
  (b) double-dielectric bilateral fin line (fins facing each other)
  (c) double-dielectric bilateral fin line (fins facing side walls)

Fig. 2.5. One obvious advantage is the flexibility offered to the designer for changing the propagation parameters by simply varying the air gap between the two substrates. The double-dielectric bilateral fin lines (Fig. 2.4(b, c)) have potential use in the design of millimeter-wave filters, especially when very sharp cut-off is desired in their characteristics. Double-dielectric fin lines also offer a convenient geometry for the design of transitions from fin line to microstrip-variant transmission lines, particularly the shielded inverted microstrip and the shielded suspended microstrip.

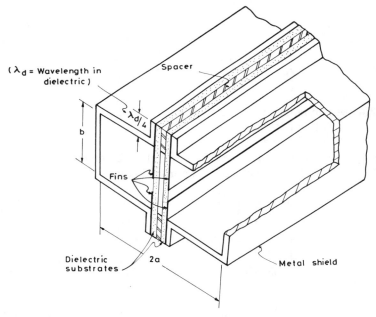

Fig. 2.5 Construction of a double-dielectric fin line.

Figure 2.6 shows a class of asymmetric fin lines. These find useful applications in filters [21] and in the construction of oscillators [22–23]. Edge-coupled fin lines in double-dielectric configuration (Fig. 2.7) form another class, which find applications in the design of filters, directional couplers, and balanced mixers [24–26]. In addition to the aforementioned structures, miscellaneous types such as the multislot fin lines (usually three or four slots) (Fig. 2.8(a)), asymmetric bilateral fin lines (Fig. 2.8(b)), edge-coupled fin lines with unequal slot widths (Fig. 2.8(c)), and edge-coupled bilateral fin lines with unequal slot widths (Fig. 2.8(d)) find application in special circuits. In a practical system, more than one fin-line configuration is generally required to realize different circuit functions.

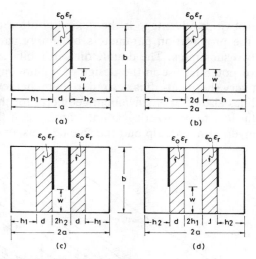

Fig. 2.6 Asymmetric fin-line structures:
  (a) unilateral
  (b) bilateral
  (c) double-dielectric bilateral (fins facing each other)
  (d) double-dielectric bilateral (fins facing side walls)

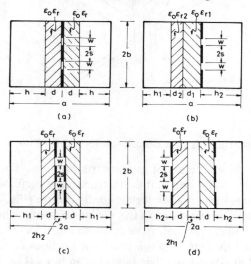

Fig. 2.7 Edge-coupled double-dielectric fin-line structures:
  (a) insulated
  (b) double layer
  (c) double-dielectric bilateral (fins facing each other)
  (d) double-dielectric bilateral (fins facing side walls)

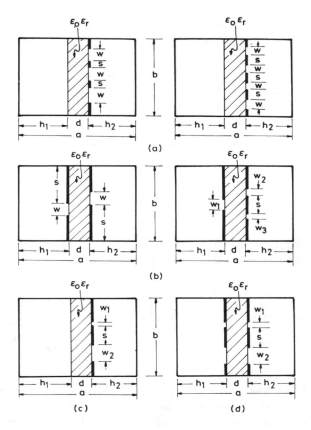

Fig. 2.8 Special fin-line structures:
  (a) multislot edge-coupled fin lines
  (b) asymmetric bilateral fin lines
  (c) edge-coupled fin line with unequal slot widths
  (d) edge-coupled bilateral fin line with unequal slot widths

2.3 ANALYSIS OF A GENERAL SYMMETRIC FIN-LINE STRUCTURE—COHN'S METHOD

Figure 2.9(a) shows the cross section of a general symmetric fin-line structure with coupled slots and layered dielectrics. The dielectrics are assumed to be isotropic, homogeneous, and lossless. In addition, metalization is assumed to be of infinite conductivity and negligible thickness. This structure can support four independent modes of propagation. They are, odd-odd (oo), even-odd (eo), odd-even (oe), and even-even (ee) modes. The structure can be analyzed for each of these modes of excitation

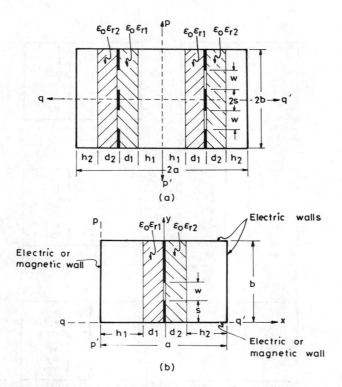

Fig. 2.9 (a) Cross section of a general symmetric fin-line structure
with coupled slots and layered dielectrics.
(b) One quarter of the structure for the purpose of analysis.

by considering the following boundary wall conditions at the planes of
symmetry pp' and qq':

Case A: odd-odd mode—pp' electric wall, qq' electric wall
Case B: even-odd mode—pp' magnetic wall, qq' electric wall
Case C: odd-even mode—pp' electric wall, qq' magnetic wall
Case D: even-even mode—pp' magnetic wall, qq' magnetic wall

Because the structure is symmetrical about pp' and qq', it suffices to
consider only one-quarter of the structure, as shown in Fig. 2.9(b), with
appropriate boundary conditions for each of the four cases. The problem
is thus reduced to that of analyzing a fin line with a single slot. Following
the analysis presented by Cohn [19] for a slotline, the solution is sought
in terms of infinite orthogonal sets of rectangular waveguide modes, and
hence an expression is derived for the susceptance at the plane of the slot.

Case A: Odd-Odd Mode Excitation

Figure 2.10(a) shows the cross section of the fin line for odd-odd mode excitation. Assume two slot waves of equal amplitude traveling in the $+z$ and $-z$ directions along the slot. Then, at transverse planes spaced by $\lambda/2$ (λ is the guide wavelength in fin line), the transverse electric and the normal magnetic fields can be set equal to zero. Now, consider two such planes at $z = 0$ and $z = \lambda/2 = c$, as shown in Fig. 2.10(b). Electric walls may be placed at these planes. The section of the fin line between these planes supports a resonant mode, and the slot can now be considered as an iris in a rectangular section of the guide, with dielectric layers on either side. The full set of modes to be considered for satisfying the boundary conditions are TE_{1n} with $n \geq 0$ and TM_{1n} with $n \geq 1$. In such a structure transverse resonance occurs, which means that the total susceptance at the plane of the slot is equal to zero. The total susceptance B_t is equal to the

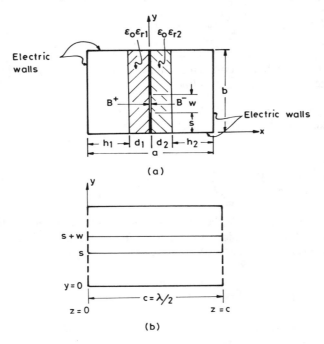

(a)

(b)

Fig. 2.10 (a) Quarter section of the fin line in Fig. 2.9(a) for odd-odd mode excitation (case A).
(b) Insertion of conducting planes at $z = 0$ and $z = c$.

sum of the susceptances of the TE_{10} mode and the capacitive iris susceptances representing the higher order modes on the $+x$ and $-x$ sides of
the iris. Thus,

$$B_t = B^+ + B^- \qquad (2.1)$$

where B^+ is the susceptance at the slot looking to the right and B^- is the
susceptance looking to the left. We first derive a formula for B^+ and then
obtain B^- by appropriately substituting the structural parameters.

In the transverse plane, the E_y and H_z components of each mode are
proportional to $\sin(\pi z/c)\,\cos(n\pi y/b)$. The total E_y and H_z fields at the
plane $x = 0$, $z = c/2$, are functions of y given by

$$E_y = R_0 + \sum_{n>0} R_n \cos(n\pi y/b) \qquad (2.2a)$$

$$H_z = y_{w0}R_0 + \sum_{n>0} y_{wn}R_n \cos(n\pi y/b) \qquad (2.2b)$$

where R_0 and R_n are constants, and n is an integer. The input wave admittances y_{w0} and y_{wn} are defined as

$$y_{w0} = \left(\frac{H_z}{E_y}\right)_{TE_{10}} \qquad (2.3)$$

$$y_{wn} = \frac{(H_z)_{TE_{1n}} + (H_z)_{TM_{1n}}}{(E_y)_{TE_{1n}} + (E_y)_{TM_{1n}}} \qquad (2.4)$$

In order to simplify the analysis, we assume that only TE_{10} mode is
present in the waveguide portion of height w at $x = 0$. E_y and H_z are
therefore specified as

$$E_y = \begin{cases} C_0, & s \le y \le s + w \\ 0, & 0 \le y < s,\ s + w < y \le b \end{cases} \qquad (2.5a)$$

$$H_z = C_0 y'_w, \qquad s \le y \le s + w \qquad (2.5b)$$

where y'_w is the input wave admittance in the waveguide of height w at
the plane $x = 0$, and C_0 is a constant. The assumption that E_y and H_z are
constant across the slot is equivalent to neglecting the higher order modes
in the region $x < 0$. The error involved in the analysis due to this assumption

is negligible for small values of w/b. Equation (2.2a) has the form of a Fourier series. Equating the series to the right-hand side of (2.5a) and solving yields the following expressions for R_0 and R_n:

$$R_0 = C_0\delta \tag{2.6a}$$

$$R_n = \frac{4C_0}{n\pi} \sin(n\pi\delta/2) \cos(n\pi\delta'/2) \tag{2.6b}$$

where

$$\delta = w/b, \ \delta' = (2s + w)/b \tag{2.6c}$$

Equating the expressions for H_z given by (2.2b) and (2.5b), we obtain

$$C_0 y'_w = y_{w0}R_0 + \sum_{n>0} y_{wn}R_n \cos(n\pi y/b) \tag{2.7}$$

Integrating over the slot width w and substituting for R_0 and R_n from (2.6), we have

$$\frac{b}{w}y'_w = y_{w0} + 2 \sum_{n>0} y_{wn} \left[\frac{\sin(n\pi\delta/2)}{(n\pi\delta/2)} \right]^2 \cos^2(n\pi\delta'/2) \tag{2.8}$$

We now replace the wave admittances by the guide admittance defined on the TE$_{10}$ mode voltage-power basis in the complete cross section of the guide at the plane of the slot. The power P_i at the plane of the slot is obtained from

$$P_i = \frac{1}{2} \int_s^{s+w} \int_0^c E_y H_z dz dy \tag{2.9}$$

After substituting for E_y and H_z from (2.5) and integrating, we get

$$P_i = (wc/2) C_0^2 y'_w \tag{2.10}$$

P_i can also be expressed in terms of the guide admittance Y_g and the slot voltage $V = wE_y$:

$$P_i = Y_g(E_y w)^2 = Y_g C_0^2 w^2 \tag{2.11}$$

Equating the right-hand sides of (2.10) and (2.11), we get

$$y'_w = (2w/c)Y_g \tag{2.12}$$

Similarly, the wave admittances y_{w0} and y_{wn} can be expressed in terms of guide admittances Y_{g0} and Y_{gn} as

$$y_{w0} = (2b/c)Y_{g0} \tag{2.13a}$$

$$y_{wn} = (2b/c)Y_{gn} \tag{2.13b}$$

Substituting for y'_w, y_{w0}, and y_{wn} from (2.12) and (2.13) in (2.8), we obtain the following expression for the guide admittance Y_g seen by the wave directed into the waveguide of length $(d_2 + h_2)$:

$$Y_g = jB^+ = Y_{g0} + 2 \sum_{n>0} Y_{gn} \left[\frac{\sin(n\pi\delta/2)}{(n\pi\delta/2)} \right]^2 \cos^2(n\pi\delta'/2) \tag{2.14}$$

B^+ represents the susceptance at the location of the slot looking in the $+x$ direction. We now obtain expressions for Y_{g0} and Y_{gn} in terms of the guide parameters.

Let Y_0, γ_0, β_0, and λ_{g0} respectively represent the TE_{10} mode characteristic admittance, propagation constant, phase constant, and guide wavelength of the air region of length h_2 in Fig. 2.10. Similarly, let Y_{20}, γ_{20}, β_{20}, and λ_{g20} represent the corresponding quantities of the TE_{10} mode for the dielectric section of length d_2. Then, the admittance Y_{g0} of the TE_{10} wave directed into the waveguide section of length $(d_2 + h_2)$ terminated in a short circuit is given by

$$Y_{g0} = Y_{20} \tanh \left\{ \gamma_{20}d_2 + \tanh^{-1} \left[\frac{Y_0}{Y_{20}} \coth(\gamma_0 h_2) \right] \right\} \tag{2.15}$$

where

$$\gamma_0 = j\beta_0 = j\frac{2\pi}{\lambda_{g0}} = j\frac{2\pi}{\lambda_0} \sqrt{1 - (\lambda_0/2c)^2} \tag{2.16a}$$

$$\gamma_{20} = j\beta_{20} = j\frac{2\pi}{\lambda_{g20}} = j\frac{2\pi}{\lambda_0} \sqrt{\epsilon_{r2} - (\lambda_0/2c)^2} \tag{2.16b}$$

$$Y_0 = \frac{c}{2b} \frac{\gamma_0}{j\eta k_0} = \frac{c}{2b\eta} (\lambda_0/\lambda_{g0}) \tag{2.17a}$$

$$Y_{20} = \frac{c}{2b} \frac{\gamma_{20}}{j\eta k_0} = \frac{c}{2b\eta} (\lambda_0/\lambda_{g20}) \tag{2.17b}$$

$$\eta = \sqrt{\frac{\mu_0}{\epsilon_0}} \tag{2.18a}$$

$$k_0 = 2\pi/\lambda_0 \tag{2.18b}$$

where η, k_0, and λ_0 are the free-space wave impedance, propagation constant, and wavelength, respectively.

For $n > 0$, both TE_{1n} and TM_{1n} modes are present. For each n, the corresponding TE and TM amplitudes must be chosen such that E_z cancels exactly at $x = 0$. With the total E_z field equal to zero, the boundary condition at $x = 0$ is satisfied. In the following we use shorter notations—namely, TE_n to represent TE_{1n}, and TM_n to represent TM_{1n}.

We now define a parameter D_n as

$$D_n = \frac{(E_y)_{TE_n}}{(E_y)_{TM_n}} \tag{2.19}$$

when

$$(E_z)_{TE_n} + (E_z)_{TM_n} = 0$$

The expressions for y_{wn} in (2.4) can now be written as

$$y_{wn} = \frac{y_{w\ TM_n} + D_n y_{w\ TE_n}}{1 + D_n} \tag{2.20}$$

By using (2.13) in (2.20), we obtain the following expression for Y_{gn}:

$$Y_{gn} = \frac{Y_{g\ TM_n} + D_n Y_{g\ TE_n}}{1 + D_n} \tag{2.21}$$

From the field component formulas for the TE and TM modes, we have

$$D_n = (b/nc)^2 \tag{2.22}$$

The input admittances $Y_{g\ TM_n}$ and $Y_{g\ TE_n}$ looking toward the $+x$ direction at the slot plane for the TM and TE modes for each n are given by

$$Y_{g\ TM_n} =$$

$$Y_{2\ TM_n} \tanh\left\{\gamma_{n2}d_2 + \tanh^{-1}\left[\frac{Y_{0\ TM_n}}{Y_{2\ TM_n}}\coth(\gamma_n h_2)\right]\right\} \tag{2.23a}$$

$$Y_{g\ TE_n} =$$

$$Y_{2\ TE_n} \coth\left\{\gamma_{n2}d_2 + \coth^{-1}\left[\frac{Y_{0\ TE_n}}{Y_{2\ TE_n}}\coth(\gamma_n h_2)\right]\right\} \tag{2.23b}$$

where

$$Y_{0\ TM_n} = \frac{c}{2b}\frac{jk_0}{\eta\gamma_n}, \quad Y_{2\ TM_n} = \frac{c}{2b}\frac{jk_2}{\eta_2\gamma_{n2}} \tag{2.24a}$$

$$Y_{0\ TE_n} = \frac{c}{2b}\frac{\gamma_n}{j\eta k_0}, \quad Y_{2\ TE_n} = \frac{c}{2b}\frac{\gamma_{n2}}{j\eta_2 k_2} \tag{2.24b}$$

$$k_2 = k_0\sqrt{\epsilon_{r2}}, \quad \eta_2 = \frac{\eta}{\sqrt{\epsilon_{r2}}} \tag{2.24c}$$

$$\gamma_n = \left[\left(\frac{\pi n}{b}\right)^2 + \left(\frac{\pi}{c}\right)^2 - \left(\frac{2\pi}{\lambda_0}\right)^2\right]^{1/2}$$

$$= \frac{\pi n}{b}\sqrt{1 - (2b/n\ \lambda_{g0})^2} = \frac{\pi n}{b}\sqrt{1 + (b\ \gamma_0/\pi n)^2} \tag{2.25a}$$

$$\gamma_{n2} = \left[\left(\frac{\pi n}{b}\right)^2 + \left(\frac{\pi}{c}\right)^2 - \left(\frac{2\pi}{\lambda_0}\right)^2\epsilon_{r2}\right]^{1/2}$$

$$= \frac{\pi n}{b}\sqrt{1 - (2b/n\ \lambda_{g20})^2} \tag{2.25b}$$

By using (2.24) in (2.23), we obtain

$$Y_{g\ TM_n} = \frac{c}{2b}\frac{jk_0\epsilon_{r2}}{\eta\gamma_{n2}}\tanh p_{n2} \tag{2.26a}$$

$$Y_{g\ TE_n} = \frac{c}{2b}\frac{\gamma_{n2}}{j\eta k_0}\coth q_{n2} \tag{2.26b}$$

where

$$p_{n2} = \gamma_{n2}d_2 + \tanh^{-1}\left[\frac{\gamma_{n2}}{\gamma_n \epsilon_{r2}} \coth(\gamma_n h_2)\right] \qquad (2.27a)$$

$$q_{n2} = \gamma_{n2}d_2 + \coth^{-1}\left[\frac{\gamma_n}{\gamma_{n2}} \coth(\gamma_n h_2)\right] \qquad (2.27b)$$

By substituting (2.22) and (2.26) in (2.21), we get

$$\eta Y_{gn} = (jck_0/2b\,\gamma_{n2})\frac{[\epsilon_{r2}\tanh p_{n2} - (b\gamma_{n2}/cnk_0)^2\coth q_{n2}]}{[1 + (b/cn)^2]} \qquad (2.28)$$

Similarly, by using (2.16) and (2.17) in (2.15), we can write

$$\eta Y_{g0} = (c\,\lambda_0/2b\,\lambda_{g20})\tanh\{(j2\pi d_2/\lambda_{g20})$$
$$+ \tanh^{-1}[(\lambda_{g20}/\lambda_{g0})\coth(\gamma_0 h_2)]\} \qquad (2.29)$$

Let

$$\xi = \lambda_0/2c \qquad (2.30)$$

Then, γ_0 and γ_{20} in (2.16) can be expressed as

$$\gamma_0 = jk_0\sqrt{1 - \xi^2} \qquad (2.31)$$

$$\gamma_{20} = jk_0\sqrt{\epsilon_{r2} - \xi^2} \qquad (2.32)$$

Define

$$u_2 = \lambda_0/\lambda_{g20} = \sqrt{\epsilon_{r2} - \xi^2} \qquad (2.33a)$$

$$v = \gamma_0/k_0 = j\,\lambda_0/\lambda_{g0} = \sqrt{\xi^2 - 1} \qquad (2.33b)$$

$$G_n = (b\,\gamma_n/\pi n) = \sqrt{1 + (b\gamma_0/\pi n)^2} = \sqrt{1 + (bv/nc\xi)^2} \qquad (2.34a)$$

$$G_{n2} = (b\,\gamma_{n2}/\pi n) = \sqrt{1 - (2b/n\lambda_{g20})^2} = \sqrt{1 - (bu_2/nc\xi)^2} \qquad (2.34b)$$

By using (2.30) and (2.34b) in (2.28), we can write

$$\eta Y_{gn} = (j/2\xi)\left\{\frac{\epsilon_{r2}\tanh p_{n2} - \xi^2 G_{n2}^2 \coth q_{n2}}{[1 + (b/cn)^2]\,nG_{n2}}\right\} \qquad (2.35)$$

where

$$p_{n2} = (\pi n/b)G_{n2}d_2 + \tanh^{-1}[(G_{n2}/G_n \, \epsilon_{r2}) \coth(\gamma_n h_2)] \qquad (2.36a)$$

$$q_{n2} = (\pi n/b)G_{n2}d_2 + \coth^{-1}[(G_n/G_{n2}) \coth(\gamma_n h_2)] \qquad (2.36b)$$

By using (2.33) in (2.29), the expression for ηY_{g0} becomes

$$
\begin{aligned}
\eta Y_{g0} = &(j \, cu_2/2b) \tan\{(\pi u_2 d_2/\xi c) \\
&- \tan^{-1}[(v/u_2) \coth(\gamma_0 h_2)]\}
\end{aligned}
\qquad (2.37)
$$

By substituting for ηY_{g0} and ηY_{gn} from (2.37) and (2.35) in (2.14), we get

$$
\begin{aligned}
\eta B^+ = &(cu_2/2b) \tan\{(\pi u_2 d_2/\xi c) - \tan^{-1}[(v/u_2) \coth (\gamma_0 h_2)]\} \\
&+ \sum_{n>0} (1/\xi)\left\{\frac{\epsilon_{r2} \tanh p_{n2} - \xi^2 G_{n2}^2 \coth q_{n2}}{[1 + (b/cn)^2]G_{n2}}\right\} \\
&\cdot \frac{\sin^2(n\pi\delta/2)}{n(n\pi\delta/2)^2} \cos^2(n\pi\delta'/2)
\end{aligned}
\qquad (2.38)
$$

The first term in (2.38) is the TE_{10} mode susceptance and the second is the discontinuity susceptance representing the effect of higher order modes. The rate of convergence of this series is very slow, but can be improved by the following system of equations (2.39) to (2.43).

Let the nth term in the series be denoted as S_n. If we let $a \to \infty$ and $f \to 0$, then $\lambda = 2c \to \infty$. Each term S_n reduces to S_n' given by

$$S_n' = (u_2^2/\xi) \frac{\sin^2(n\pi\delta/2)}{n(n\pi\delta/2)^2} \cos^2(n\pi\delta'/2) \qquad (2.39)$$

The series in (2.38) may be written as

$$\sum_{n>0} S_n = \sum_{n>0} (S_n - S_n') + \sum_{n>0} S_n' \qquad (2.40)$$

Let the second series on the right-hand side of (2.40) be written as

$$\sum_{n>0} S_n' = \frac{u_2^2 \cdot T}{\xi} \qquad (2.41a)$$

where

$$T = \sum_{n>0} \frac{\sin^2\left(\frac{n\pi\delta}{2}\right)}{n\left(\frac{n\pi\delta}{2}\right)^2} \cdot \cos^2\left(\frac{n\pi\delta'}{2}\right) \tag{2.41b}$$

By expanding, (2.41b) can be expressed in the form:

$$T = \frac{1}{(\pi\delta)^2}\left\{\sum_{n>0}\frac{1}{n^3} + \mathrm{Re}\sum_{n>0}\left[\left(\frac{e^{jn\pi\delta'}}{n^3} - \frac{e^{jn\pi\delta}}{n^3}\right)\right.\right.$$

$$\left.\left. - \frac{1}{2}\left(\frac{e^{jn\pi(\delta'+\delta)}}{n^3} + \frac{e^{jn\pi(\delta'-\delta)}}{n^3}\right)\right]\right\} \tag{2.41c}$$

Equation (2.41c) can be simplified by using the following identity, given in Collin [27]:

$$\sum_{n=1}^{\infty}\frac{e^{jnx}}{n^3} = \left(\frac{x^2}{2}\ln x - \frac{3x^2}{4} - \frac{x^4}{288} - \cdots\right)$$

$$+ \sum_{n=1}^{\infty}\frac{1}{n^3} + j\left(\frac{\pi^2 x}{6} - \frac{\pi x^2}{4} + \frac{x^3}{12}\right) \quad \text{for } 0 < x < 2\pi \tag{2.42}$$

Retaining only the first three terms of the series in x within the first bracket and using the resulting expression given by (2.42) in (2.41c), we obtain

$$T = \frac{1}{(\pi\delta)^2}\left\{\frac{(\pi\delta')^2}{2}\ln(\pi\delta') - \frac{(\pi\delta)^2}{2}\ln(\pi\delta)\right.$$

$$- \frac{[\pi(\delta'+\delta)]^2}{4}\ln[\pi(\delta'+\delta)]$$

$$- \frac{[\pi(\delta'-\delta)]^2}{4}\ln[\pi(\delta'-\delta)] + \frac{3}{2}(\pi\delta)^2$$

$$\left. + \frac{(\pi\delta)^2(\pi\delta')^2}{48} + \frac{(\pi\delta)^4}{144}\right\} \quad \text{for } 0 < s \leqslant \left(\frac{b-w}{2}\right) \tag{2.43a}$$

The above expression for T yields accurate results for $\delta' \leqslant 1$, more specifically for values of s lying in the range $0 < s \leqslant (b - w)/2$. For larger values of s in the range $(b - w)/2 \leqslant s < (b - w)$, the expression for T given in (2.41c) may be expressed in terms of another parameter δ'', instead of δ', where $\delta'' = 2(b - s - w/2)/b$. Because $\delta'' < 1$ for $(2s + w)/b > 1$, the identity given by (2.42) can be used to derive an alternative expression for T. We then get

$$
\begin{aligned}
T = \frac{1}{(\pi\delta)^2} \Bigg\{ & \frac{(\pi\delta'')^2}{2} \ln (\pi\delta'') - \frac{(\pi\delta)^2}{2} \ln (\pi\delta) \\
& - \frac{[\pi(\delta'' + \delta)]^2}{4} \ln [\pi(\delta'' + \delta)] \\
& - \frac{[\pi(\delta'' - \delta)]^2}{4} \ln [\pi(\delta'' - \delta)] + \frac{3}{2} (\pi\delta)^2 \\
& + \frac{(\pi\delta)^2(\pi\delta'')^2}{48} + \frac{(\pi\delta)^4}{144} \Bigg\} \quad \text{for} \ \left(\frac{b-w}{2}\right) \leqslant s < (b-w)
\end{aligned}
$$

(2.43b)

It may be noted that the expression for T given by (2.43b) is the same as (2.43a), except that δ' is replaced by δ''. The variation in T as a function of s is symmetric about the value $s = (b-w)/2$. This is an expected result because for a fixed slot width, as the slot is displaced along the E-plane, the variation in Z and λ/λ_0 should be symmetric about its centrally located position.

In the limiting case when $s = 0$ or $s = b - w$, we have $\delta' = \delta'' = \delta = w/b$. The expression for T simplifies to

$$
T = \left[\frac{3}{2} - \ln (2\pi\delta) + \frac{(\pi\delta)^2}{36} \right]; \quad s = 0, (b-w)
$$

(2.43c)

By using (2.40) and (2.41) in (2.38), the expression for ηB^+ becomes

$$
\begin{aligned}
\eta B^+ = & \frac{cu_2}{2b} \tan \left\{ \frac{\pi u_2 d_2}{\xi c} - \tan^{-1}\left[\frac{v}{u_2} \coth(\gamma_0 h_2) \right] \right\} + \frac{u_2^2 T}{\xi} \\
& + \frac{1}{\xi} \sum_{n=1,2}^{\infty} \left\{ \frac{\epsilon_{r2} \tanh p_{n2} - \xi^2 G_{n2}^2 \coth q_{n2}}{\left[1 + \left(\frac{b}{nc}\right)^2 \right] G_{n2}} - u_2^2 \right\} \\
& \cdot \frac{\sin^2\left(\frac{n\pi\delta}{2}\right)}{n\left(\frac{n\pi\delta}{2}\right)^2} \cos^2\left(\frac{n\pi\delta'}{2}\right)
\end{aligned}
$$

(2.44)

where

$$p_{n2} = \frac{\pi n G_{n2} d_2}{b} + \tanh^{-1}\left[\frac{G_{n2}}{G_n \epsilon_{r2}} \coth(\gamma_n h_2)\right] \qquad (2.45a)$$

$$q_{n2} = \frac{\pi n G_{n2} d_2}{b} + \coth^{-1}\left[\frac{G_n}{G_{n2}} \coth(\gamma_n h_2)\right] \qquad (2.45b)$$

$$G_{n2} = \frac{b\gamma_{n2}}{\pi n} = \sqrt{1 - \left(\frac{bu_2}{nc\xi}\right)^2} \qquad (2.45c)$$

$$u_2 = \sqrt{\epsilon_{r2} - \xi^2} \qquad (2.45d)$$

$$G_n = \frac{b\gamma_n}{\pi n} = \sqrt{1 + \left(\frac{bv}{nc\xi}\right)^2} \qquad (2.45e)$$

$$v = \sqrt{\xi^2 - 1} \qquad (2.45f)$$

$$\gamma_0 = \frac{j\pi}{c\xi}\sqrt{1 - \xi^2} \qquad (2.45g)$$

$$\xi = \frac{\lambda_0}{2c} \qquad (2.45h)$$

and T is given by (2.43)

The susceptance B^- looking toward the left at the location of the slot can be obtained from (2.44) by setting $d_2 = d_1$, $h_2 = h_1$, $\epsilon_{r2} = \epsilon_{r1}$, and $u_2 = u_1$, $\gamma_{n2} = \gamma_{n1}$, $G_{n2} = G_{n1}$, $p_{n2} = p_{n1}$, $q_{n2} = q_{n1}$. Thus,

$$\eta B^- = \frac{cu_1}{2b}\tan\left\{\frac{\pi u_1 d_1}{\xi c} - \tan^{-1}\left[\frac{v}{u_1}\coth(\gamma_0 h_1)\right]\right\} + \frac{u_1^2 T}{\xi}$$

$$+ \frac{1}{\xi}\sum_{n=1,2}^{\infty}\left\{\frac{\epsilon_{r1}\tanh p_{n1} - \xi^2 G_{n1}^2 \coth q_{n1}}{\left[1 + \left(\frac{b}{nc}\right)^2\right]G_{n1}} - u_1^2\right\}$$

$$\cdot \frac{\sin^2\left(\frac{n\pi\delta}{2}\right)}{n\left(\frac{n\pi\delta}{2}\right)^2}\cdot\cos^2\left(\frac{n\pi\delta'}{2}\right) \qquad (2.46)$$

where

$$p_{n1} = \frac{\pi n G_{n1} d_1}{b} + \tanh^{-1}\left[\frac{G_{n1}}{G_n \epsilon_{r1}} \coth(\gamma_n h_1)\right] \qquad (2.47a)$$

$$q_{n1} = \frac{\pi n G_{n1} d_1}{b} + \coth^{-1}\left[\frac{G_n}{G_{n1}} \coth(\gamma_n h_1)\right] \qquad (2.47b)$$

$$G_{n1} = \frac{b\gamma_{n1}}{\pi n} = \sqrt{1 - \left(\frac{bu_1}{nc\xi}\right)^2} \qquad (2.47c)$$

$$u_1 = \sqrt{\epsilon_{r1} - \xi^2} \qquad (2.47d)$$

The expressions for T, G_n, γ_n, v, γ_0, and ξ are defined in (2.43) and (2.45e–h).

The total susceptance B_t at the slot is obtained by adding (2.44) and (2.46). Thus,

$$\eta B_t = \eta(B^+ + B^-) \qquad (2.48)$$

The final formula for ηB_t and all the relevant parameters are consolidated and given below:

$$\eta B_t = \frac{cu_1}{2b} \tan\left\{\frac{\pi u_1 d_1}{\xi c} - \tan^{-1}\left[\frac{v}{u_1} \coth(\gamma_0 h_1)\right]\right\} + \frac{cu_2}{2b}$$

$$\cdot \tan\left\{\frac{\pi u_2 d_2}{c\xi} - \tan^{-1}\left[\frac{v}{u_2} \coth(\gamma_0 h_2)\right]\right\} + \frac{(\epsilon_{r1} + \epsilon_{r2} - 2\xi^2)T}{\xi}$$

$$+ \frac{1}{\xi} \sum_{n=1,2}^{\infty} (H_{n1} + H_{n2}) \frac{\sin^2\left(\frac{n\pi\delta}{2}\right)}{n\left(\frac{n\pi\delta}{2}\right)^2} \cos^2\left(\frac{n\pi\delta'}{2}\right) \qquad (2.49)$$

where, for $i = 1$ or $i = 2$,

$$H_{ni} = \left\{\frac{\epsilon_{ri} \tanh p_{ni} - \xi^2 G_{ni}^2 \coth q_{ni}}{\left[1 + \left(\frac{b}{nc}\right)^2\right] G_{ni}} - u_i^2\right\} \qquad (2.50a)$$

$$p_{ni} = \frac{\pi n G_{ni} d_i}{b} + \tanh^{-1}\left[\frac{G_{ni}}{G_n \epsilon_{ri}} \coth(\gamma_n h_i)\right] \qquad (2.50b)$$

$$q_{ni} = \frac{\pi n G_{ni} d_i}{b} + \coth^{-1}\left[\frac{G_n}{G_{ni}} \coth(\gamma_n h_i)\right] \tag{2.50c}$$

$$G_{ni} = \frac{b\gamma_{ni}}{\pi n} = \sqrt{1 - \left(\frac{bu_i}{nc\xi}\right)^2} \tag{2.50d}$$

$$u_i = \sqrt{\epsilon_{ri} - \xi^2} \tag{2.50e}$$

$$G_n = \frac{b}{\pi n}\gamma_n = \sqrt{1 + \left(\frac{bv}{nc\xi}\right)^2} \tag{2.50f}$$

$$v = \sqrt{\xi^2 - 1} \tag{2.50g}$$

$$\gamma_0 = \frac{j\pi}{c\xi}\sqrt{1 - \xi^2} \tag{2.50h}$$

$$\xi = \frac{\lambda_0}{2c} \tag{2.50i}$$

$$\delta = \frac{w}{b} \tag{2.50j}$$

$$T = \frac{1}{(\pi\delta)^2}\left\{\frac{(\pi\overline{\delta})^2}{2} \ln (\pi\overline{\delta}) - \frac{(\pi\delta)^2}{2} \ln (\pi\delta)\right.$$

$$- \frac{[\pi(\overline{\delta} + \delta)]^2}{4} \ln [\pi(\overline{\delta} + \delta)]$$

$$- \frac{[\pi(\overline{\delta} - \delta)]^2}{4} \ln [\pi(\overline{\delta} - \delta)] + \frac{3}{2} (\pi\delta)^2$$

$$\left. + \frac{(\pi\delta)^4}{144} + \frac{(\pi\delta)^2(\pi\overline{\delta})^2}{48}\right\};$$

$$\overline{\delta} = \delta' = \frac{2s + w}{b}, \quad 0 < s \leq \frac{b - w}{2}$$

$$\overline{\delta} = \delta'' = \frac{2\left(b - s - \dfrac{w}{2}\right)}{b}, \quad \frac{b - w}{2} \leq s < b - w \tag{2.50k}$$

For the special case of a centered slot ($\delta' = 1$), the expression for T reduces to

$$T = \frac{1}{2}\left[\ln\left(\frac{1}{2\pi\delta}\right) + \frac{3}{2}\right] \tag{2.50l}$$

In the limiting case when $s = 0$ or $s = (b - w)$, the expression for T is given by

$$T = \left[\frac{3}{2} - \ln(2\pi\delta) + \frac{(\pi\delta)^2}{36}\right] \tag{2.50m}$$

Depending on the value of ξ, G_{ni} may be real or imaginary. For G_{ni} real,

$$H_{ni} = \left\{ \frac{\epsilon_{ri}\tanh p_{ni} - \xi^2 G_{ni}^2 \coth q_{ni}}{\left[1 + \left(\dfrac{b}{cn}\right)^2\right]G_{ni}} - u_i^2 \right\} \tag{2.51a}$$

where

$$p_{ni} = \frac{\pi n G_{ni} d_i}{b} + \tanh^{-1}\left[\frac{G_{ni}}{G_n \epsilon_{ri}} \coth(\gamma_n h_i)\right] \tag{2.51b}$$

$$q_{ni} = \frac{\pi n G_{ni} d_i}{b} + \coth^{-1}\left[\frac{G_n}{G_{ni}} \coth(\gamma_n h_i)\right] \tag{2.51c}$$

If

$$\left[\frac{G_{ni}}{G_n \epsilon_{ri}} \coth(\gamma_n h_i)\right] > 1$$

then replace $\tanh(p_{ni})$ by $\coth(p_{ni})$ in (2.51a), where

$$p_{ni} = \frac{\pi n G_{ni} d_i}{b} + \coth^{-1}\left[\frac{G_{ni}}{G_n \epsilon_{ri}} \coth(\gamma_n h_i)\right] \tag{2.51d}$$

If

$$\left[\frac{G_n}{G_{ni}} \coth(\gamma_n h_i)\right] < 1,$$

then replace coth q_{ni} by tanh q_{ni} in (2.51a), where

$$q_{ni} = \frac{\pi n G_{ni} d_i}{b} + \tanh^{-1}\left[\frac{G_n}{G_{ni}} \coth(\gamma_n h_i)\right]$$
(2.51e)

For G_{ni} imaginary,

$$H_{ni} = \left\{ \frac{\epsilon_{ri} \tan p'_{ni} - \xi^2 |G_{ni}|^2 \cot q'_{ni}}{\left[1 + \left(\frac{b}{cn}\right)^2\right]|G_{ni}|} - u_i^2 \right\}$$
(2.52a)

where

$$p'_{ni} = \frac{\pi n |G_{ni}| d_i}{b} + \tan^{-1}\left[\frac{|G_{ni}|}{G_n \epsilon_{ri}} \coth(\gamma_n h_i)\right]$$
(2.52b)

$$q'_{ni} = \frac{\pi n |G_{ni}| d_i}{b} + \cot^{-1}\left[\frac{G_n}{|G_{ni}|} \coth(\gamma_n h_i)\right]$$
(2.52c)

Considering the approximations used in the analysis, the final formula (2.49) for ηB_t can be used along with (2.50) to (2.52) for fin lines satisfying the condition $w/b < 0.15$ and $w/d \leqslant 2$.

Case B: Even-Odd Mode Excitation

The structure to be analyzed for the even-odd mode excitation is shown in Fig. 2.11. The expression for ηB^+ is the same as in (2.44) and (2.45). In the expression for ηB^- given by (2.46) and (2.47), $\coth(\gamma_0 h_1)$ is replaced by $\tanh(\gamma_0 h_1)$, and $\coth(\gamma_n h_1)$ by $\tanh(\gamma_n h_1)$. The expression for the total susceptance ηB_t is obtained from (2.49) with $\coth(\gamma_0 h_1)$ and $\coth(\gamma_n h_1)$ replaced by $\tanh(\gamma_0 h_1)$ and $\tanh(\gamma_n h_1)$, respectively.

Case C: Odd-Even Mode Excitation

The structure to be analyzed for the odd-even mode excitation is shown in Fig. 2.12. The modes propagating in this structure are TE_{1n} with $n \geqslant 0$, and TM_{1n} with $n > 0$. In the transverse plane, E_y and H_z components of each mode are proportional to $\sin(\pi z/c) \sin[(2n + 1) \pi y/2b]$. Thus, at $x = 0$ and $z = c/2$, we have

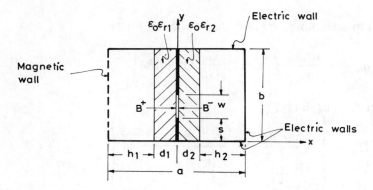

Fig. 2.11 Quarter section of the fin line in Fig. 2.9(a) for even-odd mode excitation (case B).

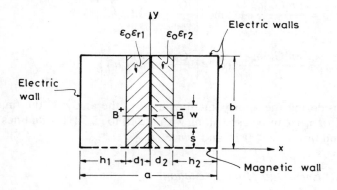

Fig. 2.12 Quarter section of the fin line in Fig. 2.9(a) for odd-even mode excitation (case C).

$$E_y = \sum_{n \geq 0} R_n \sin\left[\frac{(2n + 1)}{2b} \pi y\right] \tag{2.53a}$$

$$H_z = \sum_{n \geq 0} y_{wn} R_n \sin\left[\frac{(2n + 1)}{2b} \pi y\right] \tag{2.53b}$$

where $n = 0, 1, 2, \ldots$; R_n is a constant and y_{wn} is the input wave admittance given by (2.4). Following the steps outlined for case A, the final expression for the total susceptance ηB_t turns out to be

$$\eta B_t = (\epsilon_{r1} + \epsilon_{r2} - 2\xi^2) \frac{T}{\xi} + \frac{1}{\xi} \sum_{n \geqslant 0} (H_{n1} + H_{n2})$$

$$\cdot \frac{\left\{ \sin\left[\frac{(2n+1)}{2} \frac{\pi\delta}{2} \right] \sin\left[\frac{(2n+1)}{2} \frac{\pi\delta'}{2} \right] \right\}^2}{\frac{(2n+1)}{2} \left[\frac{(2n+1)}{2} \cdot \frac{\pi\delta}{2} \right]^2} \qquad (2.54)$$

where, for $i = 1$ or $i = 2$,

$$H_{ni} = \left\{ \frac{\epsilon_{ri} \tanh p_{ni} - \xi^2 G_{ni}^2 \coth q_{ni}}{\left[1 + \left(\frac{b}{(2n+1)c/2} \right)^2 \right] G_{ni}} - u_i^2 \right\} \qquad (2.55a)$$

$$p_{ni} = \frac{(2n+1)\pi}{2} \frac{G_{ni}d_i}{b} + \tanh^{-1}\left[\frac{G_{ni}}{G_n\epsilon_{ri}} \coth(\gamma_n h_i) \right] \qquad (2.55b)$$

$$q_{ni} = \frac{(2n+1)\pi}{2} \frac{G_{ni}d_i}{b} + \coth^{-1}\left[\frac{G_n}{G_{ni}} \coth(\gamma_n h_i) \right] \qquad (2.55c)$$

$$G_{ni} = \frac{b\gamma_{ni}}{\left(\frac{2n+1}{2} \right)\pi} = \sqrt{ 1 - \left\{ \frac{bu_i}{(2n+1)c\xi/2} \right\}^2 } \qquad (2.55d)$$

$$u_i = \sqrt{\epsilon_{ri} - \xi^2} \qquad (2.55e)$$

$$G_n = \frac{b\gamma_n}{\left(\frac{2n+1}{2} \right)\pi} = \sqrt{ 1 + \left\{ \frac{bv}{(2n+1)c\xi/2} \right\}^2 } \qquad (2.55f)$$

$$v = \sqrt{\xi^2 - 1} \qquad (2.55g)$$

$$\xi = \frac{\lambda_0}{2c} \qquad (2.55h)$$

$$\delta = w/b \qquad (2.55i)$$

$$\delta' = \frac{2s + w}{b} \qquad (2.55j)$$

For the range $0 < s \leq (b - w)/2$,

$$
\begin{aligned}
T = \{&(1/\pi\delta)^2[(-(\pi\delta)^2/2)\ln(\pi\delta/4) - ((\pi\delta')^2/2)\ln(\pi\delta'/4) \\
&+ [(\pi(\delta' + \delta))^2/4]\ln(\pi(\delta' + \delta)/4) + [(\pi(\delta' - \delta))^2/4] \\
&\cdot \ln(\pi(\delta' - \delta)/4) + ((\pi\delta)^2(\pi\delta')^2/96)]\}
\end{aligned} \tag{2.55k}
$$

For the range $(b - w)/2 \leq s < (b - w)$,

$$
\begin{aligned}
T = \frac{1}{(\pi\delta)^2} \bigg\{ &-\frac{(\pi\delta)^2}{2}\ln\left(\frac{\pi\delta}{4}\right) + \frac{(\pi\delta'')^2}{2}\ln\left(\frac{\pi\delta''}{4}\right) \\
&- \frac{[\pi(\delta'' + \delta)]^2}{4}\ln\left[\frac{\pi(\delta'' + \delta)}{4}\right] - \frac{[\pi(\delta'' - \delta)]^2}{4}\ln\left[\frac{\pi(\delta'' - \delta)}{4}\right] \\
&+ \frac{3}{2}(\pi\delta)^2 - \frac{(\pi\delta)^4}{288} - \frac{(\pi\delta)^2(\pi\delta'')^2}{96}\bigg\}
\end{aligned} \tag{2.55l}
$$

$$
\delta'' = \frac{2(b - s - w/2)}{b} \tag{2.55m}
$$

For the centered slot ($\delta' = 1$), the expression for T reduces to

$$
T = [(3/4) - (1/2)\ln(\pi\delta/4) - (\pi\delta/2)^2 \cdot (1/144)] \tag{2.56}
$$

Depending on the value of ξ, G_{ni} can be real or imaginary. For G_{ni} real, we have H_{ni}, p_{ni}, and q_{ni} as given by (2.55a–c). For G_{ni} imaginary,

$$
H_{ni} = \left\{ \frac{\epsilon_{ri}\tan p'_{ni} - \xi^2|G_{ni}|^2\cot q'_{ni}}{[1 + [b/((2n + 1)/2)c]^2]\,|G_{ni}|} - u_i^2 \right\} \tag{2.57a}
$$

$$
p'_{ni} = [(2n + 1)\pi/2]\frac{|G_{ni}|d_i}{b} + \tan^{-1}\left[\frac{|G_{ni}|}{G_n\epsilon_{ri}}\coth(\gamma_n h_i)\right] \tag{2.57b}
$$

$$
q'_{ni} = [(2n + 1)\pi/2]\frac{|G_{ni}|d_i}{b} + \cot^{-1}\left[\frac{G_n}{|G_{ni}|}\coth(\gamma_n h_i)\right] \tag{2.57c}
$$

Case D: Even-Even Mode Excitation

The structure to be analyzed for the even-even mode excitation is shown in Fig. 2.13. The expression for the total susceptance ηB_t is obtained from (2.54) by replacing $\coth(\gamma_n h_1)$ by $\tanh(\gamma_n h_1)$.

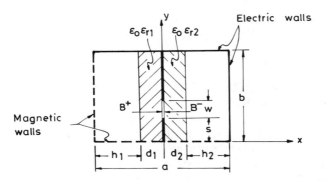

Fig. 2.13   Quarter section of the fin line in Fig. 2.9(a) for even-even
mode excitation (case D).

2.4   FORMULAS FOR GUIDE WAVELENGTH AND CHARACTERISTIC IMPEDANCE

At the transverse resonance frequency, $c = \lambda/2$, where λ is the fin-line
wavelength. Hence, the parameter $\xi = \lambda_0/2c = \lambda_0/\lambda$ when $\eta B_t = 0$. For
a given set of parameters, the value of ξ at which ηB_t becomes zero is
found numerically. The value of the free-space wavelength λ_0 is then de-
termined by using $\lambda_0 = 2c\xi$, and the frequency is calculated from $f = v_0/\lambda_0$, where v_0 is the free-space velocity. Alternatively, given the frequency
f, we can calculate λ.

The ratio of the phase velocity v_{ph} to the group velocity v_g in a fin line
can be computed from [19]:

$$\frac{v_{ph}}{v_g} = \left[1 + \frac{f}{(\lambda_0/\lambda)} \frac{\Delta(\lambda_0/\lambda)}{\Delta f} \right] \qquad (2.58)$$

where; $\Delta(\lambda_0/\lambda)$ and Δf are computed from two separate solutions of
$\eta B_t = 0$; for fixed values of ϵ_{r1}, ϵ_{r2}, w, d_1, d_2, a, and b and for two slightly
different values of $c = \lambda/2$, incremented plus and minus from the desired
value of c. The frequency f is assumed to be midway within the Δf interval.

The fin-line characteristic impedance is obtained from

$$Z = 376.7 \frac{v_{ph}}{v_g} \frac{\pi}{\xi} \frac{\Delta\xi}{-\Delta(\eta B_t)} \quad \text{(ohms)} \qquad (2.59)$$

First, $\Delta(\eta B_t)$ is computed with ϵ_{r1}, ϵ_{r2}, d_1, d_2, w, a, b, and $c = \lambda/2$ held constant, and with ξ slightly incremented plus and minus from the value $\xi = \lambda_0/\lambda$ at $\eta B_t = 0$. We obtain v_{ph}/v_g from (2.58) for the same set of parameters.

2.5 SUSCEPTANCE FORMULAS FOR SPECIFIC FIN-LINE STRUCTURES

Susceptance formulas for a number of practical structures can be obtained from the formulas derived in Sec. 2.3 for cases A, B, C, and D by the substitution of appropriate structural parameters. Formulas that can be directly programmed are listed in Appendix 2-A for commonly used fin-line structures as well as those which are considered to be of potential use in special circuit applications. These structures are listed below:

1. Unilateral fin line (Fig. 2.2(a)).
2. Insulated fin line (Fig. 2.2(c)).
3. Bilateral fin line (Fig. 2.2(b)).
4. Double-dielectric bilateral fin line with fins facing each other (Fig. 2.4(b)).
5. Double-dielectric bilateral fin line with fins facing the side walls (Fig. 2.4(c)).
6. Special cases of unilateral, insulated, bilateral, and double-dielectric fin lines: (a) Slot centered in the E-plane (Figs. 2.2(a–c) and 2.4(b, c) with $b = 2s + w$); (b) Asymmetric fin lines (Fig. 2.6).
7. Edge-coupled unilateral fin line (Fig. 2.3(a)).
8. Edge-coupled insulated fin line (Fig. 2.7(a)).
9. Edge-coupled bilateral fin line (Fig. 2.3(b)).
10. Edge-coupled double-dielectric bilateral fin line with fins facing each other (Fig. 2.7(c)).
11. Edge-coupled double-dielectric bilateral fin line with fins facing the side walls (Fig. 2.7(d)).

2.6 CLOSED-FORM DESIGN FORMULAS FOR UNILATERAL AND BILATERAL FIN LINES

In the preceding sections, we presented an approximate analysis of a general symmetric fin line, based on Cohn's method. The susceptance formulas presented in Appendix 2-A can be directly programmed to compute the propagation parameters of a class of symmetric fin lines. More exact formulas based on spectral domain methods, which are valid over a wider range of parameters, are derived in the next chapter. Both of these methods require detailed programming. From the point of view of computer-aided design and optimization, it would be desirable to have simple closed-form expressions for quickly obtaining the dispersion characteristics and, if necessary, for carrying out a tolerance analysis of fin lines.

In the following, closed-form expressions are presented for unilateral and bilateral fin lines. All the formulas presented in Secs. 2.6.1 to 2.6.4 refer to the unilateral fin line with symmetrically placed fins and centered slot as shown in Fig. 2.14(a), and to the bilateral fin line with symmetrically placed substrate and slots centered in the E-plane as shown in Fig. 2.14(b). Formulas for unilateral and bilateral fin lines with slots that are not necessarily centered in the E-plane are listed in Sec. 2.6.5. The structural parameters appearing in these formulas refer to Figs. 2.15 and 2.16.

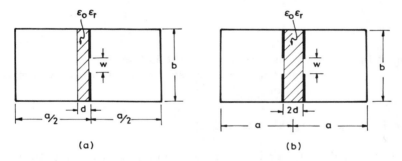

(a)   (b)

Fig. 2.14 (a) Unilateral fin line.
(b) Bilateral fin line.

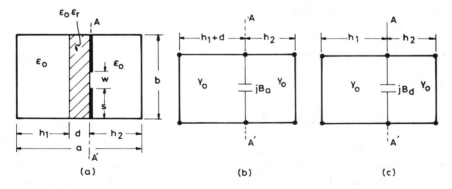

(a)   (b)   (c)

Fig. 2.15 (a) Cross section of a unilateral fin line.
(b) Equivalent transverse network at cut-off ($\epsilon_r = 1$).
(c) Equivalent transverse network at cut-off ($\epsilon_r \neq 1$).

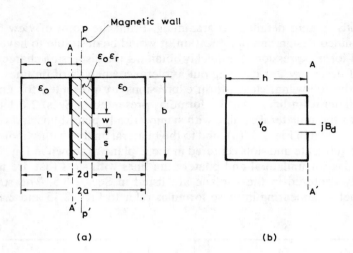

(a)   (b)

Fig. 2.16 (a) Cross section of a bilateral fin line.
(b) Equivalent transverse network at cut-off for even-mode excitation.

2.6.1 Ridge Waveguide Model [1–2]

Consider the unilateral fin line shown in Fig. 2.14(a) with aspect ratio $b/a = 1/2$, and the bilateral fin line shown in Fig. 2.14(b) with aspect ratio $b/2a = 1/2$. Recognizing that fin lines are essentially ridged waveguides with a dielectric backing, Meier [1] has presented the following approximate formulas for the guide wavelength λ and characteristic impedance Z of fin lines:

$$\lambda \approx \lambda_0/[K_e - (\lambda_0/\lambda_{cr})^2]^{1/2} \tag{2.60}$$

and

$$Z \approx Z_\infty/[K_e - (\lambda_0/\lambda_{cr})^2]^{1/2} \tag{2.61}$$

where K_e is the equivalent dielectric constant and λ_0 is the free-space wavelength; λ_{cr} and Z_∞ are respectively the cut-off wavelength and the characteristic impedance at infinite frequency of an air-filled ridge-loaded waveguide of identical dimensions. The value of K_e may be experimentally determined for a given fin-line configuration from a single cavity test [2]. The values of the characteristic admittance $(1/Z_\infty)$ of a ridge-loaded waveguide, based on a power-voltage definition, are available in the literature

[28] for a wide range of parameters. These data are directly applicable to the unilateral and bilateral fin-line structures containing thin substrates ($d/a < 0.1$) of low dielectric constant. In the expressions (2.60) and (2.61), appropriate factors may be applied to account for other aspect ratios (b/a) and configurations (symmetrical *versus* asymmetrical fin line) [29]. The definition of characteristic impedance for fin lines is not unique. For switching applications, the characteristic impedance based on voltage and current in the fin line is preferred [30]. For some other applications, the power-voltage definition of characteristic impedance is used [1]. In (2.61), Z_∞ is based on a power-voltage definition. Appropriate factors may be applied when calculating the characteristic impedance by using other definitions. In accordance with the voltage-current, power-voltage, and power-current impedance definitions for a rectangular waveguide operating in the dominant mode, we have [31]

$$Z_{\text{power, voltage}} = (4/\pi)Z_{\text{voltage, current}} \qquad (2.62a)$$

$$= (\pi^2/16)Z_{\text{power, current}} \qquad (2.62b)$$

2.6.2 Empirical Expressions [14]

In the ridge waveguide formulation, the fin line is characterized essentially as a fictitious ridged waveguide, uniformly filled with a dielectric of relative permittivity K_e. Furthermore, K_e is regarded as a constant. This approximation is satisfactory if and only if the substrate used in the fin line is very thin and its relative dielectric constant ϵ_r is close to unity. For larger values of ϵ_r, proper account must be taken of the frequency dependence.

In the following, we present closed-form expressions for the frequency-dependent equivalent permittivity K_e and the characteristic impedance, due to Sharma and Hoefer [14]. The impedances are based on a voltage-current definition, and are given for unilateral fin line (Fig. 2.14(a), $b/a = 1/2$) and bilateral fin line (Fig. 2.14(b), $b/2a = 1/2$). These expressions have been reported to be accurate in the frequency range $0.35 \leqslant b/\lambda_0 \leqslant 0.7$.

Equivalent Dielectric Constant, K_e

The expression for the frequency-dependent K_e is assumed to be of the general form:

$$K_e = K_c \cdot F(w/b, d/a, \lambda_0, \epsilon_r) \qquad (2.63)$$

where K_c is the equivalent dielectric constant at cut-off, and is given by

$$K_c = (\lambda_{cf}/\lambda_{cr})^2 \tag{2.64}$$

Here, λ_{cf} and λ_{cr} are cut-off wavelengths in the fin line and the equivalent air-filled ridged waveguide, respectively. The correction factor F is determined such that (2.60) and (2.61) yield the same results as obtained with the rigorous methods [4, 8]. The formulas for λ_{cf}, λ_{cr}, and F are given below.

Normalized Cut-Off Frequency, b/λ_{cr}

This expression is derived by assuming that the equivalent ridged waveguide is obtained by letting the substrate thickness tend toward zero, which leads to the same expression for λ_{cr} for both unilateral and bilateral fin lines:

$$b/\lambda_{cr} = 0.245(w/b)^{0.173}, \quad 1/16 \leqslant w/b \leqslant 1/4 \tag{2.65}$$

In the range $1/16 \leqslant w/b \leqslant 1/4$, the accuracy of (2.65) is reported to be within $\pm 1\%$.

Normalized Cut-Off Frequency, b/λ_{cf}

The general expression for the normalized cut-off frequency of unilateral and bilateral fin lines as a function of w/b and d/a is given by

$$b/\lambda_{cf} = A(w/b)^p (d/a)^q \tag{2.66}$$

The values of the unknown constants A, p, and q are also provided in [14] for the range of structural parameters $1/16 \leqslant w/b \leqslant 1/4$, $1/32 \leqslant d/a \leqslant 1/4$, and for two specific dielectric substrates—namely, RT-duroid™ ($\epsilon_r = 2.22$) and Kapton™ ($\epsilon_r = 3.0$). These constants are provided below.

(1) *Unilateral fin line* (Fig. 2.14(a)):
    For $\epsilon_r = 2.22$,

$$A = 0.1748$$
$$p = \begin{cases} 0.16(d/a)^{-0.07}, & 1/32 \leqslant d/a \leqslant 1/20 \\ 0.16(d/a)^{-0.07} - 0.001 \ln\left[(d/a) - (1/32)\right], & 1/20 \leqslant d/a \leqslant 1/4 \end{cases}$$
$$q = -0.0836 \tag{2.67}$$

For $\epsilon_r = 3.0$,

$A = 0.1495$

$$p = \begin{cases} 0.1732(d/a)^{-0.073}, & 1/32 \leqslant d/a \leqslant 1/10 \\ 0.1453(d/a)^{-0.1463}, & 1/10 \leqslant d/a \leqslant 1/4 \end{cases} \tag{2.68}$$

$q = -0.1223$

(2) *Bilateral fin line* (Fig. 2.14(b)):
For $\epsilon_r = 2.22$,

$A = 0.15$

$$p = \begin{cases} 0.225(d/a)^{-0.042}, & 1/32 \leqslant d/a \leqslant 1/10 \\ 0.149(d/a)^{-0.23}, & 1/10 \leqslant d/a \leqslant 1/4 \end{cases} \tag{2.69}$$

$q = -0.14$

For $\epsilon_r = 3.0$,

$A = 0.1255$

$$p = \begin{cases} 0.21772(d/a)^{-0.07155}, & 1/32 \leqslant d/a \leqslant 1/15 \\ 0.2907 - 0.3568(d/a), & 1/15 \leqslant d/a \leqslant 1/4 \end{cases} \tag{2.70}$$

$q = -0.1865$

These closed-form expressions are reported to yield results accurate to within $\pm 1\%$ when compared to the results obtained by using rigorous spectral domain methods.

Correction factor, F

The correction factor F to be substituted in (2.63) is given below for the two fin-line structures.

(1) *Unilateral fin line* (Fig. 2.14(a)):
For $\epsilon_r = 2.22$,

$$F = \begin{cases} [1.0 + 0.43(d/a)](w/b)^{p_1}, & 1/32 \leqslant d/a \leqslant 1/8 \\ [1.02 + 0.264(d/a)](w/b)^{p_1}, & 1/8 \leqslant d/a \leqslant 1/4 \end{cases} \tag{2.71}$$

$p_1 = 0.096(d/a) - 0.007$

For $\epsilon_r = 3.0$,

$$F = F' + 0.25308(b/\lambda_0) - 0.135$$

$$F' = \begin{cases} 1.368(d/a)^{0.086}(w/b)^{p_1}, & 1/32 \leqslant d/a \leqslant 1/8 \\ [1.122 + 0.176(d/a)](w/b)^{p_2}, & 1/8 \leqslant d/a \leqslant 1/4 \end{cases}$$ (2.72)

$$p_1 = 0.375(d/a) - 0.0233$$

$$p_2 = 0.032 - 3.0[(d/a) - (3/16)]^2$$

(2) *Bilateral fin line* (Fig. 2.14(b)):
For $\epsilon_r = 2.22$,

$$F = \begin{cases} 0.78(d/a)^{-0.098}(w/b)^{0.109}, & 1/32 \leqslant d/a \leqslant 1/8 \\ [1.04 - 0.2(d/a)](w/b)^{p_1}, & 1/8 \leqslant d/a \leqslant 1/4 \end{cases}$$ (2.73)

$$p_1 = 0.152 - 0.256(d/a)$$

For $\epsilon_r = 3.0$,

$$F = F' + 0.08436(b/\lambda_0) - 0.045$$

$$F' = \begin{cases} 0.975(d/a)^{-0.026}(w/b)^{p_1}, & 1/32 \leqslant d/a \leqslant 1/8 \\ [1.0769 - 0.2424(d/a)](w/b)^{p_2}, & 1/8 \leqslant d/a \leqslant 1/4 \end{cases}$$ (2.74)

$$p_1 = 0.089 + 0.288(d/a)$$

$$p_2 = 0.16 - 0.28(d/a)$$

Characteristic Impedance, Z

The characteristic impedance of unilateral and bilateral fin lines can now be computed from (2.61) by using the closed-form expressions for K_e and λ_{cr} given in (2.63) through (2.74). The closed-form expression for Z_∞, based on a voltage-current definition, is given by [14]:

$$Z_{\infty \text{ voltage-current}} =$$

$$\frac{120\pi^2(b/\lambda_{cr})}{(b/w)\sin(\pi u/\lambda_{cr}) + [(B_0/Y_0) + \tan(\pi v/2\lambda_{cr})]\cos(\pi u/\lambda_{cr})}$$ (2.75)

where

$$\frac{B_0}{Y_0} = (2b/\lambda_{cr})\left[\ln \operatorname{cosec}(\pi w/2b) + \frac{Q\cos^4(\pi w/2b)}{1 + Q\sin^4(\pi w/2b)}\right.$$

$$\left. + (1/16)(b/\lambda_{cr})^2[1 - 3\sin^2(\pi w/2b)]^2\cos^4(\pi w/2b)\right]$$ (2.76a)

$$Q = [1 - (b/\lambda_{cr})^2]^{-1/2} - 1$$ (2.76b)

The dimensional parameters u and v appearing in (2.75) are $u = 0$, $v = a$ for the unilateral fin line, and $u = 2d$, $v = 2(a - d)$ for the bilateral fin line.

2.6.3 Stationary Expressions [18]

Guide Wavelength of Unilateral Fin Line

The expressions presented in Sec. 2.6.2 are purely empirical in nature and valid for a small range of fin-line physical parameters ($1/16 \leq w/b \leq 1/4$, $1/32 \leq d/a \leq 1/4$, $b/a = 1/2$ (unilateral), $b/2a = 1/2$ (bilateral), $\epsilon_r = 2.22$, and $\epsilon_r = 3.0$). In this section, we present the closed-form expressions due to Pramanick and Bhartia [18] for the unilateral fin line (Fig. 2.14(a)). The expressions for the equivalent dielectric constant at cut-off (K_c) and the cut-off wavelength of unilateral fin-line (b/λ_{cf}) are reported to be valid over a wider range: $0 < b/a \leq 1$, $1/32 \leq w/b \leq 1.0$, $1/64 \leq d/a \leq 1/4$, and $1 \leq \epsilon_r \leq 3.75$.

The cut-off wavelength b/λ_{cf} of a unilateral fin line can be written as

$$b/\lambda_{cf} = (2a/b)(b/\lambda_{cr})(b/\lambda_{cd}) \tag{2.77}$$

Here, b/λ_{cr} is the cut-off wavelength of a finned guide ($\epsilon_r = 1$), given by [13]:

$$b/\lambda_{cr} = (b/2a)\{1 + (4/\pi)(b/a)[1 + 0.2\sqrt{(b/a)}]$$
$$\cdot \ln \csc(\pi w/2b)\}^{-1/2} \tag{2.78}$$

b/λ_{cd} is the cut-off wavelength of a dielectric loaded waveguide, modified by assuming a general field distribution in the transverse cross section of the waveguide, and also taking into account the presence of the fins. The expression for b/λ_{cd} is given by [18]:

$$b/\lambda_{cd} = (b/2a)[1 + FUN(d/a, w/b)(\epsilon_r - 1)]^{-1/2} \tag{2.79}$$

where

$$FUN(d/a, w/b) = [A_1(d/a) \ln \csc(\pi w/2b) + B_1(d/a)](d/a) \tag{2.80}$$

$A_1(d/a)$ and $B_1(d/a)$ are represented by the equations:

$$A_1(d/a) = 0.4020974[\ln(a/d)]^2$$
$$- 0.7684487 \ln(a/d) + 0.3932021 \tag{2.81a}$$

$$B_1(d/a) = 2.42 \sin[0.556 \ln(a/d)] \tag{2.81b}$$

Expressions (2.80) and (2.81) are derived so as to yield a value of b/λ_{cf} which is the same as that obtained from the rigorous spectral domain technique for the unilateral fin line with $\epsilon_r = 2.22$. These expressions are found to be valid for $\epsilon_r = 3.75$ within $\pm 1\%$. Expression (2.79) has a stationary form, and hence a small change in d/a, w/b, ϵ_r, or frequency f has a second-order effect on b/λ_{cd}. The equivalent dielectric constant at cut-off $K_c(= 2a/\lambda_{cd})$, is obtained from (2.79) as

$$K_c = 1 + (d/a)[A_1(d/a) \ln \operatorname{cosec}(\pi w/2b) + B_1(d/a)](\epsilon_r - 1) \tag{2.82}$$

Pramanick and Bhartia [18] suggest using the above expression for K_c in (2.63) to evaluate the equivalent dielectric constant K_e. The correction factor F appearing in (2.63) is due to Sharma and Hoefer [14], and is given in (2.71) for $\epsilon_r = 2.22$ and in (2.72) for $\epsilon_r = 3.0$. If we know K_e and use (2.78) for λ_{cr}, then the value of the guide wavelength λ can be calculated from (2.60).

Characteristic Impedance of Unilateral Fin Line

The frequency-dependent expression for the characteristic impedance Z of the unilateral fin line (Fig. 2.14(a)) is derived by fitting a curve to the accurate spectral domain results [18]. The expression is given by

$$Z = \frac{240\pi^2 \left[p \ln \operatorname{cosec}\left(\frac{\pi}{2}\frac{w}{b}\right) + q \right](b/a)}{\left[0.385 \ln \operatorname{cosec}\left(\frac{\pi}{2}\frac{w}{b}\right) + 1.762 \right]^2 (\lambda_0/\lambda)} \tag{2.83}$$

where

$$p = -0.763\left(\frac{b}{\lambda_0}\right)^2 + 0.58\left(\frac{b}{\lambda_0}\right) + 0.0775\left[\ln\left(\frac{a}{d}\right)\right]^2$$

$$-0.668\left[\ln\left(\frac{a}{d}\right)\right] + 1.262 \tag{2.84}$$

$$q = 0.372\left(\frac{b}{\lambda_0}\right) + 0.914, \quad \text{for } w/b > 0.3 \tag{2.85}$$

and

$$p = 0.17 \left(\frac{b}{\lambda_0}\right) + 0.0098 \tag{2.86}$$

$$q = 0.138 \left(\frac{b}{\lambda_0}\right) + 0.873, \quad \text{for } w/b \leqslant 0.3 \tag{2.87}$$

Expression (2.83) is reported to be accurate within $\pm 2\%$ for $d/a \leqslant 1/20$, and within $\pm 3\%$ for $d/a > 1/20$. All the formulas reported in Sec. 2.6.3 are valid over the normalized frequency range $0.25 \leqslant b/\lambda_0 \leqslant 0.6$.

2.6.4 Synthesis Formulas

In practical fin-line circuits, such as tapers and matching sections, it is desirable to know the normalized slot width w/b for a given set of parameters d/a, b/a, ϵ_r, and the characteristic impedance Z. For a unilateral fin line (Fig. 2.14(a), $b/a = 1/2$), the synthesis formulas are listed below [18].

$$w/b = \frac{2}{\pi} \sin^{-1}[\exp(-x)] \tag{2.88a}$$

$$(\lambda_0/\lambda) = (Cx^2 + Dx + E)/(Bx + A) \tag{2.88b}$$

and x can be obtained by solving the equation:

$$x^4 + Gx^3 + Hx^2 + Ix + J = 0 \tag{2.89}$$

where

$$G = D/C + 9.156 \tag{2.90a}$$

$$H = E/C + 9.156(D/C) + 20.95 - 6.748(pB/CF) \tag{2.90b}$$

$$I = 9.156(E/C) + 20.95(D/C) - 6.748(pA + qB)/CF \tag{2.90c}$$

$$J = 20.95(E/C) - 6.748(qA/CF) \tag{2.90d}$$

$$F = Z/[(240\pi^2)(b/a)] \tag{2.90e}$$

$$A = 8\left[1 + \frac{d}{a} B_1\left(\frac{d}{a}\right)(\epsilon_r - 1)\right]^{1/2} \tag{2.90f}$$

$$B = (4/\pi)(b/a)(1 + 0.2\sqrt{b/a})A \tag{2.90g}$$

$$C = 0.5(d/a)A_1(d/a)(\epsilon_r - 1)B/ \\ [1 + (d/a)B_1(d/a)(\epsilon_r - 1)]^{1/2} \tag{2.90h}$$

$$D = A[(B/8) + (C/B)] \tag{2.90i}$$

$$E = (A^2/8) - (b/a)^2(\lambda_0/b)^2 \tag{2.90j}$$

$A_1(d/a)$, $B_1(d/a)$, p, and q are given in (2.81) and (2.84) to (2.87).

The derivation of the above formulas is based on the assumption that the equivalent dielectric constant K_e, at the frequency f corresponding to a wavelength λ_0, is equal to the equivalent dielectric constant (K_c) at the cut-off frequency. This assumption is strictly valid for very low dielectric constants and thin substrates. The synthesis formulas given above are reported to be valid for $0 < b/a \leq 1$, $1/32 \leq w/b \leq 1$, $d/a \leq 1/20$, $1 \leq \epsilon_r \leq 3.75$, and $0.1 \leq b/\lambda_0 \leq 0.6$.

2.6.5 Transverse Resonance Method

The dispersion in fin line is approximately described by (2.60). It has been shown that if the relative dielectric constant (ϵ_r) of the fin-line substrate is low (typically < 2.5) and the substrate is very thin, K_e may be assumed as a constant [15] and can be approximated to K_c. Thus,

$$K_e \simeq K_c = (\lambda_{cf}/\lambda_{cr})^2 \tag{2.91}$$

where λ_{cf} and λ_{cr} are already defined. In this section, the transverse resonance method is used to determine λ_{cf} and λ_{cr} for unilateral and bilateral fin lines. This analysis is also based on the assumption that the substrate thickness is small as compared with the guide width. The method is valid for arbitrary slot widths (w) and slot locations (s). (See Figs. 2.15 and 2.16).

Unilateral Fin Line

In order to determine λ_{cf} and λ_{cr} of a unilateral fin line (Fig. 2.15(a)), we draw two equivalent transverse networks at the cut-off frequency of the dominant mode: one for $\epsilon_r = 1$ and another for $\epsilon_r \neq 1$. These are shown in Figs. 2.15(b) and 2.15(c), respectively. The cut-off wavelength λ_{cr} in the air-filled ridge waveguide ($\epsilon_r = 1$ in Fig. 2.15(a)) is determined by the resonance condition at the plane AA' in Fig. 2.15(b). The resonance condition is written as

$$-\cot(2\pi(h_1 + d)/\lambda_{cr}) - \cot(2\pi h_2/\lambda_{cr}) + B_a/Y_0 = 0 \qquad (2.92)$$

In (2.92), B_a is the susceptance of a window of zero thickness in a rectangular waveguide, and is given by [32]:

$$B_a/Y_0 = 4b(P_a/\lambda_{cr}) \qquad (2.93)$$

where

$$P_a = \ln[\operatorname{cosec}(\alpha_a)\,\operatorname{cosec}(\beta_a)] + \frac{2Q_1\cos^2(\alpha_a)\cos^2(\beta_a)}{1 + Q_1\sin^2(\alpha_a)\sin^2(\beta_a)}$$
$$+ Q_2[3\cos^2(\alpha_a)\cos^2(\beta_a) - \cos^2(\alpha_a) - \cos^2(\beta_a)]^2 \qquad (2.94a)$$

$$\alpha_a = \pi w/2b \qquad (2.94b)$$

$$\beta_a = \pi(w + 2s)/2b \qquad (2.94c)$$

$$Q_n = \frac{1}{\sqrt{1 - (2b/n\lambda_{cr})^2}} - 1 \qquad (2.94d)$$

The cut-off wavelength λ_{cf} in the fin line (Fig. 2.15(a)) can be obtained from the resonance condition at the plane AA' in Fig. 2.15c. The resonance condition for this case can be written as

$$-\cot(2\pi h_1/\lambda_{cf}) - \cot(2\pi h_2/\lambda_{cf}) + B_d/Y_0 = 0 \qquad (2.95)$$

where B_d is given by

$$B_d/Y_0 = (B_L/Y_0) + (B_R/Y_0) \qquad (2.96)$$

The susceptance jB_R results from the field distortion to the right of the reference plane AA'. This is the same as the susceptance of a window of zero thickness in a rectangular waveguide. The expression for jB_R has been derived in [32], and is given by

$$B_R/Y_0 = 4b(P_a/\lambda_{cf}) \qquad (2.97)$$

where P_a is given in (2.94a).

The susceptance jB_L due to the field distortion to the left of the reference plane AA' represents the influence of the dielectric and the transformation through the layer of length d. It is derived from the equivalent circuit of an open E-plane T-junction, and is approximately given by

$$B_L/Y_0 = (B_{L1}/Y_0) + (B_{L2}/Y_0) \qquad (2.98)$$

where

$$B_{L1}/Y_0 = (2b\epsilon_r/\lambda_{cf})[\alpha_{L1} \tan^{-1}(1/\alpha_{L1}) + \ln\sqrt{1 + \alpha_{L1}^2}] \qquad (2.99a)$$

$$B_{L2}/Y_0 = (2b\epsilon_r/\lambda_{cf})[\alpha_{L2} \tan^{-1}(1/\alpha_{L2}) + \ln\sqrt{1 + \alpha_{L2}^2}] \qquad (2.99b)$$

$$\alpha_{L1} = d/w; \quad \alpha_{L2} = d/b \qquad (2.99c)$$

The above formulas are valid for the centered dielectric case ($h_1 + d/2 = h_2 + d/2 = a/2$) and also for the centered fin case ($h_1 + d = h_2 = a/2$). By determining the first zero of (2.92) and (2.95), λ_{cr} and λ_{cf} can be respectively obtained.

Bilateral Fin Line

Consider the bilateral fin line shown in Fig. 2.16(a). From the practical point of view, only the even-mode excitation is considered. The equivalent transverse network at cut-off for the dominant TE_{10} mode is shown in Fig. 2.16(b). The cut-off wavelengths λ_{cr} and λ_{cf} are determined from the resonance conditions at the plane AA'. The resonance condition can be written as

$$-\cot(2\pi h/\lambda_c) + (B_d/Y_0) = 0 \qquad (2.100)$$

where

$$B_d/Y_0 = (B_{dL}/Y_0) + (B_{dR}/Y_0) \qquad (2.101)$$

The susceptance jB_{dL} models the field distortion to the left of the plane AA', and is given in [32] as

$$B_{dL}/Y_0 = (2b/\lambda_c)P_a \qquad (2.102)$$

where P_a is given by (2.94a).

The susceptance jB_{dR} models the field distortion between the plane AA' and the symmetry plane pp', and is given in [32] as

$$B_{dR}/Y_0 = (2b\epsilon_r/\lambda_c)[\alpha_{dR} \tan^{-1}(1/\alpha_{dR}) + \ln\sqrt{1 + \alpha_{dR}^2}] \qquad (2.103)$$

where

$$\alpha_{dR} = 2d/w \qquad (2.104)$$

By determining the first zero of (2.100), we can obtain the cut-off wavelength $\lambda_c = \lambda_{cr}$ for $\epsilon_r = 1$ and $\lambda_c = \lambda_{cf}$ for $\epsilon_r \neq 1$.

REFERENCES

1. P.J. Meier, "Integrated Fin-Line Millimeter Components," *IEEE Trans. Microwave Theory Tech.*, Vol. MTT-22, pp. 1209–1216, Dec. 1974.
2. P.J. Meier, "Equivalent Relative Permittivity and Unloaded Q-Factor of Integrated Fin-Line," *Electron. Lett.*, Vol. 9, No. 7 pp. 162–163, April 1973.
3. R.N. Simons, "Analysis of Millimeter-Wave Integrated Fin-Line," *IEE Proc.*, Vol. 130, Pt. H, No. 2, pp. 166–169, March 1983.
4. J.B. Knorr and P.M. Shayda, "Millimeter-Wave Fin-Line Characteristics," *IEEE Trans. Microwave Theory Tech.*, Vol. MTT-28, pp. 737–743, July 1980.
5. Y.C. Shih and W.J.R. Hoefer, "Dominant and Second-Order Mode Cut-Off Frequencies in Fin-Lines Calculated with a Two-Dimensional TLM Program," *IEEE Trans. Microwave Theory Tech.*, Vol. MTT-28, pp. 1443–1448, Dec. 1980.
6. L.P. Schmidt, T. Itoh, and H. Hofmann, "Characteristics of Unilateral Fin-Line Structures with Arbitrarily Located Slots," *IEEE Trans. Microwave Theory Tech.*, Vol. MTT-29, pp. 352–355, April 1981.
7. D.M. Syahkal and J.B. Davies, "An Accurate, Unified Solution to Various Fin Line Structures, of Phase Constant, Characteristic Impedance, and Attenuation," *IEEE Trans. Microwave Theory Tech.*, Vol. MTT-30, pp. 1854–1861, Nov. 1982.
8. L.P. Schmidt and T. Itoh, "Spectral Domain Analysis of Dominant and Higher Order Modes in Fin Lines," *IEEE Trans. Microwave Theory Tech.*, Vol. MTT-28, pp. 981–985, Sept. 1980.
9. A. Beyer, "Analysis of the Characteristics of an Earthed Fin-Line," *IEEE Trans. Microwave Theory Tech.*, Vol. MTT-29, pp. 676–680, July 1981.

10. S.B. Worm and R. Pregla, "Hybrid-Mode Analysis of Arbitrarily Shaped Planar Microwave Structures by the Method of Lines," *IEEE Trans. Microwave Theory Tech.*, Vol. MTT-32, pp. 191–196, Feb. 1984.

11. U. Schulz and R. Pregla, "A New Technique for the Analysis of the Dispersion Characteristics of Planar Waveguides," *Arch. Elek. Ubertragung,* Vol. 34, pp. 169–173, 1980.

12. Yi-Chi Shi, W.J.R. Hoefer, and A.E. Ros, "Cutoff Frequencies in Fin-Lines Calculated with a Two-Dimensional TLM Program," *IEEE MTT-S Int. Microwave Symp. Digest,* 1980, pp. 261–263.

13. W.J.R. Hoefer and M.N. Burton, "Closed Form Expressions for the Parameters of Finned and Ridged Waveguides," *IEEE Trans. Microwave Theory Tech.,* Vol. MTT-30, pp. 2190–2194, Dec. 1982.

14. A.K. Sharma and W.J.R. Hoefer, "Empirical Expressions for Fin-Line Design," *IEEE Trans. Microwave Theory Tech.,* Vol. MTT-31, pp. 350–356, April 1983.

15. A.M.K. Saad and G. Begemann, "Electrical Performance of Fin-Lines of Various Configurations," *Microwaves Opt. Acoust.,* Vol. 1, pp. 81–88, Jan. 1977.

16. A.M.K. Saad and K. Schunemann, "Closed Form Approximation for Fin-Line Eigenmodes," *IEE Proc.,* Vol. 129, Pt. H, No. 5, pp. 253–261, Oct. 1982.

17. J.K. Piotrowski, "Accurate and Simple Formulas for Dispersion in Fin-Lines," *IEEE MTT-S Int. Microwave Symp. Digest,* 1984, pp. 333–335.

18. P. Pramanick and P. Bhartia, "Accurate Analysis Equations and Synthesis Technique for Unilateral Fin Lines," *IEEE Trans. Microwave Theory Tech.,* Vol. MTT-33, pp. 24–30, Jan. 1985.

19. S.B. Cohn, "Slot-Line on a Dielectric Substrate," *IEEE Trans. Microwave Theory Tech.,* Vol. MTT-17, pp. 768–778, Oct. 1969.

20. M. Dydyk and B.D. Moore, "Shielded Microstrip Aids V-Band Receiver Designs," *Microwaves,* Vol. 21, pp. 77–82, March 1982.

21. C. Nguyen and K. Chang, "Millimeter Wave Low-Loss Fin-Line Low-Pass Filters," *Electron Lett.,* Vol. 20, No. 24, pp. 1010–1011, Nov. 1984.

22. H. Hofmann, "MM-Wave Gunn Oscillator with Distributed Feedback Fin-Line Circuit," *IEEE MTT-S Int. Microwave Symp. Digest,* 1980, pp. 59–61.

23. L.D. Cohen, "Advances in Printed Millimeter-Wave Oscillator Circuits," *IEEE MTT-S Int. Microwave Symp. Digest,* 1980, pp. 264–266.
24. Y. Konishi, K. Uenakada, N. Yazawa, and N. Hoshino, "New Microwave Components with Mounted Planar Circuit in Waveguide," NHK Laboratory Note, S1. No. 163, pp. 1–12, March 1973.
25. E. Kpodzo, K. Schunemann, and G. Begemann, "A Quadriphase Fin-Line Modulator," *IEEE Trans. Microwave Theory Tech.,* Vol. MTT-28, pp. 747–752, July 1980.
26. R. Knoechel, "A Double Balanced Fin Line Mixer with Broad IF Bandwidth Capability," *13th Eur. Microwave Conf. Digest,* 1983, pp. 567–572.
27. R.E. Collin, *Field Theory of Guided Waves,* McGraw-Hill, New York, 1960.
28. S. Hopfer, "The Design of Ridge Waveguides," *IRE Trans. Microwave Theory Tech.,* Vol. MTT-3, pp. 20–29, Oct. 1955.
29. G.C. Southworth, *Principles and Applications of Waveguide Transmission,* Van Nostrand, Princeton, NJ, 1950.
30. H. Meinel and B. Rembold, "New Millimeter Wave Fin-Line Attenuators and Switches," *IEEE MTT-S Int. Microwave Symp. Digest,* 1979, pp. 249–252.
31. E.C. Jordan and K.G. Balmain, *Electromagnetic Waves and Radiating Systems,* Prentice-Hall, India, 1976.
32. N. Marcuvitz, *Waveguide Handbook,* McGraw-Hill, New York, 1951.

APPENDIX 2-A
SUSCEPTANCE FORMULAS FOR
SPECIFIC FIN-LINE STRUCTURES

1. **Unilateral Fin Line** (Fig. 2.2(a))

$$\eta B_t = \frac{cu}{2b} \tan\left[\frac{\pi u d}{\xi c} - \tan^{-1}\left(\frac{v}{u} J_{01}\right)\right] - \frac{cv}{2b} J_{02}$$

$$+ \frac{(1 + \epsilon_r - 2\xi^2)}{\xi} T + \frac{1}{\xi} \sum_{n>0} (H_{n1} + H_{n2})W_n \qquad (2\text{-}A.1)$$

$$\xi = \lambda_0/\lambda; \quad \lambda = 2c \qquad (2\text{-}A.2a)$$

$$u = \sqrt{\epsilon_r - \xi^2} \qquad (2\text{-}A.2b)$$

$$v = \sqrt{\xi^2 - 1} \qquad (2\text{-}A.2c)$$

$$\gamma_0 = \frac{j\pi}{c\xi}\sqrt{1 - \xi^2} = \frac{\pi v}{c\xi} \qquad (2\text{-}A.2d)$$

$$G_n = \sqrt{1 + \left(\frac{bv}{nc\xi}\right)^2} = \frac{b\gamma_n}{\pi n} \qquad (2\text{-}A.2e)$$

$$G_{n1} = \sqrt{1 - \left(\frac{bu}{nc\xi}\right)^2} = \frac{b\gamma_{n1}}{\pi n} \qquad (2\text{-}A.2f)$$

$$\delta = w/b; \quad \delta' = (2s + w)/b \qquad (2\text{-}A.2g)$$

$$J_{01} = \coth(\gamma_0 h_1), \, J_{n1} = \coth(\gamma_n h_1) \qquad (2\text{-}A.2h)$$

$$J_{02} = \coth(\gamma_0 h_2), \, J_{n2} = \coth(\gamma_n h_2) \qquad (2\text{-}A.2i)$$

$$W_n = \frac{\sin^2\left(\frac{n\pi\delta}{2}\right) \cdot \cos^2\left(\frac{n\pi\delta'}{2}\right)}{n \cdot \left(\frac{n\pi\delta}{2}\right)^2} \qquad (2\text{-}A.2j)$$

$$H_{n2} = \left\{ \frac{(1 - \xi^2 G_n^2)J_{n2}}{\left[1 + \left(\dfrac{b}{nc}\right)^2\right]G_n} + v^2 \right\}$$

(2-A.3)

For G_{n1} real,

$$H_{n1} = \left\{ \frac{\epsilon_r \tanh p_{n1} - \xi^2 G_{n1}^2 \coth q_{n1}}{\left[1 + \left(\dfrac{b}{nc}\right)^2\right]G_{n1}} - u^2 \right\}$$

(2-A.4)

$$p_{n1} = \frac{\pi n G_{n1} d}{b} + \tanh^{-1}\left[\frac{G_{n1}}{G_n \epsilon_r} J_{n1}\right]$$

(2-A.5a)

$$q_{n1} = \frac{\pi n G_{n1} d}{b} + \coth^{-1}\left[\frac{G_n}{G_{n1}} J_{n1}\right]$$

(2-A.5b)

If

$$\left[\frac{G_{n1}}{G_n \epsilon_r} J_{n1}\right] > 1$$

then replace tanh p_{n1} by coth p_{n1} in (2-A.4), where

$$p_{n1} = \frac{\pi n G_{n1} d}{b} + \coth^{-1}\left[\frac{G_{n1}}{G_n \epsilon_r} J_{n1}\right]$$

(2-A.6)

If

$$\left[\frac{G_n}{G_{n1}} J_{n1}\right] < 1$$

then replace coth q_{n1} by tanh q_{n1} in (2-A.4), where

$$q_{n1} = \frac{\pi n G_{n1} d}{b} + \tanh^{-1}\left[\frac{G_n}{G_{n1}} J_{n1}\right]$$

(2-A.7)

For G_{n1} imaginary,

$$H_{n1} = \left\{ \frac{\epsilon_r \tan p'_{n1} - \xi^2 |G_{n1}|^2 \cot q'_{n1}}{\left[1 + \left(\dfrac{b}{nc}\right)^2\right]|G_{n1}|} - u^2 \right\} \tag{2-A.8}$$

$$p'_{n1} = \frac{\pi n |G_{n1}| d}{b} + \tan^{-1}\left[\frac{|G_{n1}|}{G_n \epsilon_r} J_{n1}\right] \tag{2-A.9a}$$

$$q'_{n1} = \frac{\pi n |G_{n1}| d}{b} + \cot^{-1}\left[\frac{G_n}{|G_{n1}|} J_{n1}\right] \tag{2-A.9b}$$

$$T = \frac{1}{(\pi\delta)^2} \left\{ \frac{(\pi\delta)^2}{2} \ln(\pi\delta) - \frac{(\pi\delta)^2}{2} \cdot \ln(\pi\delta) \right.$$

$$- \frac{\pi(\delta + \bar{\delta})^2}{4} \cdot \ln[\pi(\delta + \bar{\delta})] - \frac{[\pi(\bar{\delta} - \delta)]^2}{4} \ln[\pi(\bar{\delta} - \delta)]$$

$$\left. + \frac{3}{2} \cdot (\pi\delta)^2 + \frac{(\pi\delta)^4}{144} + \frac{(\pi\delta)^2(\pi\bar{\delta})^2}{48} \right\},$$

$$\delta = \begin{cases} \dfrac{2s + w}{b}, \; 0 < s \le \dfrac{(b - w)}{2} \\[2mm] \dfrac{2(b - s - w/2)}{b}, \; \dfrac{(b - w)}{2} \le s < (b - w) \end{cases} \tag{2-A.10}$$

2. Insulated Fin Line (Fig. 2.2(c))

$$\eta B_t = \frac{cu}{b} \left\{ \tan\frac{\pi u d}{\xi c} - \tan^{-1}\left[\frac{v}{u} \coth\gamma_0 h\right] \right\}$$

$$+ \frac{2}{\xi} (\epsilon_r - \xi^2) T + \frac{2}{\xi} \sum_{n>0} H_{n1} W_n \tag{2-A.11}$$

where ξ, u, v, γ_0, G_n, G_{n1}, δ, δ', W_n, and T are given in (2-A.2a) to (2-A.2g), (2-A.2j) and (2-A.10), respectively. For the two cases, G_{n1} real and G_{n1} imaginary, H_{n1} in (2-A.11) is obtained using (2-A.4) to (2-A.7) and (2-A.8) to (2-A.9), respectively, with h_1 replaced by h.

3. Bilateral Fin Line (Fig. 2.2(b))

Even-Mode Excitation

$$\eta B_t = \frac{cu}{2b} \tan\left(\frac{\pi u d}{\xi c}\right) - \frac{cv}{2b} \coth(\gamma_0 h)$$

$$+ (1 + \epsilon_r - 2\xi^2)\frac{T}{\xi} + \frac{1}{\xi}\sum_{n>0}(H_{n1} + H_{n2})W_n \qquad (2\text{-A}.12)$$

where ξ, u, v, γ_0, G_n, G_{n1}, δ, δ', W_n, and T are given in (2-A.2a) to (2-A.2g), (2-A.2j), and (2-A.10), respectively.

$$H_{n2} = \left\{\frac{(1 - \xi^2 G_n^2)\coth\left(\dfrac{\pi n G_n h}{b}\right)}{\left[1 + \left(\dfrac{b}{nc}\right)^2\right]G_n} + v^2\right\} \qquad (2\text{-A}.13)$$

For G_{n1} real,

$$H_{n1} = \left\{\frac{(\epsilon_r - \xi^2 G_{n1}^2)\tanh\left(\dfrac{\pi n G_{n1} d}{b}\right)}{\left[1 + \left(\dfrac{b}{nc}\right)^2\right]G_{n1}} - u^2\right\} \qquad (2\text{-A}.14)$$

For G_{n1} imaginary,

$$H_{n1} = \left\{\frac{\epsilon_r + \xi^2|G_{n1}|^2\tan\left(\dfrac{\pi n|G_{n1}|d}{b}\right)}{\left[1 + \left(\dfrac{b}{nc}\right)^2\right]|G_{n1}|} - u^2\right\} \qquad (2\text{-A}.15)$$

Odd-Mode Excitation

$$\eta B_t = \frac{-cu}{2b}\cot\left(\frac{\pi u d}{\xi c}\right) - \frac{cv}{2b}\coth(\gamma_0 h)$$

$$+ (1 + \epsilon_r - 2\xi^2)\frac{T}{\xi} + \frac{1}{\xi}\sum_{n>0}(H_{n1} + H_{n2})W_n \qquad (2\text{-A}.16)$$

where ξ, u, v, γ_0, G_n, G_{n1}, δ, δ', W_n, T, H_{n2} are given by (2-A.2a) − (2-A.2g), (2-A.2j), (2-A.10) and (2-A.13), respectively.

For G_{n1} real,

$$H_{n1} = \left\{ \frac{(\epsilon_r - \xi^2 G_{n1}^2)\, \coth\!\left(\dfrac{\pi n G_{n1} d}{b}\right)}{\left[1 + \left(\dfrac{b}{nc}\right)^2\right] G_{n1}} - u^2 \right\} \tag{2-A.17}$$

For G_{n1} imaginary,

$$H_{n1} = \left\{ -\frac{(\epsilon_r + \xi^2 |G_{n1}|^2)\, \cot\!\left(\dfrac{\pi n |G_{n1}| d}{b}\right)}{\left[1 + \left(\dfrac{b}{nc}\right)^2\right] |G_{n1}|} - u^2 \right\} \tag{2-A.18}$$

4. Double-Dielectric Bilateral Fin Line with Fins Facing Each Other (Fig. 2.4(b))

Odd-Mode Excitation

Use (2-A.1) to (2-A.10).

Even-Mode Excitation

Replace J_{02} and J_{n2} given in (2-A.2i) by

$$J_{02} = \tanh(\gamma_0 h_2), \ J_{n2} = \tanh(\gamma_n h_2) \tag{2-A.19}$$

and then use (2-A.1) to (2-A.10).

5. Double-Dielectric Bilateral Fin Line with Fins Facing Side Walls (Fig. 2.4(c))

Odd-Mode Excitation

Use (2-A.1) to (2-A.10).

Even-Mode Excitation

Replace J_{01} and J_{n1} given in (2-A.2h) by

$$J_{01} = \tanh(\gamma_0 h_1), \quad J_{n1} = \tanh(\gamma_n h_1) \tag{2-A.20}$$

and then use (2-A.1) to (2-A.10).

6. Special cases of Unilateral, Insulated, Bilateral, and Double-Dielectric Fin Lines (Figs. 2.2(a–c) and 2.4(b, c))

Slots Centered in the E-Plane ($b = w + 2s$)

In the above-mentioned fin-line structures, if the slot is centered in the E-plane, the following changes need to be incorporated in each of the expressions for ηB_t. This would also result in considerable saving in the computational time

$$\delta = \frac{w}{b}, \quad \delta' = 1 \tag{2-A.21}$$

$$W_n = \frac{\sin^2\left(\dfrac{n\pi\delta}{2}\right)}{n\left(\dfrac{n\pi\delta}{2}\right)^2} \tag{2-A.22}$$

$$T = \frac{1}{2}\left[\frac{3}{2} - \ln(2\pi\delta) + \frac{(\pi\delta)^2}{36}\right] \tag{2-A.23}$$

The summation in the expressions for ηB_t is to be carried out for only even values of n ($n \neq 0$).

Asymmetric Fin Lines (Fig. 2.6)

For asymmetric fin-line configurations ($s = 0$), the following changes need to be incorporated in the expressions for ηB_t:

$$\delta = \delta' = w/b \tag{2-A.24}$$

$$W_n = \frac{\sin^2(n\pi\delta)}{n(n\pi\delta)^2} \tag{2-A.25}$$

$$T = \left[\frac{3}{2} - \ln(2\pi\delta) + \frac{(\pi\delta)^2}{36} \right] \tag{2-A.26}$$

The summation in the expressions for ηB_t is to be carried out for all values of $n > 0$ ($n = 1, 2, 3, \ldots$).

7. Edge-Coupled Unilateral Fin Line (Fig. 2.3(a))

Odd-Mode Excitation

Use (2-A.1) to (2-A.10).

Even-Mode Excitation

$$\eta B_t = (1 + \epsilon_r - 2\xi^2)\frac{T'}{\xi} + \frac{1}{\xi}\sum_{n\geq0}(H_{n1} + H_{n2})W_n' \tag{2-A.27}$$

where ξ, u, and v are given in (2-A.2a) to (2-A.2c), respectively, while δ and δ' are given in (2-A.2g).

$$W_n' = \frac{\left\{ \sin\left[\left(\frac{2n+1}{2}\right)\frac{\pi\delta}{2} \right] \sin\left[\left(\frac{2n+1}{2}\right)\frac{\pi\delta'}{2} \right] \right\}^2}{\left(\frac{2n+1}{2}\right)\left[\left(\frac{2n+1}{2}\right)\frac{\pi\delta}{2} \right]^2} \tag{2-A.28}$$

$$G_n = \sqrt{1 + \left\{ \frac{bv}{\left(\frac{2n+1}{2}\right)c\xi} \right\}^2} = \frac{b\gamma_n}{\left(\frac{2n+1}{2}\right)\pi} \tag{2-A.29a}$$

$$G_{n1} = \sqrt{1 - \left\{ \frac{bu}{\left(\frac{2n+1}{2}\right)c\xi} \right\}^2} = \frac{b\gamma_{n1}}{\left(\frac{2n+1}{2}\right)\pi} \tag{2-A.29b}$$

$$H_{n2} = \left\{ \frac{(1 - \xi^2 G_n^2)\coth(\gamma_n h_2)}{\left[1 + \left(\frac{b}{(2n+1)c/2}\right)^2 \right]G_n} + v^2 \right\} \tag{2-A.30}$$

For G_{n1} real,

$$H_{n1} = \left\{ \frac{\epsilon_r \tanh p_{n1} - \xi^2 G_{n1}^2 \coth q_{n1}}{\left[1 + \left(\dfrac{b}{(2n+1)c/2}\right)^2\right] G_{n1}} - u^2 \right\}$$

(2-A.31)

$$p_{n1} = \left(\frac{2n+1}{2}\right)\frac{\pi G_{n1} d}{b} + \tanh^{-1}\left[\frac{G_{n1}}{G_n \epsilon_r} \coth(\gamma_n h_1)\right]$$

(2-A.32)

$$q_{n1} = \left(\frac{2n+1}{2}\right)\frac{\pi G_{n1} d}{b} + \coth^{-1}\left[\frac{G_n}{G_{n1}} \coth(\gamma_n h_1)\right]$$

(2-A.33)

If

$$\left[\frac{G_{n1}}{G_n \epsilon_r} \coth(\gamma_n h_1)\right] > 1$$

then replace $\tanh p_{n1}$ by $\coth p_{n1}$ in (2-A.31), with

$$p_{n1} = \left(\frac{2n+1}{2}\right)\frac{\pi G_{n1} d}{b} + \coth^{-1}\left[\frac{G_{n1}}{G_n \epsilon_r} \coth(\gamma_n h_1)\right]$$

(2-A.34)

If

$$\left[\frac{G_n}{G_{n1}} \coth(\gamma_n h_1)\right] < 1$$

then replace $\coth q_{n1}$ by $\tanh q_{n1}$ in (2-A.31), with

$$q_{n1} = \left(\frac{2n+1}{2}\right)\frac{\pi G_{n1} d}{b} + \tanh^{-1}\left[\frac{G_n}{G_{n1}} \coth(\gamma_n h_1)\right]$$

(2-A.35)

For G_{n1} imaginary,

$$H_{n1} = \left\{ \frac{\epsilon_r \tan p'_{n1} - \xi^2 |G_{n1}|^2 \cot q'_{n1}}{\left[1 + \left(\dfrac{b}{(2n+1)c/2}\right)^2\right] |G_{n1}|} - u^2 \right\}$$

(2-A.36)

where

$$p'_{n1} = \left(\frac{2n + 1}{2}\right)\frac{\pi|G_{n1}|d}{b} + \tan^{-1}\left[\frac{|G_{n1}|}{G_n\epsilon_r}\coth(\gamma_n h_1)\right] \qquad (2\text{-A.37})$$

$$q'_{n1} = \left(\frac{2n + 1}{2}\right)\frac{\pi|G_{n1}|d}{b} + \cot^{-1}\left[\frac{G_n}{|G_{n1}|}\coth(\gamma_n h_1)\right] \qquad (2\text{-A.38})$$

The expression for T' in (2-A.27) is given by

$$\begin{aligned}
T' = \frac{1}{(\pi\delta)^2}\Bigg\{ &-\frac{(\pi\delta)^2}{2}\ln\left(\frac{\pi\delta}{4}\right) - \frac{(\pi\delta')^2}{2}\ln\left(\frac{\pi\delta'}{4}\right) \\
&+ \frac{[\pi(\delta' + \delta)]^2}{4}\cdot\ln\left[\frac{\pi(\delta' + \delta)}{4}\right] \\
&+ \frac{[\pi(\delta' - \delta)]^2}{4}\ln\left[\frac{\pi(\delta' - \delta)}{4}\right] + \frac{(\pi\delta)^2(\pi\delta')^2}{96}\Bigg\}, \\
&\qquad \text{for } 0 < s \leqslant (b - w)/2 \qquad (2\text{-A.39a})
\end{aligned}$$

$$\begin{aligned}
T' = \frac{1}{(\pi\delta)^2}\Bigg\{ &-\frac{(\pi\delta)^2}{2}\ln\left(\frac{\pi\delta}{4}\right) + \frac{(\pi\delta'')^2}{2}\ln\left(\frac{\pi\delta''}{4}\right) \\
&- \frac{[\pi(\delta'' + \delta)]^2}{4}\ln\left[\frac{\pi(\delta'' + \delta)}{4}\right] \\
&- \frac{[\pi(\delta'' - \delta)]^2}{4}\ln\left[\frac{\pi(\delta'' - \delta)}{4}\right] \\
&+ \frac{3}{2}(\pi\delta)^2 - \frac{(\pi\delta)^4}{288} - \frac{(\pi\delta)^2(\pi\delta'')^2}{96}\Bigg\}, \\
\delta'' = \frac{2(b - s - w/2)}{b} &\text{ for } \left(\frac{b - w}{2}\right) \leqslant s < (b - w) \quad (2\text{-A.39b})
\end{aligned}$$

8. Edge-Coupled Insulated Fin Line (Fig. 2.7(a))

Odd-Mode Excitation

Use (2-A.11).

Even-Mode Excitation

$$\eta B_t = (\epsilon_r - \xi^2) \frac{2T'}{\xi} + \frac{2}{\xi} \sum_{n \geqslant 0} H_{n1} W'_n \tag{2-A.40}$$

where ξ, u, v, G_n, G_{n1}, T', and W'_n are given in (2-A.2a) to (2-A.2c), (2-A.29a), (2-A.29b), (2-A.39), and (2-A.28), respectively. For the two cases, G_{n1} real and G_{n1} imaginary, H_{n1} in (2-A.40) is obtained from (2-A.31) and (2-A.36), respectively, with h_1 replaced by h.

9. Edge-Coupled Bilateral Fin Line (Fig. 2.3(b))

Odd-Odd Mode Excitation

Use the formulas for the odd mode excitation of a bilateral fin line (2-A.16) to (2-A.18).

Even-Odd Mode Excitation

Use the formulas for the even mode of a bilateral fin line (2-A.12) to (2-A.15).

Odd-Even Mode Excitation

$$\eta B_t = (1 + \epsilon_r - 2\xi^2) \frac{T'}{\xi} + \frac{1}{\xi} \sum_{n \geqslant 0} (H_{n1} + H_{n2}) W'_n \tag{2-A.41}$$

where ξ, u, v, G_n, G_{n1}, T', and W'_n are given in (2-A.2a) to (2-A.2c), (2-A.29a), (2-A.29b), (2-A.39), and (2-A.28), respectively, while δ and δ' are given in (2-A.2g).

$$H_{n2} = \left\{ \frac{(1 - \xi^2 G_n^2)\coth(\gamma_n h)}{\left[1 + \left(\frac{b}{(2n+1)c/2}\right)^2 G_n\right]} + v^2 \right\} \tag{2-A.42}$$

For G_{n1} real,

$$H_{n1} = \left\{ \frac{(\epsilon_r - \xi^2 G_{n1}^2)\coth\left[\left(\frac{2n + 1}{2}\right)\frac{\pi G_{n1}d}{b}\right]}{\left[1 + \left(\frac{b}{(2n + 1)c/2}\right)^2\right]G_{n1}} - u^2 \right\} \quad (2\text{-A.43})$$

For G_{n1} imaginary,

$$H_{n1} = \left\{ -\frac{(\epsilon_r + \xi^2|G_{n1}|^2)\cot\left[\left(\frac{2n + 1}{2}\right)\frac{\pi|G_{n1}|d}{b}\right]}{\left[1 + \left(\frac{b}{(2n + 1)c/2}\right)^2\right]|G_{n1}|} - u^2 \right\} \quad (2\text{-A.44})$$

Even-Even Mode Excitation

Use (2-A.41)–(2-A.44) with

$$\coth\left[\left(\frac{2n + 1}{2}\right)\frac{\pi G_{n1}d}{b}\right]$$

replaced by

$$\tanh\left[\left(\frac{2n + 1}{2}\right)\frac{\pi G_{n1}d}{b}\right]$$

and

$$\cot\left[\left(\frac{2n + 1}{2}\right)\frac{\pi|G_{n1}|d}{b}\right]$$

replaced by

$$-\tan\left[\left(\frac{2n + 1}{2}\right)\frac{\pi|G_{n1}|d}{b}\right]$$

10. Edge-Coupled Double-Dielectric Bilateral Fin Line with Fins Facing Each Other (Fig. 2.7(c))

Odd-Odd Mode Excitation

 Use (2-A.1) to (2-A.10).

Even-Odd Mode Excitation

 Use (2-A.1) to (2-A.10) with (2-A.2i) replaced by (2-A.19).

Odd-Even Mode Excitation

 Use (2-A.27) to (2-A.39).

Even-Even Mode Excitation

 Use (2-A.27) to (2-A.39) with coth $\gamma_n h_2$ replaced by tanh $\gamma_n h_2$.

11. Edge-Coupled Double-Dielectric Bilateral Fin Line with Fins Facing Side Walls (Fig. 2.7(d))

Odd-Odd Mode Excitation
 Use (2-A.1) to (2-A.10).

Even-Odd Mode Excitation

 Use (2-A.1) to (2-A.10) with (2-A.2h) replaced by (2-A.20).

Odd-Even Mode Excitation

 Use (2-A.27) to (2-A.39)

Even-Even Mode Excitation

 Use (2-A.27) to (2-A.39) with coth $\gamma_n h_1$ replaced by tanh $\gamma_n h_1$.

Chapter 3
Analysis of Fin Lines: Rigorous Methods

3.1 INTRODUCTION

Approximate methods for the analysis of fin-line structures were presented in Ch. 2. These methods can be used within the following limitations: (1) they are known to yield accurate results for guide wavelength and characteristic impedance of fin lines having narrow slot widths; (2) only dominant mode propagation characteristics are obtained; and (3) they are applicable to fin-line configurations possessing certain types of symmetry.

In a practical system, the symmetric fin lines are not necessarily favored for many applications. For example, the characteristic impedances of conventional unilateral and bilateral fin lines are quite high, and impedance matching to active devices is often difficult. This problem can somewhat be alleviated by using antipodal fin line, but the mounting of active devices becomes difficult.

In order to extend the range of application and increase the degree of integration, there is a need to utilize more general types of fin lines, not necessarily possessing symmetry. The asymmetry could serve as an additional parameter to control the propagation characteristics, thereby providing more flexibility in actual circuit design. For practical applications, the knowledge of higher order modes is also essential: first, to assess the single-mode operating bandwidth; and, second, to evaluate the equivalent circuit parameters of discontinuities incorporated in the circuit. In addition, such influences as finite metalization thickness and waveguide housing grooves need to be studied for accurate design of fin-line circuits.

In this chapter, we present rigorous methods of analyzing symmetric as well as asymmetric fin lines. First, the *spectral domain technique* [1–3] is applied to a fin-line structure. In this method, the information on the propagation constant at a given frequency is extracted from algebraic equations that relate Fourier transforms of the electric fields at the dielectric-air interface to those of the currents on the fins. An advantage of this method is that the accuracy can be checked by comparing the results obtained by using different basis functions. A convergence check could also be performed by increasing the number of basis functions for one of the sets. In addition, dispersion characteristics for the higher order modes can be generated.

Generalized multilayer fin lines, which consist of slots located on more than one dielectric interface, can be easily analyzed by using the *spectral-domain immittance approach* [4–6] in conjunction with Galerkin's method. In this approach, an immittance matrix for the structure is derived from the combination of equivalent transmission lines in the transverse direction. This technique is quite general and allows computation of propagation constants for the dominant as well as the higher order modes. The method allows any number of slots of equal or unequal widths to be arbitrarily located at each interface.

Fin lines with multilayer dielectrics can be more easily analyzed by applying the spectral domain technique using the concept of chain matrix [7–8]. This is the most general method and can be applied to symmetric as well as asymmetric fin lines having slots located on more than one interface between the dielectric layers. Several other rigorous analytical and numerical methods, which include the modal analysis [9–10], method of lines [11], and TLM method [12], are also reported in the literature. These methods are useful for analyzing dispersion characteristics of fin lines with (1) finite metalization thickness, (2) grooves in the waveguide housing, and (3) varying slot width profile.

3.2 DERIVATION OF ELECTROMAGNETIC FIELDS

In a region containing no sources, the electromagnetic fields satisfy the following Maxwell's equations:

$$\nabla \times \overrightarrow{E} = -\frac{\partial \overrightarrow{B}}{\partial t} \tag{3.1a}$$

$$\nabla \times \overrightarrow{H} = \frac{\partial \overrightarrow{D}}{\partial t} \tag{3.1b}$$

$$\nabla \cdot \overrightarrow{D} = 0 \tag{3.1c}$$

$$\nabla \cdot \vec{B} = 0 \qquad (3.1d)$$

Electric and Magnetic Potentials

From (3.1d), we can write

$$\vec{B} = \nabla \times \vec{A}^e \qquad (3.2a)$$

Substitute (3.2a) in (3.1a) to obtain

$$\nabla \times \left(\vec{E} + \frac{\partial \vec{A}^e}{\partial t}\right) = 0 \qquad (3.2b)$$

or

$$\vec{E} = -\nabla \Phi^e - \frac{\partial \vec{A}^e}{\partial t} \qquad (3.2c)$$

$\vec{A}^e$ and Φ^e are known as the electric vector potential and electric scalar potential, respectively.

Substituting (3.2a) and (3.2c) in (3.1b), we get

$$\nabla \times \nabla \times \vec{A}^e = \mu\epsilon \frac{\partial}{\partial t}\left(-\nabla \Phi^e - \frac{\partial \vec{A}^e}{\partial t}\right)$$

or

$$\nabla(\nabla \cdot \vec{A}^e) - \nabla^2 \vec{A}^e = -\mu\epsilon \frac{\partial^2 \vec{A}^e}{\partial t^2} - \mu\epsilon \frac{\partial}{\partial t} \nabla \Phi^e$$

or

$$-\nabla^2 \vec{A}^e + \mu\epsilon \frac{\partial^2 \vec{A}^e}{\partial t^2} + \nabla\left[\nabla \cdot \vec{A}^e + \mu\epsilon \frac{\partial \Phi^e}{\partial t}\right] = 0 \qquad (3.3)$$

If we impose the Lorentz condition, namely,

$$\nabla \cdot \vec{A}^e + \mu\epsilon \frac{\partial \Phi^e}{\partial t} = 0 \tag{3.4}$$

then (3.3) becomes

$$\nabla^2 \vec{A}^e - \mu\epsilon \frac{\partial^2 \vec{A}^e}{\partial t^2} = 0 \tag{3.5}$$

From (3.1c), we can write

$$\vec{D} = -\nabla \times \vec{A}^h \tag{3.6a}$$

Substituting (3.6a) in (3.1b), we have

$$\nabla \times \left(\vec{H} + \frac{\partial \vec{A}^h}{\partial t} \right) = 0 \tag{3.6b}$$

$$\vec{H} = -\nabla\Phi^h - \frac{\partial \vec{A}^h}{\partial t} \tag{3.6c}$$

$\vec{A}^h$ and Φ^h are known as the magnetic vector potential and magnetic scalar potential, respectively.

Substituting (3.6a) and (3.6c) in (3.1a), we have

$$-\nabla \times \nabla \times \vec{A}^h = \mu\epsilon \frac{\partial}{\partial t} \left(\nabla\Phi^h + \frac{\partial \vec{A}^h}{\partial t} \right)$$

or

$$\nabla^2 \vec{A}^h - \mu\epsilon \frac{\partial^2 \vec{A}^h}{\partial t^2} - \nabla \left[\left(\nabla \cdot \vec{A}^h \right) + \mu\epsilon \frac{\partial \Phi^h}{\partial t} \right] = 0 \tag{3.7}$$

If we impose the Lorentz condition:

$$\nabla \cdot \vec{A}^h + \mu\epsilon \frac{\partial \Phi^h}{\partial t} = 0 \tag{3.8}$$

then (3.7) becomes

$$\nabla^2 \vec{A}^h - \mu\epsilon \frac{\partial^2 \vec{A}^h}{\partial t^2} = 0 \tag{3.9}$$

Hertz Potential

Define

$$\vec{A}^e = \mu\epsilon \frac{\partial \vec{\pi}^e}{\partial t} \tag{3.10a}$$

and

$$\vec{A}^h = \mu\epsilon \frac{\partial \vec{\pi}^h}{\partial t} \tag{3.10b}$$

where $\vec{\pi}^e$ and $\vec{\pi}^h$ are known as the electric Hertz potential and magnetic Hertz potential, respectively.

With (3.10a), (3.4) can be rewritten as

$$\mu\epsilon \frac{\partial}{\partial t} \nabla \cdot \vec{\pi}^e = -\mu\epsilon \frac{\partial \Phi^e}{\partial t} \tag{3.11a}$$

or

$$\Phi^e = -\nabla \cdot \vec{\pi}^e \tag{3.11b}$$

With (3.11b) and (3.10a), (3.2a) and (3.2c) can be rewritten as

$$\vec{B} = \mu\epsilon \frac{\partial}{\partial t} \nabla \times \vec{\pi}^e \tag{3.12a}$$

$$\vec{E} = \nabla(\nabla \cdot \vec{\pi}^e) - \mu\epsilon \frac{\partial^2 \vec{\pi}^e}{\partial t^2} \tag{3.12b}$$

Similarly, using the definition of $\vec{A}^h$ given by (3.10b) in (3.8), we get

$$\Phi^h = -\nabla \cdot \vec{\pi}^h \tag{3.13}$$

With (3.10b) and (3.13), $\vec{D}$ and $\vec{H}$ given by (3.6a) and (3.6c) can be expressed as

$$\vec{D} = -\mu\epsilon \frac{\partial}{\partial t} \nabla \times \vec{\pi}^h \tag{3.14a}$$

$$\vec{H} = \nabla(\nabla \cdot \vec{\pi}^h) - \mu\epsilon \frac{\partial^2 \vec{\pi}^h}{\partial t^2} \tag{3.14b}$$

The Hertz potentials $\vec{\pi}^e$ and $\vec{\pi}^h$ satisfy the wave equations:

$$\nabla^2 \vec{\pi}^e - \mu\epsilon \frac{\partial^2 \vec{\pi}^e}{\partial t^2} = 0 \tag{3.15a}$$

$$\nabla^2 \vec{\pi}^h - \mu\epsilon \frac{\partial^2 \vec{\pi}^h}{\partial t^2} = 0 \tag{3.15b}$$

Assuming a time dependence of $e^{j\omega t}$ and setting $k^2 = \omega^2\mu\epsilon$, the field and wave equations can be written as

$$\vec{E}^e = \nabla(\nabla \cdot \vec{\pi}^e) + k^2\vec{\pi}^e \tag{3.16a}$$

$$\vec{H}^e = j\omega\epsilon \nabla \times \vec{\pi}^e \tag{3.16b}$$

$$\vec{E}^h = -j\omega\mu \nabla \times \vec{\pi}^h \tag{3.17a}$$

$$\vec{H}^h = \nabla(\nabla \cdot \vec{\pi}^h) + k^2\vec{\pi}^h \tag{3.17b}$$

and

$$\nabla^2 \vec{\pi}^e + k^2 \vec{\pi}^e = 0 \tag{3.18a}$$

$$\nabla^2 \vec{\pi}^h + k^2 \vec{\pi}^h = 0 \tag{3.18b}$$

TE and TM Waves

The electromagnetic fields in general can be expressed as the super-position of TE and TM fields. For ease of mathematical analysis presented in the following sections, the fields are expressed in terms of the Hertz potential functions $\phi^e(x, y, z)$ and $\phi^h(x, y, z)$.

Let us consider TE and TM modes with respect to the z-direction, and define

$$\vec{\pi}^e = \hat{z}\phi^e(x, y, z), \text{ for TM or E-Waves} \tag{3.19a}$$

$$\vec{\pi}^h = \hat{z}\phi^h(x, y, z), \text{ for TE or H-waves} \tag{3.19b}$$

Then, from (3.18), we get the following wave equations in terms of ϕ^e and ϕ^h:

$$\nabla^2\phi^e + k^2\phi^e = 0 \tag{3.20a}$$

$$\nabla^2\phi^h + k^2\phi^h = 0 \tag{3.20b}$$

The electric and magnetic fields are expressed as

$$\vec{E}^e = \nabla(\nabla \cdot \vec{\pi}^e) + k^2\vec{\pi}^e$$
$$= \left(\nabla\frac{\partial}{\partial z} + k^2\hat{z}\right)\phi^e \tag{3.21a}$$

$$\vec{H}^e = j\omega\epsilon \nabla \times \phi^e\hat{z} \tag{3.21b}$$

$$\vec{E}^h = -j\omega\mu \nabla \times \phi^h\hat{z} \tag{3.21c}$$

$$\vec{H}^h = \left(\nabla\frac{\partial}{\partial z} + k^2\hat{z}\right)\phi^h \tag{3.21d}$$

Expanding (3.21), we get

$$\vec{E}^e = \hat{x}\frac{\partial^2\phi^e}{\partial x\partial z} + \hat{y}\frac{\partial^2\phi^e}{\partial y\partial z} + \hat{z}\left(\frac{\partial^2\phi^e}{\partial z^2} + k^2\phi^e\right) \tag{3.22a}$$

$$\overrightarrow{H^e} = j\omega\epsilon\left(\hat{x}\frac{\partial\phi^e}{\partial y} - \hat{y}\frac{\partial\phi^e}{\partial x}\right) \tag{3.22b}$$

$$\overrightarrow{E^h} = -j\omega\mu\left(\hat{x}\frac{\partial\phi^h}{\partial y} - \hat{y}\frac{\partial\phi^h}{\partial x}\right) \tag{3.22c}$$

$$\overrightarrow{H^h} = \hat{x}\frac{\partial^2\phi^h}{\partial x\partial z} + \hat{y}\frac{\partial^2\phi^h}{\partial y\partial z} + \hat{z}\left(\frac{\partial^2\phi^h}{\partial z^2} + k^2\phi^h\right) \tag{3.22d}$$

The total $\overrightarrow{E}$ and $\overrightarrow{H}$ fields are then given by

$$\overrightarrow{E} = \overrightarrow{E^e} + \overrightarrow{E^h} \tag{3.23a}$$

$$\overrightarrow{H} = \overrightarrow{H^e} + \overrightarrow{H^h} \tag{3.23b}$$

3.3   SPECTRAL DOMAIN TECHNIQUE

In this section, we present application of the spectral domain technique to analyze the propagation characteristics of an unilateral fin line. This technique can be easily extended to the analysis of other fin-line structures.

3.3.1   Basic Formulation

Consider the unilateral fin line shown in Fig. 3.1. The fin line supports a hybrid field. For the purpose of analysis, we consider the electromagnetic fields existing in each of the three regions as the superposition of TE (to z) and TM (to z) fields. By using (3.22) and (3.23), the fields are first expressed in terms of $\phi^e(x, y, z)$ and $\phi^h(x, y, z)$ as follows:

$$E_{zi}(x, y, z) = \left(\frac{\partial^2}{\partial z^2} + k_i^2\right)\phi_i^e(x, y, z) \tag{3.24a}$$

$$H_{zi}(x, y, z) = \left(\frac{\partial^2}{\partial z^2} + k_i^2\right)\phi_i^h(x, y, z) \tag{3.24b}$$

$$E_{xi}(x, y, z) = \frac{\partial^2}{\partial x\partial z}\phi_i^e(x, y, z) - j\omega\mu_0\frac{\partial}{\partial y}\phi_i^h(x, y, z) \tag{3.24c}$$

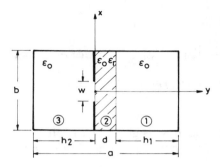

Fig. 3.1 Cross section of a unilateral fin line.

$$H_{xi}(x, y, z) = j\omega\epsilon_i\frac{\partial}{\partial y}\phi_i^e(x, y, z) + \frac{\partial^2}{\partial x\partial z}\phi_i^h(x, y, z) \qquad (3.24d)$$

$$E_{yi}(x, y, z) = \frac{\partial^2}{\partial y\partial z}\phi_i^e(x, y, z) + j\omega\mu_0\frac{\partial}{\partial x}\phi_i^h(x, y, z) \qquad (3.24e)$$

$$H_{yi}(x, y, z) = -j\omega\epsilon_i\frac{\partial}{\partial x}\phi_i^e(x, y, z) + \frac{\partial^2}{\partial y\partial z}\phi_i^h(x, y, z) \qquad (3.24f)$$

where $i = 1$, 2, and 3 refer to regions 1, 2, and 3, respectively. Thus, ϕ_i^e and ϕ_i^h satisfy the Helmholtz equation:

$$(\nabla^2 + k_i^2)\phi_i^e = 0 \qquad (3.25a)$$

$$(\nabla^2 + k_i^2)\phi_i^h = 0 \qquad (3.25b)$$

For the present problem, we have

$$\epsilon_1 = \epsilon_3 = \epsilon_0, \quad \epsilon_2 = \epsilon_0\epsilon_r \qquad (3.26a)$$

$$k_1^2 = k_3^2 = k_0^2 = \omega^2\mu_0\epsilon_0, \quad k_2^2 = k_0^2\epsilon_r \qquad (3.26b)$$

Assume propagation in the z-direction, with a z-dependence $e^{j\beta z}$. In order to convert (3.24) and (3.25) into the spectral domain, we define the Fourier transform as

$$\hat{\phi}_i^{e,h}(\alpha_n, y) = \int_{-b/2}^{b/2}\phi_i^{e,h}(x, y)\, e^{j\alpha_n x}dx \qquad (3.27)$$

where, in general,

$$\alpha_n = \begin{cases} (2n-1)\pi/b, & \phi_i^h \text{ odd in } x/\phi_i^e \text{ even in } x \qquad (3.28a) \\ 2n\pi/b, & \phi_i^h \text{ even in } x/\phi_i^e \text{ odd in } x \qquad (3.28b) \end{cases}$$

For the present problem, α_n is given by (3.28b).

The transform of the field equations (3.24) are now given by

$$\hat{E}_{zi}(\alpha_n, y) = (k_i^2 - \beta^2)\hat{\phi}_i^e(\alpha_n, y) \qquad (3.29a)$$

$$\hat{H}_{zi}(\alpha_n, y) = (k_i^2 - \beta^2)\hat{\phi}_i^h(\alpha_n, y) \qquad (3.29b)$$

$$\hat{E}_{xi}(\alpha_n, y) = -\alpha_n\beta\,\hat{\phi}_i^e(\alpha_n, y) - j\omega\mu_0\frac{d}{dy}\,\hat{\phi}_i^h(\alpha_n, y) \qquad (3.29c)$$

$$\hat{H}_{xi}(\alpha_n, y) = j\omega\epsilon_i\frac{d}{dy}\,\hat{\phi}_i^e(\alpha_n, y) - \alpha_n\beta\,\hat{\phi}_i^h(\alpha_n, y) \qquad (3.29d)$$

$$\hat{E}_{yi}(\alpha_n, y) = j\beta\frac{d}{dy}\,\hat{\phi}_i^e(\alpha_n, y) - \omega\mu_0\alpha_n\hat{\phi}_i^h(\alpha_n, y) \qquad (3.29e)$$

$$\hat{H}_{yi}(\alpha_n, y) = \omega\epsilon_i\alpha_n\hat{\phi}_i^e(\alpha_n, y) + j\beta\frac{d}{dy}\,\hat{\phi}_i^h(\alpha_n, y) \qquad (3.29f)$$

and $\hat{\phi}_i^e$ and $\hat{\phi}_i^h$ satisfy the equation:

$$\left(\frac{d^2}{dy^2} - \gamma_i^2\right)\hat{\phi}_i^{e,h}(\alpha_n, y) = 0 \qquad (3.30)$$

where

$$\gamma_i^2 = \alpha_n^2 + \beta^2 - k_i^2 \qquad (3.31a)$$

For the three regions $i = 1, 2,$ and 3, we can write

$$\gamma_1^2 = \gamma_3^2 = \alpha_n^2 + \beta^2 - k_0^2 = \gamma_0^2 \qquad (3.31b)$$

$$\gamma_2^2 = \alpha_n^2 + \beta^2 - k_0^2\epsilon_r = \gamma^2 \qquad (3.31c)$$

The solution of (3.30) for the three regions is written as

$$\hat{\phi}_1^e(\alpha_n, y) = A^e(\alpha_n) \sinh[\gamma_1(h_1 + d - y)] \tag{3.32a}$$

$$\hat{\phi}_1^h(\alpha_n, y) = A^h(\alpha_n) \cosh[\gamma_1(h_1 + d - y)] \tag{3.32b}$$

$$\hat{\phi}_2^e(\alpha_n, y) = B^e(\alpha_n) \sinh \gamma_2 y + C^e(\alpha_n) \cosh \gamma_2 y \tag{3.32c}$$

$$\hat{\phi}_2^h(\alpha_n, y) = B^h(\alpha_n) \sinh \gamma_2 y + C^h(\alpha_n) \cosh \gamma_2 y \tag{3.32d}$$

$$\hat{\phi}_3^e(\alpha_n, y) = D^e(\alpha_n) \sinh[\gamma_3(h_2 + y)] \tag{3.32e}$$

$$\hat{\phi}_3^h(\alpha_n, y) = D^h(\alpha_n) \cosh[\gamma_3(h_2 + y)] \tag{3.32f}$$

where $A^e(\alpha_n) \ldots D^h(\alpha_n)$ are unknown constants. In order to solve for these unknowns, we apply the boundary conditions at the interfaces, $y = 0$ and $y = d$:

At $y = d$:

$$E_{x1}(x, d) = E_{x2}(x, d) \tag{3.33a}$$

$$E_{z1}(x, d) = E_{z2}(x, d) \tag{3.33b}$$

$$H_{x1}(x, d) = H_{x2}(x, d) \tag{3.33c}$$

$$H_{z1}(x, d) = H_{z2}(x, d) \tag{3.33d}$$

At $y = 0$:

$$E_{x2}(x, 0) = E_{x3}(x, 0) \tag{3.34a}$$

$$E_{z2}(x, 0) = E_{z3}(x, 0) \tag{3.34b}$$

$$E_{x3}(x, 0) = \begin{cases} e_x(x), & \text{in the slot} \\ 0, & \text{elsewhere} \end{cases} \tag{3.34c}$$

$$E_{z3}(x, 0) = \begin{cases} e_z(x), & \text{in the slot} \\ 0, & \text{elsewhere} \end{cases} \tag{3.34d}$$

$$J_x(x) = \begin{cases} 0, & \text{in the slot} \\ H_{z2}(x, 0) - H_{z3}(x, 0), & \text{elsewhere} \end{cases} \tag{3.34e}$$

$$J_z(x) = \begin{cases} 0, & \text{in the slot} \\ -H_{x2}(x, 0) + H_{x3}(x, 0), & \text{elsewhere} \end{cases} \tag{3.34f}$$

where $e_x(x)$ and $e_z(x)$ are the unknown electric fields across the slot at $y = 0$, and $J_x(x)$ and $J_z(x)$ are the unknown current density functions on the fins at $y = 0$. Taking the Fourier transform of (3.33) and (3.34), we obtain

At $y = d$:

$$\hat{E}_{x1}(\alpha_n, d) = \hat{E}_{x2}(\alpha_n, d) \tag{3.35a}$$

$$\hat{E}_{z1}(\alpha_n, d) = \hat{E}_{z2}(\alpha_n, d) \tag{3.35b}$$

$$\hat{H}_{x1}(\alpha_n, d) = \hat{H}_{x2}(\alpha_n, d) \tag{3.35c}$$

$$\hat{H}_{z1}(\alpha_n, d) = \hat{H}_{z2}(\alpha_n, d) \tag{3.35d}$$

At $y = 0$:

$$\hat{E}_{x2}(\alpha_n, 0) = \hat{E}_{x3}(\alpha_n, 0) = \hat{e}_x(\alpha_n) \tag{3.36a}$$

$$\hat{E}_{z2}(\alpha_n, 0) = \hat{E}_{z3}(\alpha_n, 0) = \hat{e}_z(\alpha_n) \tag{3.36b}$$

$$\hat{J}_x(\alpha_n) = \hat{H}_{z2}(\alpha_n, 0) - \hat{H}_{z3}(\alpha_n, 0) \tag{3.36c}$$

$$\hat{J}_z(\alpha_n) = -\hat{H}_{x2}(\alpha_n, 0) + \hat{H}_{x3}(\alpha_n, 0) \tag{3.36d}$$

By applying the boundary conditions given in (3.35) and (3.36) and solving, we get the following algebraic equations relating $\hat{J}_x(\alpha_n)$ and $\hat{J}_z(\alpha_n)$ with $\hat{e}_x(\alpha_n)$ and $\hat{e}_z(\alpha_n)$:

$$\begin{bmatrix} \hat{J}_x(\alpha_n) \\ \hat{J}_z(\alpha_n) \end{bmatrix} = \begin{bmatrix} \hat{G}_{11}(\alpha_n, \beta) & \hat{G}_{12}(\alpha_n, \beta) \\ \hat{G}_{21}(\alpha_n, \beta) & \hat{G}_{22}(\alpha_n, \beta) \end{bmatrix} \begin{bmatrix} \hat{e}_z(\alpha_n) \\ \hat{e}_x(\alpha_n) \end{bmatrix} \tag{3.37}$$

where $\hat{G}_{11}(\alpha_n, \beta)$, $\hat{G}_{12}(\alpha_n, \beta)$, $\hat{G}_{21}(\alpha_n, \beta)$, and $\hat{G}_{22}(\alpha_n, \beta)$ are the elements of the dyadic Green's function in the Fourier transformed domain. With some algebraic manipulation, the expressions for the values of G can be arranged as follows:

$$\hat{G}_{11}(\alpha_n, \beta) = \frac{-j\alpha_n\beta}{P_0}(P_1 \sinh \gamma d \cosh \gamma d$$
$$+ P_2 \sinh^2 \gamma d + P_3) \tag{3.38a}$$

$$\hat{G}_{12}(\alpha_n, \beta) = \frac{-j}{P_0}(P_4 \sinh \gamma d \cosh \gamma d + P_5 \sinh^2 \gamma d + P_6) \tag{3.38b}$$

$$\hat{G}_{21}(\alpha_n, \beta) = \frac{-j}{P_0}(P_7 \sinh \gamma d \cosh \gamma d + P_8 \sinh^2 \gamma d + P_9) \tag{3.38c}$$

$$\hat{G}_{22}(\alpha_n, \beta) = \hat{G}_{11}(\alpha_n, \beta) \tag{3.38d}$$

where

$$P_1 = \gamma[k_0^2\gamma_0^2(\coth^2\gamma_0 h_1 + \epsilon_r) + (k^2\gamma_0^2 + k_0^2\gamma^2)$$
$$\coth \gamma_0 h_1 \coth \gamma_0 h_2] \tag{3.39a}$$

$$P_2 = \gamma_0[(k^2\gamma_0^2 + k_0^2\gamma^2) \coth \gamma_0 h_1$$
$$+ k_0^2\gamma^2(\coth^2\gamma_0 h_1 + \epsilon_r)\coth \gamma_0 h_2] \tag{3.39b}$$

$$P_3 = k^2\gamma_0\gamma^2(\coth \gamma_0 h_1 + \coth \gamma_0 h_2) \tag{3.39c}$$

$$P_4 = \gamma[k_0^2\gamma_0^2(k^2 - \beta^2)(\coth^2\gamma_0 h_1 + \epsilon_r) + (k_0^2 - \beta^2)$$
$$(k^2\gamma_0^2 + k_0^2\gamma^2) \coth \gamma_0 h_1 \coth \gamma_0 h_2] \tag{3.39d}$$

$$P_5 = \gamma_0[k_0^2\gamma^2(k_0^2 - \beta^2)(\coth^2\gamma_0 h_1 + \epsilon_r) \coth \gamma_0 h_2$$
$$+ (k^2 - \beta^2)(k^2\gamma_0^2 + k_0^2\gamma^2)\coth \gamma_0 h_1] \tag{3.39e}$$

$$P_6 = k^2\gamma_0\gamma^2(k_0^2 - \beta^2)(\coth \gamma_0 h_1 + \coth \gamma_0 h_2) \tag{3.39f}$$

$$P_7 = \gamma[k_0^2\gamma_0^2(k^2 - \alpha_n^2)(\coth^2\gamma_0 h_1 + \epsilon_r) + (k_0^2 - \alpha_n^2)$$
$$(k^2\gamma_0^2 + k_0^2\gamma^2) \coth \gamma_0 h_1 \coth \gamma_0 h_2] \tag{3.39g}$$

$$P_8 = \gamma_0[(k^2 - \alpha_n^2)(k^2\gamma_0^2 + k_0^2\gamma^2) \coth \gamma_0 h_1$$
$$+ k_0^2\gamma^2(k_0^2 - \alpha_n^2)(\epsilon_r + \coth^2 \gamma_0 h_1) \coth \gamma_0 h_2] \tag{3.39h}$$

$$P_9 = k^2\gamma_0\gamma^2(k_0^2 - \alpha_n^2)(\coth \gamma_0 h_1 + \coth \gamma_0 h_2) \tag{3.39i}$$

$$P_0 = \omega\mu_0\gamma_0\gamma[(k^2\gamma_0^2 + k_0^2\gamma^2) \coth \gamma_0 h_1 \sinh \gamma d \cosh \gamma d$$
$$+ k_0^2\gamma_0\gamma(\coth^2\gamma_0 h_1 + \epsilon_r) \sinh^2 \gamma d + k^2\gamma_0\gamma] \tag{3.39j}$$

3.3.2   Characteristic Equation

In the matrix equation (3.37), $\hat{e}_x(\alpha_n)$, $\hat{e}_z(\alpha_n)$, $\hat{J}_x(\alpha_n)$, and $\hat{J}_z(\alpha_n)$ are unknown functions. Because the electric fields and currents are nonzero in complementary regions at the interface $y = 0$, it is possible to eliminate $\hat{J}_x(\alpha_n)$ and $\hat{J}_z(\alpha_n)$ by using Galerkin's method and Parseval's theorem [13-14] and solving for $\hat{e}_x(\alpha_n)$ and $\hat{e}_z(\alpha_n)$. To this end, we define an inner product of the two functions as

$$\langle \hat{\psi}_1(\alpha_n),\ \hat{\psi}_2^*(\alpha_n) \rangle = \sum_{n=-\infty}^{\infty} \hat{\psi}_1(\alpha_n)\hat{\psi}_2^*(\alpha_n) \qquad (3.40\text{a})$$

According to Parseval's theorem, we have

$$\int_{-b/2}^{b/2} \psi_1(x)\psi_2(x)\mathrm{d}x = \frac{1}{b} \sum_{n=-\infty}^{\infty} \hat{\psi}_1(\alpha_n)\hat{\psi}_2^*(\alpha_n) \qquad (3.40\text{b})$$

Next, the aperture electric fields $\hat{e}_x(\alpha_n)$ and $\hat{e}_z(\alpha_n)$ are expanded in terms of known basis functions $\hat{f}_{xm}(\alpha_n)$ and $\hat{g}_{zm}(\alpha_n)$, respectively

$$\hat{e}_x(\alpha_n) = \sum_{m=1}^{M} \xi_m \hat{f}_{xm}(\alpha_n) \qquad (3.41\text{a})$$

$$\hat{e}_z(\alpha_n) = \sum_{m=1}^{N} \zeta_m \hat{g}_{zm}(\alpha_n) \qquad (3.41\text{b})$$

where ξ_m and ζ_m are unknown constants. Substituting (3.41) in (3.37), we get

$$\hat{G}_{11}(\alpha_n, \beta) \sum_{m=1}^{N} \zeta_m \hat{g}_{zm}(\alpha_n) + \hat{G}_{12}(\alpha_n, \beta) \sum_{m=1}^{M} \xi_m \hat{f}_{xm}(\alpha_n)$$

$$= \hat{J}_x(\alpha_n) \qquad (3.42\text{a})$$

$$\hat{G}_{21}(\alpha_n, \beta) \sum_{m=1}^{N} \zeta_m \hat{g}_{zm}(\alpha_n) + \hat{G}_{22}(\alpha_n, \beta) \sum_{m=1}^{M} \xi_m \hat{f}_{xm}(\alpha_n)$$

$$= \hat{J}_z(\alpha_n) \qquad (3.42\text{b})$$

If we take the inner products with respect to $\hat{f}_{xi}^*(\alpha_n)$ and $\hat{g}_{zi}^*(\alpha_n)$, respectively, and apply Parseval's theorem, we get the following set of equations:

$$\sum_{m=1}^{N} P_{im}\zeta_m + \sum_{m=1}^{M} Q_{im}\xi_m = 0, \quad i = 1, 2, \ldots, M \qquad (3.43a)$$

$$\sum_{m=1}^{N} R_{im}\zeta_m + \sum_{m=1}^{M} S_{im}\xi_m = 0, \quad i = 1, 2, \ldots, N \qquad (3.43b)$$

where

$$P_{im} = \sum_{n=-\infty}^{\infty} \hat{f}_{xi}^*(\alpha_n)\hat{G}_{11}(\alpha_n, \beta)\hat{g}_{zm}(\alpha_n), \quad i = 1, 2, \ldots, M \qquad (3.44a)$$

$$Q_{im} = \sum_{n=-\infty}^{\infty} \hat{f}_{xi}^*(\alpha_n)\hat{G}_{12}(\alpha_n, \beta)\hat{f}_{xm}(\alpha_n), \quad i = 1, 2, \ldots, M \qquad (3.44b)$$

$$R_{im} = \sum_{n=-\infty}^{\infty} \hat{g}_{zi}^*(\alpha_n)\hat{G}_{21}(\alpha_n, \beta)\hat{g}_{zm}(\alpha_n), \quad i = 1, 2, \ldots, N \qquad (3.44c)$$

$$S_{im} = \sum_{n=-\infty}^{\infty} \hat{g}_{zi}^*(\alpha_n)\hat{G}_{22}(\alpha_n, \beta)\hat{f}_{xm}(\alpha_n), \quad i = 1, 2, \ldots, N \qquad (3.44d)$$

The inner products on the right-hand side of (3.42) vanish upon application of Parseval's theorem because the inverse transforms of the electric fields $\hat{e}_x(\alpha_n)$ and $\hat{e}_z(\alpha_n)$ and the current densities $\hat{J}_x(\alpha_n)$ and $\hat{J}_z(\alpha_n)$ are nonzero in the complementary regions at the interface $y = 0$. The characteristic equation for determining the desired propagation constant of the dominant and higher order modes is obtained by setting the determinant of the coefficient matrix in (3.43) equal to zero.

3.3.3 Choice of Basis Functions

The numerical solution of (3.43) is obtained by introducing a known set of basis functions. The accuracy of the final solution depends on the accuracy with which the basis functions represent the true electric field distribution in the slot.

For slots of small width, fairly accurate solutions for the guide wavelength can be obtained by neglecting the longitudinal component of the electric field along the length of the slot in comparison with the transverse component across the width of the slot, i.e., by setting $e_z(x, z) = 0$. This assumption is exact when $w = b$, which corresponds to purely dielectric slab loaded waveguide. Also, for other slot widths this assumption results in simplicity as well as numerical efficiency, while retaining adequate accuracy required in practice. The dispersion equation for determining the guide wavelength then reduces to a single equation:

$$\sum_{m=1}^{M} \sum_{n=-\infty}^{\infty} \hat{G}_{12}(\alpha_n, \beta)|\hat{f}_{xm}(\alpha_n)|^2 = 0 \tag{3.45}$$

Furthermore, if we use one-term approximation and set $M = 1$, the characteristic equation reduces to

$$\sum_{n=-\infty}^{\infty} \hat{G}_{12}(\alpha_n, \beta)|\hat{f}_x(\alpha_n)|^2 = 0 \tag{3.46}$$

where $\hat{f}_{x1}(\alpha_n)$ is replaced by $\hat{f}_x(\alpha_n)$.

With a suitable choice of the basis function corresponding to one term approximation, reasonably accurate results can be obtained for the guide wavelength.

Simple Basis Functions for the Slot Field

As a first approximation, we assume the z-directed electric field to be zero within the slot, so that

$$g_z(x) = 0 \tag{3.47}$$

For the x-directed electric field, we can consider the following three choices of one-term basis functions. The first choice:

(1)

$$f_x(x) = 1 \tag{3.48a}$$

the Fourier transform of which is

$$\hat{f}_x(\alpha_n) = \frac{\sin\left(\dfrac{\alpha_n w}{2}\right)}{(\alpha_n/2)} \tag{3.48b}$$

The choice of basis function (1) has been shown to give accurate results in the case of slotlines having narrow slot widths ($w/d \leqslant 2$, where d is the thickness of the substrate); for dielectric loaded waveguide ($w/d = 1$), it is exact [3].

The second choice:

(2)

$$f_x(x) = \frac{1}{\sqrt{\left(\frac{w}{2}\right)^2 - x^2}} \qquad (3.49a)$$

$$\hat{f}_x(\alpha_n) = \pi J_0\left(\frac{w}{2}\,|\alpha_n|\right) \qquad (3.49b)$$

where J_0 is the Bessel function of *zero*th order. Then, the third choice:

(3)

$$f_x(x) = \left(1 + \left|\frac{2x}{w}\right|^3\right) \qquad (3.50a)$$

$$\hat{f}_x(\alpha_n) = 2w \left[\frac{\sin\left(\frac{\alpha_n w}{2}\right)}{\left(\frac{\alpha_n w}{2}\right)} + \frac{3w}{\left(\frac{\alpha_n w}{2}\right)^2}\right]$$

$$\cdot \left[\cos\left(\frac{\alpha_n w}{2}\right) - 2\,\frac{\sin\left(\frac{\alpha_n w}{2}\right)}{\left(\frac{\alpha_n w}{2}\right)} + \frac{\sin^2\left(\frac{\alpha_n w}{4}\right)}{\left(\frac{\alpha_n w}{4}\right)^2}\right] \qquad (3.50b)$$

More Accurate Basis Functions for $w/d > 2$ and $w/b < 1$

An important feature of the spectral domain method as applied here is that quite accurate solutions are possible, even if an extremely small sized matrix such as $M = N = 1$ is used. This is achieved by suitably incorporating the edge condition of the aperture electric field into the choice of the basis functions.

The following four basis functions may be chosen in practice. All of these can be readily Fourier transformed.

(1) *Qualified one-term expansions satisfying the "edge condition" at* $|x| = w/2$ *(Fig. 3.2):*

$$f_{x1}(x) = \frac{1}{\sqrt{\left(\frac{w}{2}\right)^2 - x^2}} \tag{3.51a}$$

$$g_{z1}(x) = x\sqrt{\left(\frac{w}{2}\right)^2 - x^2} \tag{3.51b}$$

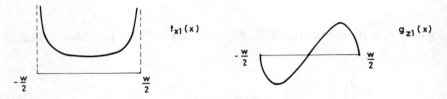

Fig. 3.2   Qualified one term basis function satisfying edge condition at $|x| = w/2$.

(2) *Trains of rectangular pulses with unknown amplitudes* (Fig. 3.3) [2]:

$$f_{xm}(x) = \begin{cases} 1, & (m-1)\Delta x < |x| < m\Delta x \\ 0, & \text{elsewhere} \end{cases} \tag{3.52a}$$

with

$$\Delta x = \frac{w}{2M}$$

$$g_{zm}(x) = \begin{cases} 1, & (m-1)\Delta x' < x < m\Delta x' \\ -1, & -m\Delta x' < x < -(m-1)\Delta x' \\ 0, & \text{elsewhere} \end{cases} \tag{3.52b}$$

with

$$\Delta x' = \frac{w}{2N}$$

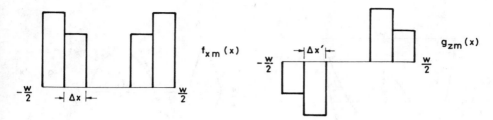

Fig. 3.3   Basis functions consisting of trains of rectangular pulses with unknown amplitudes.

(3) *Sinusoidal functions modified by an edge-condition term* (Fig. 3.4) [2]:

$$f_{xm}(x) = \frac{\cos\left[(m-1)\pi\left(\frac{2x}{w} + 1\right)\right]}{\sqrt{1 - \left(\frac{2x}{w}\right)^2}} \qquad (3.53a)$$

$$g_{zm}(x) = \frac{\sin\left[(m-1)\pi\left(\frac{2x}{w} + 1\right)\right]}{\sqrt{1 - \left(\frac{2x}{w}\right)^2}} \qquad (3.53b)$$

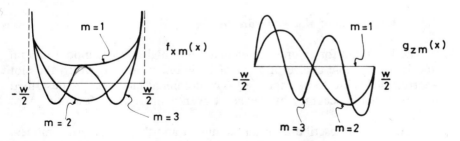

Fig. 3.4   Sinusoidal basis functions modified by an edge-condition term.

(4) *Legendre polynomials for unbounded fields and trignometric functions for bounded fields* (Fig. 3.5):

$$f_{xm}(x) = P_{2(m-1)}\left(\frac{2x}{w}\right), \quad 0 < |x| < \frac{w}{2} \qquad (3.54a)$$

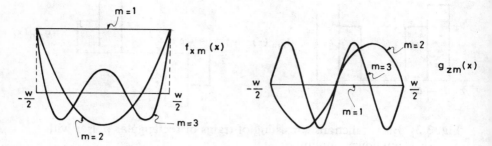

Fig. 3.5 Basis functions consisting of Legendre polynomials for
unbounded fields and trigonometric functions for bounded
fields.

$$g_{zm}(x) = \sin\left[(m - 1)\pi\left(\frac{2x}{w}\right)\right] \tag{3.54b}$$

Of the above four basis functions, the second set (3.52) is less advantageous numerically, because it requires an inherently large matrix order,
and the edge-condition cannot be directly incorporated. Its useful feature
is that it is quite flexible and generally applicable, and the expansion
coefficients ξ_m and ζ_m are adjusted automatically to represent the aperture
field distributions. For better numerical efficiency, either (3.53) or (3.54)
is recommended.

3.3.4 Evaluation of Higher Order Modes

The key point for an efficient evaluation of higher order modes in a fin
line is the suitable choice of a set of basis functions into which the slot
aperture fields are to be expanded. The dominant mode can be described
to a reasonable accuracy by means of even a single basis function, e.g.,
(3.50).

However, to describe both the dominant and the higher order modes,
we could choose (3.53) or (3.54) as the basis functions. A simpler set of
basis functions, which describe at least the first five eigenmodes in a unilateral fin line, are given below [15]:

$$f_{x1}(x) = \begin{cases} 1; \ |x| \leq \dfrac{w}{2} \\[2mm] 0; \ \text{otherwise} \end{cases} \tag{3.55a}$$

$$
f_{x2}(x) = \begin{cases} \dfrac{1}{\sqrt{1 - (2x/w)^2}}; & |x| \leqslant \dfrac{w}{2} \\ 0; & \text{otherwise} \end{cases} \tag{3.55b}
$$

$$
g_{z1}(x) = \begin{cases} \dfrac{2x}{w} \sqrt{(1 - (2x/w)^2)}; & |x| \leqslant \dfrac{w}{2} \\ 0; & \text{otherwise} \end{cases} \tag{3.55c}
$$

$$
g_{z2}(x) = \begin{cases} \dfrac{\sin(4\pi x/w)}{\sqrt{(1 - (2x/w)^2}}; & |x| \leqslant \dfrac{w}{2} \\ 0; & \text{otherwise} \end{cases} \tag{3.55d}
$$

3.3.5   Application to Some Variants of Unilateral Fin Line

In order to demonstrate the generality of the spectral domain technique, we shall consider three variants of unilateral fin line. These are (1) *unilateral fin line with arbitrarily located slot* (Fig. 3.6(a)), (2) *edge-coupled unilateral fin line* (Fig. 3.6(b)), and (3) *multislot edge-coupled unilateral fin line* (Fig. 3.6(c)).

(1) *Unilateral fin line with arbitrarily located slot* (Fig. 3.6(a)):
The characteristic equation for determining the propagation constant is the same as given in (3.43) and (3.44) with values of $\hat{G}_{ij}$ ($i = 1, 2; j = 1, 2$) given in (3.38) and (3.39). For the present problem, the Fourier transform is defined as

$$
\hat{\phi}_i^{e,h}(\alpha_n, y) = \int_0^b \phi_i^{e,h}(x, y) \, e^{j\alpha_n x} dx \tag{3.56}
$$

where

$$
\alpha_n = \frac{n\pi}{b}; \quad n = 0, \pm 1, \pm 2, \ldots, \infty \tag{3.57}
$$

If we choose a sinusoidal basis function modified by an edge condition term, we have

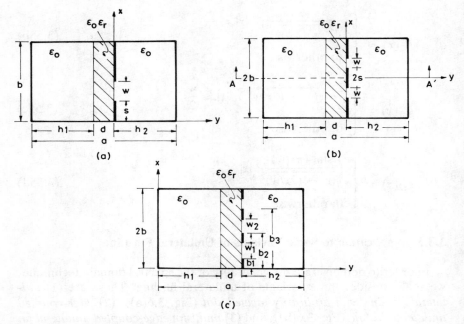

Fig. 3.6 Cross sections of:
   (a) unilateral fin line with arbitrarily located slot
   (b) edge-coupled unilateral fin line
   (c) multislot edge-coupled unilateral fin line

$$f_{xm}(x) = \frac{\cos\left[m\pi\left(\dfrac{x-s}{w}\right)\right]}{\sqrt{1 - \left[\dfrac{2(x-s)}{w} - 1\right]^2}}; \quad s \le x \le s + w \qquad (3.58a)$$

$$g_{zm}(x) = \frac{\sin\left[m\pi\left(\dfrac{x-s}{w}\right)\right]}{\sqrt{1 - \left[\dfrac{2(x-s)}{w} - 1\right]^2}}; \quad s \le x \le s + w \qquad (3.58b)$$

The Fourier transform of (3.58) is given by

$$\hat{f}_{xm}(\alpha_n) = \text{Re}\left[\frac{\pi w}{4}\, e^{j\alpha_n(s+w/2)}\left\{e^{jm\pi/2}J_0\left[\frac{1}{2}\left(\alpha_n w + m\pi\right)\right]\right.\right.$$

$$\left.\left. + e^{-jm\pi/2}J_0\left[\frac{1}{2}\left(\alpha_n w - m\pi\right)\right]\right\}\right] \qquad (3.59\text{a})$$

$$\hat{g}_{zm}(\alpha_n) = \text{Im}\left[-\frac{j\pi w}{4}\, e^{j\alpha_n(s+w/2)}\left\{e^{jm\pi/2}J_0\left[\frac{1}{2}\left(\alpha_n w + m\pi\right)\right]\right.\right.$$

$$\left.\left. - e^{-jm\pi/2}J_0\left[\frac{1}{2}\left(\alpha_n w - m\pi\right)\right]\right\}\right] \qquad (3.59\text{b})$$

where J_0 is the Bessel function.

If we use (3.59) in (3.43) and (3.44), the propagation constant can be determined by setting the determinant of the coefficient matix in (3.43) equal to zero.

For a slot centered in the E-plane ($b = 2s + w$), we use even values of m and n in (3.56) to (3.59), i.e., $n = 0, \pm2, \pm4, \ldots, m = 0, 2, 4, \ldots$ We may note that, with the basis function defined as in (3.58), the summations in (3.43) and (3.44) start from $m = 0$ and $i = 0$.

(2) *Edge-coupled unilateral fin line* (Fig. 3.6(b)):

This structure supports two orthogonal modes—namely, the even- and odd-modes. For the even-mode excitation, the symmetry plane AA' is replaced by a magnetic wall, and for the odd-mode excitation, it is replaced by an electric wall.

Odd-Mode Excitation

The formulas derived for the unilateral fin line with arbitrarily located slot are also valid for an edge-coupled unilateral fin line excited in the odd-mode.

Even-Mode Excitation

For this case, the Fourier transform is defined as

$$\hat{\phi}_i^{e,h}(\alpha_n, y) = \int_0^b \phi_i^{e,h}(x, y)\, e^{j\alpha_n x}dx \qquad (3.60)$$

where

$$\alpha_n = \left(n - \frac{1}{2}\right)\frac{\pi}{b}, \quad n = 0, \pm 1, \pm 2, \pm 3, \ldots \qquad (3.61)$$

If we use the definition given in (3.60), the Fourier transform of the basis function (3.58) is given by

$$\hat{f}_{xm}(\alpha_n) = \text{Im}\left\{\frac{\pi w}{4} e^{j\alpha_n(s+w/2)}\left[e^{jm\pi/2} J_0\left(\frac{1}{2}(\alpha_n w + m\pi)\right)\right.\right.$$
$$\left.\left. + e^{-jm\pi/2} J_0\left(\frac{1}{2}(\alpha_n w - m\pi)\right)\right]\right\} \qquad (3.62a)$$

$$\hat{g}_{zm}(\alpha_n) = \text{Re}\left\{-\frac{j\pi w}{4} e^{j\alpha_n(s+w/2)}\left[e^{jm\pi/2} J_0\left(\frac{1}{2}(\alpha_n w + m\pi)\right)\right.\right.$$
$$\left.\left. - e^{-jm\pi/2} J_0\left(\frac{1}{2}(\alpha_n w - m\pi)\right)\right]\right\} \qquad (3.62b)$$

If we use (3.62) in (3.43) and (3.44) with the values $\hat{G}_{ij}$ ($i = 1, 2; j = 1, 2$) given in (3.38) and (3.39), the propagation constant can be determined by setting the determinant of the coefficient matrix in (3.43) equal to zero. For the basis function (3.58), the summations in (3.43) and (3.44) start from $m = 0$ and $i = 0$.

(3) *Multislot edge-coupled unilateral fin line* (Fig. 3.6(c)):
  For this case, the Fourier transform is defined as

$$\hat{\phi}_i^{e,h}(\alpha_n, y) = \int_0^{2b} \phi_i^{e,h}(x, y) e^{j\alpha_n x} dx \qquad (3.63)$$

where

$$\alpha_n = \frac{n\pi}{2b} \qquad (3.64)$$

The basis functions f_{xm} and g_{zm} can be chosen as

$$f_{xmi}(x) = \frac{\cos\left[m\pi\left(\dfrac{x - b_i}{w_i}\right)\right]}{\sqrt{1 - \left[\dfrac{2(x - b_i)}{w_i} - 1\right]^2}}; \quad b_i \leq x \leq b_i + w_i \qquad (3.65a)$$

$$g_{zmi}(x) = \frac{\sin\left[m\pi\left(\dfrac{x - b_i}{w_i}\right)\right]}{\sqrt{1 - \left[\dfrac{2(x - b_i)}{w_i} - 1\right]^2}}; \quad b_i \leq x \leq b_i + w_i \qquad (3.65b)$$

If we substitute the Fourier transform of (3.65) in (3.43) and (3.44) (summations in (3.43) and (3.44) starting from $m = 0$ and $i = 0$) with the values of $\hat{G}_{ij}$ ($i = 1, 2; j = 1, 2$) given in (3.38) and (3.39), the propagation constant can be determined by setting the determinant of the coefficient matrix in (3.43) equal to zero.

For the aforementioned three cases, we have chosen sinusoidal basis functions. We could also choose other basis functions such as the Legendre polynomials.

3.4 FORMULAS FOR CHARACTERISTIC IMPEDANCE

In the preceding section, we presented formulas for evaluating the propagation constants of dominant and higher order modes. The characteristic impedance of the dominant mode is another important quantity, essential for the design of microwave and millimeter-wave integrated circuits. Because it is a non-TEM line, the definition of characteristic impedance in fin line is not unique. Three commonly used definitions of the characteristic impedance (Z) are based on

1. Voltage-current, $Z = V/I$;
2. Power-current, $Z = 2P/I^2$;
3. Power-voltage, $Z = V^2/2P$;

where P is the transmitted power, V is the voltage across the slot, and I is the current on the fins. For switching applications, the characteristic impedance based on voltage and current in the fin line is preferred [16]. For some other applications, the power-voltage definition of characteristic impedance is used [17]. However, the most suitable definition, following the argument given in [18], is

$$Z = \frac{V^2}{2P_{avg}} \qquad (3.66)$$

where P_{avg} is the time-averaged power flow. The expression for the voltage V across the slot is given by

$$V = \int_{\text{slot}} E_x(x)\mathrm{d}x \tag{3.67}$$

This expression can be evaluated because the x-dependence of the integrand is known from the slot-field series expansion. The coefficients ξ_m and ζ_m result from inverting the eigenvalue matrix equation (3.43) after the propagation constant has been computed.

The average power transported in the case of a unilateral fin line (Fig. 3.1) is given by

$$P_{\text{avg}} = \frac{1}{2} \operatorname{Re} \int_{-b/2}^{b/2} \int_{-h2}^{h_1+d} (E_x H_y^* - E_y H_x^*)\mathrm{d}y\,\mathrm{d}x \tag{3.68}$$

By applying Parseval's theorem, we get

$$P_{\text{avg}} = \frac{1}{2b} \operatorname{Re} \sum_{n=-\infty}^{\infty} \int_{-h2}^{h_1+d} \mathrm{d}y[\hat{E}_x(\alpha_n, y)\hat{H}_y^*(\alpha_n, y)$$
$$- \hat{E}_y(\alpha_n, y)\hat{H}_x^*(\alpha_n, y)] \tag{3.69}$$

The integration with respect to y can be carried out analytically, by substituting the spectral field components. This gives an equation of the form:

$$P_{\text{avg}} = \frac{1}{2b} \sum_{n=-\infty}^{\infty} \hat{F}(\alpha_n, \beta) \tag{3.70}$$

which is evaluated numerically for each of the three regions.

Consider the unilateral fin line shown in Fig. 3.1. By applying the boundary conditions (3.35) and (3.36) to the field equations (3.29) and (3.32), and assuming $\hat{e}_z(\alpha_n) = 0$, we can relate the constants $A^{e,h}(\alpha_n)$ ... $D^{e,h}(\alpha_n)$ to $\hat{e}_x(\alpha_n)$. The expressions for the various constants are given by

$$A^e = \frac{(k_2^2 - \beta^2)}{(k_1^2 - \beta^2)} \frac{(B^e \sinh \gamma_2 d)}{\sinh \gamma_1 h_1} \tag{3.71a}$$

$$B^e = -\frac{\hat{G}_{22}(\alpha_n, \beta)\hat{e}_x(\alpha_n)}{j\omega\epsilon_0\epsilon_r\gamma_2} + \frac{\alpha_n\beta C^h}{j\omega\epsilon_0\epsilon_r\gamma_2} - \frac{\alpha_n\beta}{j\omega\epsilon_0\epsilon_r\gamma_2}D^h \cosh \gamma_1 h_2 \tag{3.71b}$$

$$C^e = 0 \tag{3.71c}$$

$$D^e = 0 \tag{3.71d}$$

$$A^h = \frac{(k_2^2 - \beta^2)}{(k_1^2 - \beta^2)} \frac{(B^h \sinh \gamma_2 d + C^h \cosh \gamma_2 d)}{\cosh \gamma_1 h_1} \tag{3.71e}$$

$$B^h = -\frac{\hat{e}_x(\alpha_n)}{j\omega\mu_0\gamma_2} \tag{3.71f}$$

$$C^h = \frac{\hat{e}_x(\alpha_n)}{(k_2^2 - \beta^2)}\left[\hat{G}_{12}(\alpha_n, \beta) - \frac{(k_1^2 - \beta^2) \coth \gamma_1 h_2}{j\omega\mu_0\gamma_1}\right] \tag{3.71g}$$

$$D^h = -\frac{\hat{e}_x(\alpha_n)}{j\omega\mu_0\gamma_1 \sinh \gamma_1 h_2} \tag{3.71h}$$

The characteristic impedance Z is given by (3.66), where

$$V = \int_{-w/2}^{w/2} E_x(x)dx = \int_{-w/2}^{w/2} e_x(x)dx \tag{3.72}$$

P_{avg} given in (3.69) can be rewritten as

$$P_{avg} = P_{avg1} + P_{avg2} + P_{avg3} \tag{3.73a}$$

where

$$P_{avg1} = \frac{1}{2b} \text{Re} \sum_{n=-\infty}^{\infty} \int_{d}^{h_1+d} dy[\hat{E}_{x1}(\alpha_n, y)\hat{H}_{y1}^*(\alpha_n, y)$$

$$- \hat{E}_{y1}(\alpha_n, y)\hat{H}_{x1}^*(\alpha_n, y)] \tag{3.73b}$$

$$P_{avg2} = \frac{1}{2b} \text{Re} \sum_{n=-\infty}^{\infty} \int_{0}^{d} dy[\hat{E}_{x2}(\alpha_n, y)\hat{H}_{y2}^*(\alpha_n, y)$$

$$- \hat{E}_{y2}(\alpha_n, y) \hat{H}_{x2}^*(\alpha_n, y)] \tag{3.73c}$$

$$P_{avg3} = \frac{1}{2b} \text{Re} \sum_{n=-\infty}^{\infty} \int_{-h_2}^{0} dy[\hat{E}_{x3}(\alpha_n, y)\hat{H}_{y3}^*(\alpha_n, y)$$

$$- \hat{E}_{y3}(\alpha_n, y)\hat{H}_{x3}^*(\alpha_n, y)] \tag{3.73d}$$

Consider region 3. The fields in this region can be expressed in terms of $\hat{e}_x(\alpha_n)$ by combining (3.29), (3.32), and (3.71):

$$\hat{E}_{x3}(\alpha_n, y) = \frac{\hat{e}_x(\alpha_n) \sinh \gamma_1(h_2 + y)}{\sinh(\gamma_1 h_2)} \tag{3.74a}$$

$$\hat{E}_{y3}(\alpha_n, y) = -\frac{j\alpha_n \hat{e}_x(\alpha_n) \cosh \gamma_1(h_2 + y)}{\gamma_1 \sinh(\gamma_1 h_2)} \tag{3.74b}$$

$$\hat{H}_{x3}(\alpha_n, y) = \frac{\alpha_n \beta \hat{e}_x(\alpha_n)}{j\omega\mu_0\gamma_1} \frac{\cosh \gamma_1(h_2 + y)}{\sinh (\gamma_1 h_2)} \tag{3.74c}$$

$$\hat{H}_{y3}(\alpha_n, y) = -\frac{\beta \hat{e}_x(\alpha_n)}{\omega\mu_0} \frac{\sinh \gamma_1(h_2 + y)}{\sinh (\gamma_1 h_2)} \tag{3.74d}$$

By substituting (3.74) in (3.73d) and evaluating the integral, we get

$$P_{avg3} = \frac{1}{2b} \sum_{n=-\infty}^{\infty} -\frac{\beta[\hat{e}_x(\alpha_n)]^2}{\omega\mu_0} \left[\frac{\coth(\gamma_1 h_2)}{2\gamma_1} \left(1 + \frac{\alpha_n^2}{\gamma_1^2} \right) \right.$$
$$\left. - \frac{h_2}{2 \sinh^2(\gamma_1 h_2)} \left(1 - \frac{\alpha_n^2}{\gamma_1^2} \right) \right] \tag{3.75}$$

P_{avg1} and P_{avg2} can be evaluated in a similar way. The final expressions are

$$P_{avg1} = \frac{1}{2b} \sum_{n=-\infty}^{\infty} \left\{ \frac{T_1}{2} \left[\frac{\sinh(2\gamma_1 h_1)}{2\gamma_1} - h_1 \right] \right.$$
$$\left. + \frac{T_2}{2} \left[\frac{\sinh(2\gamma_1 h_1)}{2\gamma_1} + h_1 \right] \right\} \tag{3.76}$$

$$P_{avg2} = \frac{1}{2b} \sum_{n=-\infty}^{\infty} \left\{ \frac{T_3}{2} \left[\frac{\sinh(2\gamma_2 d)}{2\gamma_2} - d \right] \right.$$
$$\left. + \frac{T_4}{2} \left[\frac{\cosh(2\gamma_2 d)}{2\gamma_2} - \frac{1}{2\gamma_2} \right] + T_5 d \right\} \tag{3.77}$$

where

$$T_1 = (-\alpha_n\beta A^e + j\omega\mu_0\gamma_1 A^h)(\omega\epsilon_0\alpha_n A^e - j\beta\gamma_1 A^h) \tag{3.78a}$$

$$T_2 = (j\beta\gamma_1 A^e + \omega\mu_0\alpha_n A^h)(j\omega\epsilon_0\gamma_1 A^e + \alpha_n\beta A^h) \qquad (3.78b)$$

$$T_3 = -\frac{\beta}{\omega\mu_0}\left(1 + \frac{\alpha_n^2}{\gamma_2^2}\right)[\hat{e}_x^2(\alpha_n) + k_2^2\gamma_2^2 B^{e^2} - \omega^2\mu_0^2\gamma_2^2 C^{h^2}]$$
$$- 2j\alpha_n\gamma_2(k_2^2 + \beta^2)C^h B^e \qquad (3.78c)$$

$$T_4 = 2\left[\frac{\alpha_n}{\omega\mu_0}(k_2^2 + \beta^2)B^e + \frac{j\beta}{\gamma_2}(\alpha_n^2 + \gamma_2^2)C^h\right]\hat{e}_x(\alpha_n) \qquad (3.78d)$$

$$T_5 = -\frac{\beta}{\omega\mu_0}\hat{e}_x^2(\alpha_n) + (j\beta\gamma_2 B^e - \omega\mu_0\alpha_n C^h)$$
$$\cdot (j\omega\epsilon_0\epsilon_r\gamma_2 B^e - \alpha_n\beta C^h) \qquad (3.78e)$$

After having determined V and P_{avg} as described above, the characteristic impedance can be evaluated by substituting them in (3.66). In deriving the above expressions, it was assumed that $\hat{e}_z(\alpha_n) = 0$. We could also derive the above expressions for the case in which $\hat{e}_z(\alpha_n) \neq 0$.

It is worthwhile mentioning here that the definition of characteristic impedance (3.66) also holds good for coupled or uncoupled slots, either symmetrically or asymmetrically located.

3.5 SPECTRAL DOMAIN IMMITTANCE APPROACH

In the preceding section, we presented the spectral domain analysis of unilateral fin lines. This method becomes quite complicated for multidielectric fin lines as well as fin lines consisting of slots located on more than one dielectric interface. The analysis of such structures is greatly simplified by the introduction of the *spectral domain immittance matrix* concept [5]. Instead of lengthy field formulations, the matrix elements can be obtained almost by inspection. In this section, we shall first present an analysis of a double-layer unilateral fin line by using the spectral domain immittance approach. Next, the method is extended to a more general fin-line structure, consisting of slots on more than one dielectric interface.

3.5.1 Basic Formulation

Consider a double-layer unilateral fin line, as shown in Fig. 3.7. In conventional spectral domain analysis, hybrid field components in each region are written in terms of E_z and H_z. In the present analysis, E_y and H_y components are used rather than E_z and H_z. This simplifies the formulation considerably and allows us to use the equivalent transmission

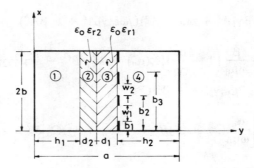

Fig. 3.7 Cross section of a double layer unilateral fin line.

line concept. This is because, in the absence of any metalization on the interface, the modal spectrum consists of TM-to-y and TE-to-y modes only. The field in the fin line can be expressed as the superposition of these modal fields.

Assume that the field propagates in the z-direction, according to $\exp(-j\beta z)$. The Fourier transform of the field components along the y-direction is given by

$$\hat{E}_y(\alpha_n, y) = \int_0^{2b} E_y(x, y)e^{j\alpha_n x}dx \tag{3.79}$$

where

$$\alpha_n = \frac{n\pi}{2b}, \quad n = 0, \pm 1, \pm 2, \ldots \tag{3.80}$$

and similarly for $\hat{H}_y(\alpha_n, y)$. From the inverse Fourier transform, we have

$$E_y(x, y)e^{-j\beta z} = \frac{1}{4b} \sum_{n=-\infty}^{\infty} \hat{E}_y(\alpha_n, y)e^{-j(\alpha_n x + \beta z)} \tag{3.81}$$

From this equation, we can see that the field components are the super-position of inhomogeneous plane waves propagating in the θ direction with respect to the z-axis, where $\theta = \cos^{-1}(\beta/\sqrt{\alpha_n^2 + \beta^2})$. By taking this into account, we transform the (x, z) coordinate system into a (u, v) coordinate system, u being taken along the propagation direction and v being trans-verse to u and y (see Fig. 3.8). This transformation has the form:

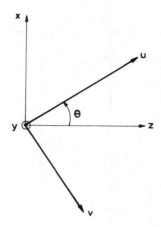

Fig. 3.8 Transformation from u, v coordinate system to x, y coordinate system.

$$\begin{bmatrix} u \\ v \end{bmatrix} = \begin{bmatrix} \sin\theta & \cos\theta \\ -\cos\theta & \sin\theta \end{bmatrix} \begin{bmatrix} x \\ z \end{bmatrix} \tag{3.82a}$$

where

$$\theta = \cos^{-1}(\beta/\sqrt{\alpha_n^2 + \beta^2}) \tag{3.82b}$$

The plane waves in the u-direction are now decomposed into TE-to-y ($\hat{H}_y$, $\hat{E}_v$, $\hat{H}_u$) and TM-to-y ($\hat{E}_y$, $\hat{E}_u$, $\hat{H}_v$). The metalization at $y = d_1 + d_2 + h_1$ is taken into account by introducing current densities $\hat{J}_u$ and $\hat{J}_v$, the first generating only the TM fields and the second generating only the TE fields.

We can now draw equivalent circuits for each spectral component of the TM and TE waves, as shown in Fig. 3.9. The wave admittances for TM and TE waves are defined as

$$Y_{TMi} = \frac{\hat{H}_v}{\hat{E}_u} = \frac{j\omega\epsilon_0\epsilon_{ri}}{\gamma_i}, \quad i = 1, \ldots, 4 \tag{3.83a}$$

$$Y_{TEi} = -\frac{\hat{H}_u}{\hat{E}_v} = \frac{\gamma_i}{j\omega\mu_0}, \quad i = 1, \ldots, 4 \tag{3.83b}$$

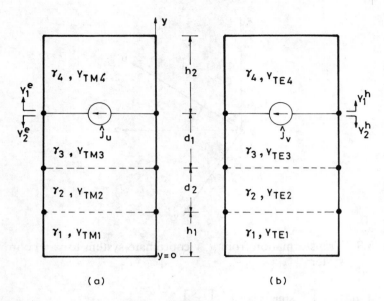

Fig. 3.9   Equivalent transmission line network for the double layer
unilateral fin line shown in Fig. 3.7.

where $\gamma_i = \sqrt{\alpha_n^2 + \beta^2 - \epsilon_{ri}k_0^2}$ is the propagation constant in the y-direction
in the ith region. All the boundary conditions for the TM and TE waves
are incorporated in the equivalent circuits.

By using transmission line theory, the currents and voltages (electric
fields) at $y = d_1 + d_2 + h_1$ are related via

$$\hat{J}_u(\alpha_n, y_0) = Y_{11}^e \hat{E}_u(\alpha_n, y_0) \qquad (3.84a)$$

$$\hat{J}_v(\alpha_n, y_0) = Y_{11}^h \hat{E}_v(\alpha_n, y_0) \qquad (3.84b)$$

where

$$y_0 = d_1 + d_2 + h_1 \qquad (3.84c)$$

Y_{11}^e and Y_{11}^h are the driving-point admittances at $y = d_1 + d_2 + h_1$ for
the TM and TE modes, respectively. Equation (3.84) can be rewritten in
matrix notation as

$$
\begin{bmatrix} \hat{J}_u(\alpha_n, y_0) \\ \hat{J}_v(\alpha_n, y_0) \end{bmatrix} = \begin{bmatrix} Y_{11}^e & 0 \\ 0 & Y_{11}^h \end{bmatrix} \begin{bmatrix} \hat{E}_u(\alpha_n, y_0) \\ \hat{E}_v(\alpha_n, y_0) \end{bmatrix}
$$

(3.85)

From the equivalent circuit shown in Fig. 3.9(a), we have

$$
Y_{11}^e = Y_1^e + Y_2^e
$$

(3.86a)

where

$$
Y_1^e = Y_{TM4} \coth(\gamma_4 h_2)
$$

(3.86b)

$$
Y_2^e = \frac{Y_{TM3}[Y_{TM3} + Y_3^e \coth(\gamma_3 d_1)]}{[Y_3^e + Y_{TM3} \coth(\gamma_3 d_1)]}
$$

(3.86c)

$$
Y_3^e = \frac{Y_{TM2}[Y_{TM2} + Y_4^e \coth(\gamma_2 d_2)]}{[Y_4^e + Y_{TM2} \coth(\gamma_2 d_2)]}
$$

(3.86d)

$$
Y_4^e = Y_{TM1} \coth(\gamma_1 h_1)
$$

(3.86e)

From the equivalent circuit shown in Fig. 3.9(b), we have

$$
Y_{11}^h = Y_1^h + Y_2^h
$$

(3.87a)

where

$$
Y_1^h = Y_{TE4} \coth(\gamma_4 h_2)
$$

(3.87b)

$$
Y_2^h = \frac{Y_{TE3}[Y_{TE3} + Y_3^h \coth(\gamma_3 d_1)]}{[Y_3^h + Y_{TE3} \coth(\gamma_3 d_1)]}
$$

(3.87c)

$$
Y_3^h = \frac{Y_{TE2}[Y_{TE2} + Y_4^h \coth(\gamma_2 d_2)]}{[Y_4^h + Y_{TE2} \coth(\gamma_2 d_2)]}
$$

(3.87d)

$$
Y_4^h = Y_{TE1} \coth(\gamma_1 h_1)
$$

(3.87e)

It may be noted that for the present problem,

$$
\gamma_1 = \gamma_4 = \sqrt{\alpha_n^2 + \beta^2 - k_0^2} \text{ and } \epsilon_{r1} = \epsilon_{r4} = 1
$$

By using the coordinate transformation (3.82a), we can rewrite (3.85) in terms of the (x, z) coordinate system as

$$
\begin{bmatrix} \hat{J}_x(\alpha_n, y_0) \\ \hat{J}_z(\alpha_n, y_0) \end{bmatrix} = \begin{bmatrix} \sin\theta & -\cos\theta \\ \cos\theta & \sin\theta \end{bmatrix} \begin{bmatrix} Y_{11}^e & 0 \\ 0 & Y_{11}^h \end{bmatrix}
$$
$$
\times \begin{bmatrix} \sin\theta & \cos\theta \\ -\cos\theta & \sin\theta \end{bmatrix} \begin{bmatrix} \hat{E}_x(\alpha_n, y_0) \\ \hat{E}_z(\alpha_n, y_0) \end{bmatrix} \tag{3.88a}
$$

If we multiply the matrices on the right-hand side of (3.88a) and rearrange, we obtain

$$
\begin{bmatrix} \hat{J}_x(\alpha_n, y_0) \\ \hat{J}_z(\alpha_n, y_0) \end{bmatrix} = \begin{bmatrix} \hat{G}_{11}(\alpha_n, \beta) & \hat{G}_{12}(\alpha_n, \beta) \\ \hat{G}_{21}(\alpha_n, \beta) & \hat{G}_{22}(\alpha_n, \beta) \end{bmatrix} \begin{bmatrix} \hat{E}_z(\alpha_n, y_0) \\ \hat{E}_x(\alpha_n, y_0) \end{bmatrix} \tag{3.88b}
$$

where

$$
\hat{G}_{11}(\alpha_n, \beta) = (Y_{11}^e - Y_{11}^h) \sin\theta \cos\theta \tag{3.89a}
$$

$$
\hat{G}_{12}(\alpha_n, \beta) = Y_{11}^e \sin^2\theta + Y_{11}^h \cos^2\theta \tag{3.89b}
$$

$$
\hat{G}_{21}(\alpha_n, \beta) = Y_{11}^h \sin^2\theta + Y_{11}^e \cos^2\theta \tag{3.89c}
$$

$$
\hat{G}_{22}(\alpha_n, \beta) = \hat{G}_{11}(\alpha_n, \beta) \tag{3.89d}
$$

With the determination of the elements of the dyadic Green's function, the propagation constant and characteristic impedance can be obtained by using the procedure described in the preceding section.

3.5.2 Application to Fin Line with Slots at More Than One Dielectric Interface

In order to demonstrate the generality of the spectral domain immittance approach, we will consider a general fin-line structure, as shown in Fig. 3.10. The slots are printed at the interfaces $y = h_1$ and $y = h_1 + d$. Following the procedure given above, we can draw transmission line equivalents for the spectral components of the TE and TM waves. These equivalent circuits are shown in Fig. 3.11. By using transmission line theory,

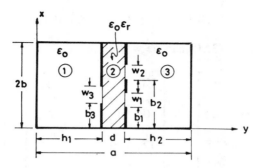

Fig. 3.10 Cross section of a general fin line having slots at more than one dielectric interface.

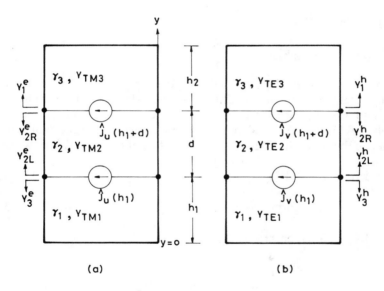

Fig. 3.11 Equivalent transmission line networks for the structure shown in Fig. 3.10.

the currents and voltages (electric fields) at $y = h_1$ and $h_1 + d$ are related via

$$\hat{J}_u(\alpha_n, h_1 + d) = Y_{11}^e \hat{E}_u(\alpha_n, h_1 + d) + Y_{12}^e \hat{E}_u(\alpha_n, h_1) \quad (3.90a)$$

$$\hat{J}_v(\alpha_n, h_1 + d) = Y_{11}^h \hat{E}_v(\alpha_n, h_1 + d) + Y_{12}^h \hat{E}_v(\alpha_n, h_1) \quad (3.90b)$$

$$\hat{J}_u(\alpha_n, h_1) = Y_{21}^e \hat{E}_u(\alpha_n, h_1 + d) + Y_{22}^e \hat{E}_u(\alpha_n, h_1) \quad (3.90c)$$

$$\hat{J}_v(\alpha_n, h_1) = Y_{21}^h \hat{E}_v(\alpha_n, h_1 + d) + Y_{22}^h \hat{E}_v(\alpha_n, h_1) \qquad (3.90d)$$

In matrix notation (3.90) can be written as

$$\begin{bmatrix} \hat{J}_u(\alpha_n, h_1 + d) \\[1em] \hat{J}_v(\alpha_n, h_1 + d) \\[1em] \hat{J}_u(\alpha_n, h_1) \\[1em] \hat{J}_v(\alpha_n, h_1) \end{bmatrix} = \begin{bmatrix} Y_{11}^e & 0 & Y_{12}^e & 0 \\[1em] 0 & Y_{11}^h & 0 & Y_{12}^h \\[1em] Y_{21}^e & 0 & Y_{22}^e & 0 \\[1em] 0 & Y_{21}^h & 0 & Y_{22}^h \end{bmatrix} \begin{bmatrix} \hat{E}_u(\alpha_n, h_1 + d) \\[1em] \hat{E}_v(\alpha_n, h_1 + d) \\[1em] \hat{E}_u(\alpha_n, h_1) \\[1em] \hat{E}_v(\alpha_n, h_1) \end{bmatrix}$$

$$(3.91a)$$

or, in a short form:

$$[\hat{J}]_{uv} = [Y]_{uv}[\hat{E}]_{uv} \qquad (3.91b)$$

where Y_{11}^e, Y_{22}^e and Y_{12}^e, Y_{21}^e are the driving-point and transfer admittances, respectively, of the TM wave equivalent circuit. Similarly, Y_{11}^h, Y_{22}^h and Y_{12}^h, Y_{21}^h are the driving-point and transfer admittances, respectively, of TE wave equivalent circuit. By applying conventional transmission line theory to the TM wave equivalent circuit (Fig. 3.11(a)), we obtain

$$Y_{11}^e = Y_1^e + Y_{2R}^e \qquad (3.92a)$$

$$Y_1^e = Y_{TM3} \coth(\gamma_3 h_2) \qquad (3.92b)$$

$$Y_{2R}^e = Y_{TM2} \coth(\gamma_2 d) \qquad (3.92c)$$

$$Y_{22}^e = Y_3^e + Y_{2L}^e \qquad (3.92d)$$

$$Y_{2L}^e = Y_{2R}^e \qquad (3.92e)$$

$$Y_3^e = Y_{TM1} \coth(\gamma_1 h_1) \qquad (3.92f)$$

$$Y_{12}^e = -Y_{2R}^e / \cosh(\gamma_2 d) \qquad (3.92g)$$

$$Y_{21}^e = -Y_{2L}^e / \cosh(\gamma_2 d) \qquad (3.92h)$$

Similarly, from the TE wave equivalent circuit (Fig. 3.11(b)), we can write down the expressions for Y_{11}^h ... Y_{22}^h. The matrix equation (3.91) can now be transformed to the (x, z) coordinate system as follows:

$$[\hat{J}]_{xz} = [L]^{-1}[Y]_{uv}[L][\hat{E}]_{xz} \tag{3.93a}$$

where

$$[L] = \begin{bmatrix} \sin\theta & \cos\theta & 0 & 0 \\ -\cos\theta & \sin\theta & 0 & 0 \\ 0 & 0 & \sin\theta & \cos\theta \\ 0 & 0 & -\cos\theta & \sin\theta \end{bmatrix} \tag{3.93b}$$

If we carry out the matrix multiplication in (3.93a) and rearrange, we obtain

$$\begin{bmatrix} \hat{J}_x(\alpha_n, h_1 + d) \\ \hat{J}_z(\alpha_n, h_1 + d) \\ \hat{J}_x(\alpha_n, h_1) \\ \hat{J}_z(\alpha_n, h_1) \end{bmatrix} = \begin{bmatrix} \hat{G}_{xx}^{11} & \hat{G}_{xz}^{11} & \hat{G}_{xx}^{12} & \hat{G}_{xz}^{12} \\ \hat{G}_{zx}^{11} & \hat{G}_{zz}^{11} & \hat{G}_{zx}^{12} & \hat{G}_{zz}^{12} \\ \hat{G}_{xx}^{21} & \hat{G}_{xz}^{21} & \hat{G}_{xx}^{22} & \hat{G}_{xz}^{22} \\ \hat{G}_{zx}^{21} & \hat{G}_{zz}^{21} & \hat{G}_{zx}^{22} & \hat{G}_{zz}^{22} \end{bmatrix} \begin{bmatrix} \hat{E}_z(\alpha_n, h_1 + d) \\ \hat{E}_x(\alpha_n, h_1 + d) \\ \hat{E}_z(\alpha_n, h_1) \\ \hat{E}_x(\alpha_n, h_1) \end{bmatrix}$$

$$\tag{3.94}$$

where

$$\hat{G}_{xx}^{11} = (Y_{11}^e - Y_{11}^h)\sin\theta \cos\theta = \hat{G}_{zz}^{11} \tag{3.95a}$$

$$\hat{G}_{xz}^{11} = Y_{11}^e \sin^2\theta + Y_{11}^h \cos^2\theta \tag{3.95b}$$

$$\hat{G}_{xz}^{12} = Y_{12}^e \sin^2\theta + Y_{12}^h \cos^2\theta \tag{3.95c}$$

$$\hat{G}_{zx}^{12} = Y_{12}^e \cos^2\theta + Y_{12}^h \sin^2\theta \tag{3.95d}$$

and so on.

The matrix equation (3.94) relates the fin current density components and the tangential electric field components in the slots at $y = h_1$ and $y = h_1 + d$. The equation is similar to (3.37). The slot fields E_x and E_z can now be expanded with respect to basis functions such as (3.65). The application of Galerkin's procedure in the spectral domain results in a homogeneous eigenvalue matrix equation in terms of slot field expansion coefficients. A nontrivial solution of this homogeneous matrix equation yields the modal propagation constant of the fin-line structure shown in Fig. 3.10. This procedure is described in detail in Sec. 3.3. The characteristic impedance can be derived by following the method described in Sec. 3.4.

3.6 SPECTRAL DOMAIN TECHNIQUE USING THE CONCEPT OF A CHAIN MATRIX

The spectral domain technique using the concept of a *chain matrix* is the most general method of analyzing multilayer fin lines with several strip conductors sandwiched between two successive layers [7–8]. The key point of this method is that the potential function coefficients of one layer are easily connected to those of subsequent layers through the introduction of a chain matrix. Because of this, the overall computing time is linearly dependent on the number of dielectric layers. This is a distinct advantage of this method when analyzing a structure with large number of dielectric layers.

In this section, the spectral domain technique using the concept of a chain matrix is first applied to analyze a general N-layer unilateral fin line. As an application of this technique, the elements of the dyadic Green's function are derived for a bilateral fin line.

3.6.1 Analysis of N-Layer Unilateral Fin Line

Consider a general N-layer unilateral fin line as shown in Fig. 3.12. We begin with the expressions for the electric and magnetic fields in the ith region (same as (3.29)):

$$\hat{E}_{zi}(\alpha_n, y) = (k_i^2 - \beta^2)\, \hat{\phi}_i^e(\alpha_n, y) \tag{3.96a}$$

$$\hat{H}_{zi}(\alpha_n, y) = (k_i^2 - \beta^2)\, \hat{\phi}_i^h(\alpha_n, y) \tag{3.96b}$$

$$\hat{E}_{xi}(\alpha_n, y) = -\alpha_n \beta\, \hat{\phi}_i^e(\alpha_n, y) - j\omega\mu_0 \frac{\mathrm{d}}{\mathrm{d}y}\, \hat{\phi}_i^h(\alpha_n, y) \tag{3.96c}$$

$$\hat{H}_{xi}(\alpha_n, y) = j\omega\epsilon_i \frac{\mathrm{d}}{\mathrm{d}y}\, \hat{\phi}_i^e(\alpha_n, y) - \alpha_n\beta\, \hat{\phi}_i^h(\alpha_n, y) \tag{3.96d}$$

where

$$\hat{\phi}_i^{e,h}(\alpha_n, y) = \int_0^{2b} \hat{\phi}_i^{e,h}(x, y)e^{j\alpha_n x}\mathrm{d}x \tag{3.97a}$$

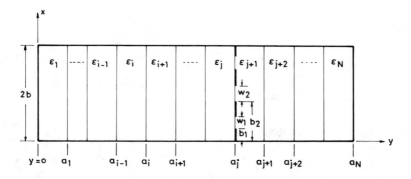

Fig. 3.12   Cross section of a generalized N-layer fin line.

and

$$\alpha_n = \frac{n\pi}{2b}, \quad n = 0, \pm 1, \pm 2, \ldots \tag{3.97b}$$

$\hat{\phi}_i^{e,h}(\alpha_n, y)$ can be obtained by solving the Helmholtz equation:

$$\left(\frac{d^2}{dy^2} - \gamma_i^2\right)\hat{\phi}_i^{e,h}(\alpha_n, y) = 0 \tag{3.98a}$$

where

$$\gamma_i^2 = \alpha_n^2 + \beta^2 - k_i^2; \quad k_i^2 = \omega^2\mu_i\epsilon_i \tag{3.98b}$$

The solution of (3.98) for an arbitrary region can be written as follows. For $a_{i-1} < y < a_i; i \leq j$:

$$\hat{\phi}_i^e(\alpha_n, y) = A_i^e \sinh(\gamma_i y) + B_i^e \cosh(\gamma_i y) \tag{3.99a}$$

$$\hat{\phi}_i^h(\alpha_n, y) = A_i^h \sinh(\gamma_i y) + B_i^h \cosh(\gamma_i y) \tag{3.99b}$$

For $a_{i-1} < y < a_i; i \geq j + 1$:

$$\hat{\phi}_i^e(\alpha_n, y) = A_i^e \sinh \gamma_i(a_i - y) + B_i^e \cosh \gamma_i(a_i - y) \tag{3.100a}$$

$$\hat{\phi}_i^h(\alpha_n, y) = A_i^h \sinh \gamma_i(a_i - y) + B_i^h \cosh \gamma_i(a_i - y) \tag{3.100b}$$

The boundary conditions at the various dielectric interfaces, except for those with strips sandwiched between them, are given by the following.

At $y = a_i$:

$$\hat{E}_{zi}(\alpha_n) = \hat{E}_{zi+1}(\alpha_n) \tag{3.101a}$$

$$\hat{H}_{zi}(\alpha_n) = \hat{H}_{zi+1}(\alpha_n) \tag{3.101b}$$

$$\hat{E}_{xi}(\alpha_n) = \hat{E}_{xi+1}(\alpha_n) \tag{3.101c}$$

$$\hat{H}_{xi}(\alpha_n) = \hat{H}_{xi+1}(\alpha_n) \tag{3.101d}$$

At $y = a_j$, the interface where the strips are situated, we have

$$\hat{E}_{zj}(\alpha_n) = \hat{E}_{zj+1}(\alpha_n) = \hat{E}_z(\alpha_n) \tag{3.102a}$$

$$\hat{E}_{xj}(\alpha_n) = \hat{E}_{xj+1}(\alpha_n) = \hat{E}_x(\alpha_n) \tag{3.102b}$$

$$\hat{H}_{zj}(\alpha_n) - \hat{H}_{zj+1}(\alpha_n) = \hat{J}_x(\alpha_n) \tag{3.102c}$$

$$\hat{H}_{xj+1}(\alpha_n) - \hat{H}_{xj}(\alpha_n) = \hat{J}_z(\alpha_n) \tag{3.102d}$$

By substituting (3.99) and (3.100) in (3.96) and using (3.101), we can relate the coefficients of the potential function for any layer to its subsequent one, except for the layers sandwiching the strip conductors. The relation is as follows:

$$\begin{bmatrix} A_{i+1}^e \\ B_{i+1}^e \\ A_{i+1}^h \\ B_{i+1}^h \end{bmatrix} = [P_{i+1,i}] \begin{bmatrix} A_i^e \\ B_i^e \\ A_i^h \\ B_i^h \end{bmatrix} \tag{3.103}$$

where

$$[P_{i+1,i}] = [\gamma_{i+1} \, u_i]^{-1}[\gamma_i \, v_i] \tag{3.104}$$

$$[\gamma_i v_i] = \begin{bmatrix} (k_i^2 - \beta^2) & (k_j^2 - \beta^2) & 0 & 0 \\ \cdot \sinh(\gamma_i v_i) & \cdot \cosh(\gamma_i v_i) & & \\ 0 & 0 & (k_i^2 - \beta^2) & (k_i^2 - \beta^2) \\ & & \cdot \sinh(\gamma_i v_i) & \cdot \cosh(\gamma_i v_i) \\ \alpha_n\beta \sinh(\gamma_i v_i) & \alpha_n\beta \cosh(\gamma_i v_i) & \mp j\omega\mu_i\gamma_i & \mp j\omega\mu_i\gamma_i \\ & & \cdot \cosh(\gamma_i v_i) & \cdot \sinh(\gamma_i v_i) \\ \pm j\omega\epsilon_i\gamma_i & \pm j\omega\epsilon_i\gamma_i & \alpha_n\beta \sinh(\gamma_i v_i) & \alpha_n\beta \cosh(\gamma_i v_i) \\ \cdot \cosh(\gamma_i v_i) & \cdot \sinh(\gamma_i v_i) & & \end{bmatrix} \tag{3.105}$$

$$[\gamma_{i+1}u_i] = \begin{bmatrix} (k_{i+1}^2 - \beta^2) \\ \cdot \sinh(\gamma_{i+1}u_i) & (k_{i+1}^2 - \beta^2) \\ \cdot \cosh(\gamma_{i+1}u_i) & 0 & 0 \\ 0 & 0 & (k_{i+1}^2 - \beta^2) \\ \cdot \sinh(\gamma_{i+1}u_i) & (k_{i+1}^2 - \beta^2) \\ \cdot \cosh(\gamma_{i+1}u_i) \\ \alpha_n\beta \sinh(\gamma_{i+1}u_i) & \alpha_n\beta \cosh(\gamma_{i+1}u_i) & \mp j\omega\mu_{i+1}\gamma_{i+1} \\ \cdot \cosh(\gamma_{i+1}u_i) & \mp j\omega\mu_{i+1}\gamma_{i+1} \\ \cdot \sinh(\gamma_{i+1}u_i) \\ \pm j\omega\epsilon_{i+1}\gamma_{i+1} \\ \cdot \cosh(\gamma_{i+1}u_i) & \pm j\omega\epsilon_{i+1}\gamma_{i+1} \\ \cdot \sinh(\gamma_{i+1}u_i) & \alpha_n\beta \sinh(\gamma_{i+1}u_i) & \alpha_n\beta \cosh(\gamma_{i+1}u_i) \end{bmatrix}$$

(3.106)

In the above matrices, $v_i = u_i = a_i$ for $i \le j$, and $v_i = 0$, $u_i = a_{i+1} - a_i$ for $i \ge j + 1$. Furthermore, the upper signs (plus or minus) are for $i \le j$, whereas the lower signs hold for $i \ge j + 1$. The matrix $[P_{i+1,i}]$ is called the chain matrix. By using (3.103), the coefficients of potential function for any layer (as long as strips do not enter into the successive layers) can be obtained; e.g., the relation between the $(i + 3)$th layer and ith layer is written as

$$\begin{bmatrix} A_{i+3}^e \\ B_{i+3}^e \\ A_{i+3}^h \\ B_{i+3}^h \end{bmatrix} = [P_{i+3,i+2}][P_{i+2,i+1}][P_{i+1,i}] \begin{bmatrix} A_i^e \\ B_i^e \\ A_i^h \\ B_i^h \end{bmatrix}$$

(3.107)

The coefficients of the potential function can be related to the fields in the dielectric layers above and below the strip conductors by using the relation:

$$\begin{bmatrix} \hat{E}_{zj}(\alpha_n) \\ \hat{H}_{zj}(\alpha_n) \\ \hat{E}_{xj}(\alpha_n) \\ \hat{H}_{xj}(\alpha_n) \end{bmatrix} = [\gamma_j a_j] \begin{bmatrix} A_j^e \\ B_j^e \\ A_j^h \\ B_j^h \end{bmatrix}$$

(3.108)

and

$$\begin{bmatrix} \hat{E}_{zj+1}(\alpha_n) \\ \hat{H}_{zj+1}(\alpha_n) \\ \hat{E}_{xj+1}(\alpha_n) \\ \hat{H}_{xj+1}(\alpha_n) \end{bmatrix} = [\gamma_{j+1}(a_{j+1} - a_j)] \begin{bmatrix} A_{j+1}^e \\ B_{j+1}^e \\ A_{j+1}^h \\ B_{j+1}^h \end{bmatrix}$$

(3.109)

By using the chain matrix (3.103), we can rewrite (3.108) and (3.109) as

$$\begin{bmatrix} \hat{E}_{zj}(\alpha_n) \\ \hat{H}_{zj}(\alpha_n) \\ \hat{E}_{xj}(\alpha_n) \\ \hat{H}_{xj}(\alpha_n) \end{bmatrix} = [\gamma_j a_j][P_{j,j-1}] \ldots [P_{2,1}] \begin{bmatrix} A_1^e \\ B_1^e \\ A_1^h \\ B_1^h \end{bmatrix}$$

(3.110)

and

$$
\begin{bmatrix} \hat{E}_{zj+1}(\alpha_n) \\ \hat{H}_{zj+1}(\alpha_n) \\ \hat{E}_{xj+1}(\alpha_n) \\ \hat{H}_{xj+1}(\alpha_n) \end{bmatrix} = [\gamma_{j+1}(a_{j+1} - a_j)][P_{j+2,j+1}]^{-1}
$$

$$
\ldots [P_{N,N-1}]^{-1} \begin{bmatrix} A_N^e \\ B_N^e \\ A_N^h \\ B_N^h \end{bmatrix} \tag{3.111}
$$

At this point, we shall consider four different cases separately.

Case 1: Electric Walls at $y = 0$ and $y = a_N$

$$
B_1^e = B_N^e = 0 \tag{3.112}
$$

$$
A_1^h = A_N^h = 0 \tag{3.113}
$$

By subtracting (3.111) from (3.110) and using (3.102), (3.112), and (3.113), we get

$$
[Q] \begin{bmatrix} A_1^e \\ 0 \\ 0 \\ B_1^h \end{bmatrix} - [R] \begin{bmatrix} A_N^e \\ 0 \\ 0 \\ B_N^h \end{bmatrix} = \begin{bmatrix} 0 \\ \hat{J}_x(\alpha_n) \\ 0 \\ -\hat{J}_z(\alpha_n) \end{bmatrix} \tag{3.114}
$$

where

$$
[Q] = [\gamma_j a_j][P_{j,j-1}][P_{j-1,j-2}] \ldots [P_{2,1}] \tag{3.115a}
$$

and

$$
[R] = [\gamma_{j+1}(a_{j+1} - a_j)][P_{j+2,j+1}]^{-1} \ldots [P_{N,N-1}]^{-1} \tag{3.115b}
$$

Equation (3.114) can be rewritten as

$$
\begin{bmatrix} A_1^e \\ B_1^h \\ A_N^e \\ B_N^h \end{bmatrix} = [U] \begin{bmatrix} 0 \\ \hat{J}_x(\alpha_n) \\ 0 \\ -\hat{J}_z(\alpha_n) \end{bmatrix} \tag{3.116}
$$

The matrix $[U] = [T]^{-1}$, where the elements of $[T]$ are $T_{mn} = S_{pq}$, $q \neq 2, 3, 6, 7$. The matrix $[S]$ is obtained from matrices $[Q]$ and $[R]$ by using the relation:

$$[S] = \{[Q], \ - [R]\} \tag{3.117}$$

From (3.116), we have

$$A_1^e = U_{12}\hat{J}_x(\alpha_n) - U_{14}\hat{J}_z(\alpha_n) \tag{3.118a}$$

$$B_1^h = U_{22}\hat{J}_x(\alpha_n) - U_{24}\hat{J}_z(\alpha_n) \tag{3.118b}$$

By substituting (3.112), (3.113), and (3.118) in (3.110) and simplifying, we have

$$\begin{bmatrix} \hat{J}_x(\alpha_n) \\ \hat{J}_z(\alpha_n) \end{bmatrix} = \begin{bmatrix} \hat{G}_{11}(\alpha_n, \beta) & \hat{G}_{12}(\alpha_n, \beta) \\ \hat{G}_{21}(\alpha_n, \beta) & \hat{G}_{22}(\alpha_n, \beta) \end{bmatrix} \begin{bmatrix} \hat{E}_z(\alpha_n) \\ \hat{E}_x(\alpha_n) \end{bmatrix} \tag{3.119}$$

where

$$\hat{G}_{22}(\alpha_n, \beta) = -(Q_{11}U_{12} + Q_{14}U_{22})/\Delta \tag{3.120a}$$

$$\hat{G}_{21}(\alpha_n, \beta) = (Q_{31}U_{12} + Q_{34}U_{22})/\Delta \tag{3.120b}$$

$$\hat{G}_{12}(\alpha_n, \beta) = -(Q_{11}U_{14} + Q_{14}U_{24})/\Delta \tag{3.120c}$$

$$\hat{G}_{11}(\alpha_n, \beta) = (Q_{31}U_{14} + Q_{34}U_{24})/\Delta \tag{3.120d}$$

and

$$\Delta = (Q_{11}Q_{34} - Q_{14}Q_{31})(U_{12}U_{24} - U_{14}U_{22}) \tag{3.121}$$

Case 2: Magnetic Walls at $y = 0$ and $y = a_N$

$$A_1^e = B_1^h = 0 \tag{3.122a}$$

$$A_N^e = B_N^h = 0 \tag{3.122b}$$

By subtracting (3.111) from (3.110) and using (3.102) and (3.122), we get

$$
\begin{bmatrix} B_1^e \\ A_1^h \\ B_N^e \\ A_N^h \end{bmatrix} = [U] \begin{bmatrix} 0 \\ \hat{J}_x(\alpha_n) \\ 0 \\ -\hat{J}_z(\alpha_n) \end{bmatrix} \tag{3.123}
$$

The matrix $[U] = [T]^{-1}$, where the elements of $[T]$ are $T_{mn} = S_{pq}$, $q \neq 1, 4, 5, 8$. The matrix $[S]$ is obtained from (3.117). From (3.123), we have

$$
B_1^e = U_{12}\hat{J}_x(\alpha_n) - U_{14}\hat{J}_z(\alpha_n) \tag{3.124a}
$$

$$
A_1^h = U_{22}\hat{J}_x(\alpha_n) - U_{24}\hat{J}_z(\alpha_n) \tag{3.124b}
$$

By substituting (3.122) and (3.124) in (3.110) and simplifying, the equation reduces to the same form as (3.119), where

$$
\hat{G}_{22}(\alpha_n, \beta) = -(Q_{12}U_{12} + Q_{13}U_{22})/\Delta \tag{3.125a}
$$

$$
\hat{G}_{21}(\alpha_n, \beta) = (Q_{32}U_{12} + Q_{33}U_{22})/\Delta \tag{3.125b}
$$

$$
\hat{G}_{12}(\alpha_n, \beta) = -(Q_{12}U_{14} + Q_{13}U_{24})/\Delta \tag{3.125c}
$$

$$
\hat{G}_{11}(\alpha_n, \beta) = (Q_{32}U_{14} + Q_{33}U_{24})/\Delta \tag{3.125d}
$$

and

$$
\Delta = (Q_{12}Q_{33} - Q_{13}Q_{32})(U_{12}U_{24} - U_{14}U_{22}) \tag{3.126}
$$

Case 3: Magnetic Wall at $y = 0$ and Electric Wall at $y = a_N$

$$
A_1^e = B_1^h = 0 \tag{3.127a}
$$

$$
B_N^e = A_N^h = 0 \tag{3.127b}
$$

By subtracting (3.111) from (3.110) and using (3.102) and (3.127), we get

$$
\begin{bmatrix} B_1^e \\ A_1^h \\ A_N^e \\ B_N^h \end{bmatrix} = [U] \begin{bmatrix} 0 \\ \hat{J}_x(\alpha_n) \\ 0 \\ -\hat{J}_z(\alpha_n) \end{bmatrix} \tag{3.128}
$$

The matrix $[U] = [T]^{-1}$, where elements of $[T]$ are $T_{mn} = S_{pq}$, $q \neq$ 1, 4, 6, 7. The matrix $[S]$ is obtained from (3.117). Following the procedure given above, we obtain

$$\hat{G}_{22}(\alpha_n, \beta) = -(Q_{12}U_{12} + Q_{13}U_{22})/\Delta \qquad (3.129a)$$

$$\hat{G}_{21}(\alpha_n, \beta) = (Q_{32}U_{12} + Q_{33}U_{22})/\Delta \qquad (3.129b)$$

$$\hat{G}_{12}(\alpha_n, \beta) = -(Q_{12}U_{14} + Q_{13}U_{24})/\Delta \qquad (3.129c)$$

$$\hat{G}_{11}(\alpha_n, \beta) = (Q_{32}U_{14} + Q_{33}U_{24})/\Delta \qquad (3.129d)$$

and

$$\Delta = (Q_{12}Q_{33} - Q_{13}Q_{32})(U_{12}U_{24} - U_{14}U_{22}) \qquad (3.130)$$

Case 4: Magnetic Wall at $y = a_N$ and Electric Wall at $y = 0$

$$A_N^e = B_N^h = 0 \qquad (3.131a)$$

$$A_1^h = B_1^e = 0 \qquad (3.131b)$$

By subtracting (3.111) from (3.110) and using (3.102) and (3.131), we get

$$\begin{bmatrix} A_1^e \\ B_1^h \\ B_N^e \\ A_N^h \end{bmatrix} = [U] \begin{bmatrix} 0 \\ \hat{J}_x(\alpha_n) \\ 0 \\ -\hat{J}_z(\alpha_n) \end{bmatrix} \qquad (3.132)$$

The matrix $[U] = [T]^{-1}$, where the elements of $[T]$ are $T_{mn} = S_{pq}$, $q \neq$ 2, 3, 5, 8. The matrix $[S]$ is obtained from (3.117). Following the procedure given above, we get

$$\hat{G}_{22}(\alpha_n, \beta) = -(Q_{11}U_{12} + Q_{14}U_{22})/\Delta \qquad (3.133a)$$

$$\hat{G}_{21}(\alpha_n, \beta) = (Q_{31}U_{12} + Q_{34}U_{22})/\Delta \qquad (3.133b)$$

$$\hat{G}_{12}(\alpha_n, \beta) = -(Q_{11}U_{14} + Q_{14}U_{24})/\Delta \qquad (3.133c)$$

$$\hat{G}_{11}(\alpha_n, \beta) = (Q_{31}U_{14} + Q_{34}U_{24})/\Delta \qquad (3.133d)$$

and

$$\Delta = (Q_{11}Q_{34} - Q_{31}Q_{14})(U_{12}U_{24} - U_{14}U_{22}) \tag{3.134}$$

Once the elements of the dyadic Green's function are determined, the propagation constant and the characteristic impedance can be obtained by following the procedure described in Sec. 3.3 and 3.4.

3.6.2 Application to Bilateral Fin Line

The generalized formulas that have been developed by using the method of the chain matrix can be readily applied to a variety of fin lines. We will demonstrate the procedure by considering the example of a bilateral fin line (Fig. 3.13) for its two orthogonal modes (even and odd) of excitation.

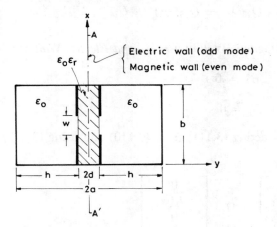

Fig. 3.13 Cross section of a bilateral fin line.

Odd-Mode Case

Consider the symmetric right half of the structure. The boundaries at $y = 0$ and $y = d + h$ represent electric walls for the odd-mode. Hence, formulas (3.120) and (3.121) are applicable for the determination of elements of the dyadic Green's function. In order to determine the various Q_{ij} and U_{ij} values appearing in these formulas, we proceed as follows:

$$[Q] = [\gamma_1 d] \tag{3.135}$$

$$[R] = [\gamma_2 h] \tag{3.136}$$

The matrices $[\gamma_1 d]$ and $[\gamma_2 h]$ can be obtained from (3.105) and (3.106), respectively. We have $[U] = [T]^{-1}$, where the elements of $[T]$ are $T_{mn} = S_{pq}$, $q \neq 2, 3, 6, 7$. Matrix $[S]$ is obtained from (3.117). Matrix $[T]$ for the bilateral fin line excited in the odd-mode is given by

$$
[T] =
\begin{bmatrix}
(k^2 - \beta^2) & 0 & -(k_0^2 - \beta^2) & 0 \\
\cdot \sinh(\gamma d) & & \cdot \sinh(\gamma_0 h) & \\[2ex]
0 & (k^2 - \beta^2) & 0 & -(k_0^2 - \beta^2) \\
& \cdot \cosh(\gamma d) & & \cdot \cosh(\gamma_0 h) \\[2ex]
\alpha_n\beta \sinh(\gamma d) & -j\omega\mu_0\gamma & -\alpha_n\beta \sinh(\gamma_0 h) & -j\omega\mu_0\gamma_0 \\
& \cdot \sinh(\gamma d) & & \cdot \sinh(\gamma_0 h) \\[2ex]
j\omega\epsilon_0\epsilon_r\gamma & \alpha_n\beta \cosh(\gamma d) & j\omega\epsilon_0\gamma_0 & -\alpha_n\beta \cosh(\gamma_0 h) \\
\cdot \cosh(\gamma d) & & \cdot \cosh(\gamma_0 h) &
\end{bmatrix}
$$

where $\hspace{10cm}$ (3.137)

$$
\gamma_1 = \gamma = \sqrt{\alpha_n^2 + \beta^2 - k^2}; \quad k^2 = \omega^2\mu_0\epsilon_0\epsilon_r \tag{3.138a}
$$

$$
\gamma_2 = \gamma_0 = \sqrt{\alpha_n^2 + \beta^2 - k_0^2}; \quad k_0^2 = \omega^2\mu_0\epsilon_0 \tag{3.138b}
$$

From (3.105) and (3.135), we have

$$
Q_{11} = (k^2 - \beta^2)\sinh(\gamma d) \tag{3.139a}
$$

$$
Q_{14} = 0 \tag{3.139b}
$$

$$
Q_{31} = \alpha_n\beta \sinh(\gamma d) \tag{3.139c}
$$

$$
Q_{34} = -j\omega\mu_0\gamma \sinh(\gamma d) \tag{3.139d}
$$

The elements of matrix $[U]$ can be obtained from the matrix $[T]^{-1}$. These are given by

$$
U_{12} = -\frac{(k_0^2 - \beta^2)\sinh(\gamma_0 h)}{\det[T]} [j\omega\mu_0\gamma \, \alpha_n\beta \sinh(\gamma d) \cosh(\gamma_0 h)
$$
$$
+ j\omega \, \alpha_n\beta \, \mu_0\gamma_0 \sinh(\gamma_0 h)\cosh(\gamma d)] \tag{3.140a}
$$

$$
U_{14} = -\frac{(k_0^2 - \beta^2)\sinh(\gamma_0 h)}{\det[T]} [-j\omega\mu_0\gamma_0(k^2 - \beta^2) \cosh(\gamma d) \sinh(\gamma_0 h)
$$
$$
- j\omega\mu_0\gamma(k_0^2 - \beta^2) \sinh(\gamma d) \cosh(\gamma_0 h)] \tag{3.140b}
$$

$$U_{22} = -\frac{(k_0^2 - \beta^2)\sinh(\gamma_0 h)}{\det[T]} [-(k^2 - \beta^2)(k_0^2 - \alpha_n^2)$$

$$\cdot \sinh(\gamma d) \cosh(\gamma_0 h) + \alpha_n^2 \beta^2 \sinh(\gamma d) \cosh(\gamma_0 h)$$

$$+ k^2 \gamma_0 \gamma \sinh(\gamma_0 h) \cosh(\gamma d)] \qquad (3.140c)$$

$$U_{24} = -\frac{(k_0^2 - \beta^2) \sinh(\gamma_0 h)}{\det[T]} [(k^2 - k_0^2)$$

$$\cdot \alpha_n \beta \sinh(\gamma d) \cosh(\gamma_0 h)] \qquad (3.140d)$$

By substituting (3.139) and (3.140) in (3.120) and after some algebraic manipulations, we get the following expressions for the elements of the dyadic Green's function:

$$\hat{G}_{11}(\alpha_n, \beta) = \frac{-j\alpha_n\beta}{\omega\mu_0\gamma_0\gamma} [\gamma_0 \coth(\gamma d) + \gamma \coth(\gamma_0 h)] \qquad (3.141a)$$

$$\hat{G}_{12}(\alpha_n, \beta) = \frac{-j}{\omega\mu_0\gamma_0\gamma} [\gamma_0(k^2 - \beta^2) \coth(\gamma d)$$

$$+ \gamma(k_0^2 - \beta^2) \coth(\gamma_0 h)] \qquad (3.141b)$$

$$\hat{G}_{21}(\alpha_n, \beta) = \frac{-j}{\omega\mu_0\gamma_0\gamma} [\gamma_0(k^2 - \alpha_n^2) \coth(\gamma d)$$

$$+ \gamma(k_0^2 - \alpha_n^2) \coth(\gamma_0 h)] \qquad (3.141c)$$

$$\hat{G}_{22}(\alpha_n, \beta) = \hat{G}_{11}(\alpha_n, \beta) \qquad (3.141d)$$

Even-Mode Case

For this case we have a magnetic wall at $y = 0$ and an electric wall at $y = d + h$. Hence, formulas (3.129) and (3.130) are applicable. Following the procedure given above, we obtain the elements of dyadic Green's function as given in (3.141) with $\coth(\gamma d)$ replaced by $\tanh(\gamma d)$.

The propagation constants and the characteristic impedances for the even-mode and odd-mode can now be obtained following the procedure described in Sec. 3.3 and 3.4.

3.7 CHARACTERISTIC EQUATIONS FOR SPECIFIC FIN-LINE STRUCTURES

The characteristic equations for a number of practical structures can be obtained from the formulas derived in Sec. 3.3, 3.5, and 3.6 by the substitution of appropriate structural parameters. Formulas that can be directly programmed are listed in Appendix 3-A for commonly used fin-line structures as well as for some considered to be of potential use in special circuit applications. These structures are listed below:

1. Unilateral fin line (Fig. 2.2(a)).
2. Insulated fin line (Fig. 2.2(c)).
3. Bilateral fin line (Fig. 2.2(b)).
4. Double-dielectric bilateral fin line with fins facing each other (Fig. 2.4(b)).
5. Double-dielectric bilateral fin line with fins facing the side walls (Fig. 2.4(c)).
6. Special cases of unilateral, insulated, bilateral, and double-dielectric fin lines: (a) slots centered in the E-plane (Fig. 2.2(a–c) and Fig. 2.4(b, c) with $b = 2s + w$); (b) asymmetric fin lines (Fig. 2.6).
7. Edge-coupled unilateral fin line (Fig. 2.3(a)).
8. Edge-coupled insulated fin line (Fig. 2.7(a)).
9. Edge-coupled bilateral fin line (Fig. 2.3(b)).

For structures not given above, appropriate characteristic equation can be obtained by following the procedures outlined in Sec. 3.3, 3.5, and 3.6.

3.8 MODAL ANALYSIS OF FIN LINES

The spectral domain methods described in the earlier sections are the most commonly used hybrid-mode analyses of fin lines. However, for certain problems, like discontinuities in a fin line, modal analysis offers certain special features. Furthermore, the effect of finite metalization thickness and waveguide grooves to fix the dielectric substrate can be easily taken into account in this method. The metalization thickness and the groove depths play a significant role in the design of circuits, especially at millimeter-wave frequencies.

In this section, we present the modal analysis of a unilateral fin line with zero metalization thickness and no waveguide grooves to provide a basic understanding of the technique. Application of the technique to a more general fin line consisting of grooves and finite metalization thickness is also discussed.

3.8.1 Derivation of Electric and Magnetic Fields

Consider the electromagnetic field propagating in the $+z$-direction and having x, z, and time dependence as $e^{-jk_x x}$, $e^{-j\beta z}$, and $e^{j\omega t}$, respectively. In a region containing no sources, this electromagnetic field satisfies the following Maxwell's equations:

$$\nabla \times \vec{H} = j\omega\epsilon_0\epsilon_r \vec{E} \qquad (3.142a)$$

$$\nabla \times \vec{E} = -j\omega\mu_0 \vec{H} \qquad (3.142b)$$

where ϵ_r is the dielectric constant of the medium. By expanding (3.142), we have

$$j\omega\epsilon_0\epsilon_r \, E_x = \frac{\partial H_z}{\partial y} - \frac{\partial H_y}{\partial z} \qquad (3.143a)$$

$$j\omega\epsilon_0\epsilon_r \, E_y = \frac{\partial H_x}{\partial z} - \frac{\partial H_z}{\partial x} \qquad (3.143b)$$

$$j\omega\epsilon_0\epsilon_r \, E_z = \frac{\partial H_y}{\partial x} - \frac{\partial H_x}{\partial y} \qquad (3.143c)$$

$$-j\omega\mu_0 \, H_x = \frac{\partial E_z}{\partial y} - \frac{\partial E_y}{\partial z} \qquad (3.143d)$$

$$-j\omega\mu_0 \, H_y = \frac{\partial E_x}{\partial z} - \frac{\partial E_z}{\partial x} \qquad (3.143e)$$

$$-j\omega\mu_0 \, H_z = \frac{\partial E_y}{\partial x} - \frac{\partial E_x}{\partial y} \qquad (3.143f)$$

By substituting (3.143c) in (3.143e) and after some algebraic manipulations, we have

$$H_y = \frac{1}{(k_0^2\epsilon_r - k_x^2)} \left[\frac{\partial^2 H_x}{\partial x \partial y} + j\omega\epsilon_0\epsilon_r \frac{\partial E_x}{\partial z} \right] \qquad (3.144a)$$

Similarly, we express H_z, E_y, and E_z in terms of E_x and H_x:

$$H_z = \frac{1}{(k_0^2\epsilon_r - k_x^2)} \left[\frac{\partial^2 H_x}{\partial x \partial z} - j\omega\epsilon_0\epsilon_r \frac{\partial E_x}{\partial y} \right] \qquad (3.144b)$$

$$E_y = \frac{1}{(k_0^2\epsilon_r - k_x^2)}\left[\frac{\partial^2 E_x}{\partial x \partial y} - j\omega\mu_0 \frac{\partial H_x}{\partial z}\right] \tag{3.144c}$$

$$E_z = \frac{1}{(k_0^2\epsilon_r - k_x^2)}\left[\frac{\partial^2 E_x}{\partial x \partial z} + j\omega\mu_0 \frac{\partial H_x}{\partial y}\right] \tag{3.144d}$$

If we combine (3.144a) and (3.144b) vectorially, we obtain

$$\vec{H}_t = (\hat{y}\,H_y + \hat{z}\,H_z)$$

$$= \frac{1}{(k_0^2\epsilon_r - k_x^2)}\left[\frac{\partial}{\partial x}\nabla_t H_x - j\omega\epsilon_0\epsilon_r\hat{x} \times \nabla_t E_x\right] \tag{3.145}$$

Similarly, combining (3.144c) and (3.144d) vectorially gives

$$\vec{E}_t = (\hat{y}\,E_y + \hat{z}\,E_z)$$

$$= \frac{1}{(k_0^2\epsilon_r - k_x^2)}\left[\frac{\partial}{\partial x}\nabla_t E_x + j\omega\mu_0\hat{x} \times \nabla_t H_x\right] \tag{3.146}$$

From (3.145) and (3.146), we can write

$$\begin{bmatrix} \vec{E}_t \\ \vec{H}_t \end{bmatrix} = \frac{1}{(k_0^2\epsilon_r - k_x^2)} \begin{bmatrix} \dfrac{\partial}{\partial x} & j\omega\mu_0\hat{x}\ \times \\ -j\omega\epsilon_0\epsilon_r\hat{x}\ \times & \dfrac{\partial}{\partial x} \end{bmatrix} \begin{bmatrix} \nabla_t E_x \\ \nabla_t H_x \end{bmatrix} \tag{3.147}$$

3.8.2 Elements of Dyadic Green's Function Matrix

Consider the unilateral fin line shown in Fig. 3.14. The y- and z-components of the electric and magnetic fields can be obtained from (3.147). The x-components of the electric and magnetic fields satisfy the Helmholtz equation:

$$\left[\frac{\partial^2}{\partial x^2} + \frac{\partial^2}{\partial y^2} + (k_0^2\epsilon_r - \beta^2)\right]\begin{bmatrix} E_x \\ H_x \end{bmatrix} = 0 \tag{3.148a}$$

where

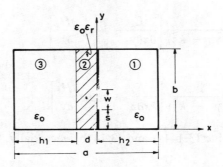

Fig. 3.14   Cross section of a unilateral fin line with arbitrarily located slot.

$$k_x^2 + k_y^2 + \beta^2 = k_0^2\epsilon_r \quad (\epsilon_r = 1 \text{ for regions 1 and 3}) \tag{3.148b}$$

The solution of (3.148a) in the three regions shown in Fig. 3.14 are given below.

Region 1:

$$E_x^{(1)} = \sum_{n=1}^{\infty} A_{n1} \cos[\gamma_{n1}(x - h_2)] \sin(\alpha_n y) \tag{3.149a}$$

$$H_x^{(1)} = \sum_{n=0}^{\infty} B_{n1} \sin[\gamma_{n1}(x - h_2)] \cos(\alpha_n y) \tag{3.149b}$$

Region 2:

$$E_x^{(2)} = \sum_{n=1}^{\infty} [A_{n2} \sin(\gamma_{n2}x) \sin(\alpha_n y) \\ + A'_{n2} \cos(\gamma_{n2}x) \sin(\alpha_n y)] \tag{3.149c}$$

$$H_x^{(2)} = \sum_{n=0}^{\infty} [B_{n2} \cos(\gamma_{n2}x) \cos(\alpha_n y) \\ + B'_{n2} \sin(\gamma_{n2}x) \cos(\alpha_n y)] \tag{3.149d}$$

Region 3:

$$E_x^{(3)} = \sum_{n=1}^{\infty} A_{n3} \cos[\gamma_{n1}(x + d + h_1)] \sin(\alpha_n y) \tag{3.149e}$$

$$H_x^{(3)} = \sum_{n=0}^{\infty} B_{n3} \sin[\gamma_{n1}(x + d + h_1)] \cos(\alpha_n y) \qquad (3.149f)$$

where

$$\gamma_{n1} = k_{x1} = k_{x3}, \; \gamma_{n2} = k_{x2}, \; k_{y1} = k_{y2} = k_{y3} = \alpha_n$$

$$\gamma_{n1} = \sqrt{k_0^2 - \beta^2 - \alpha_n^2} \qquad (3.150a)$$

$$\gamma_{n2} = \sqrt{k_0^2 \epsilon_r - \beta^2 - \alpha_n^2} \qquad (3.150b)$$

and

$$\alpha_n = \begin{cases} \dfrac{n\pi}{b}; \; (b \neq 2s + w) & (3.151a) \\[3mm] \dfrac{2n\pi}{b}; \; (b = 2s + w) & (3.151b) \end{cases}$$

By substituting (3.149) in (3.147), we get the expressions for the y- and z-components of the electric and magnetic fields as given below.

Region 1:

$$E_y^{(1)} = \sum_{n=0}^{\infty} S_{n1} \sin[\gamma_{n1}(x - h_2)] \cos(\alpha_n y) \qquad (3.152a)$$

$$H_y^{(1)} = \sum_{n=1}^{\infty} M_{n1} \cos[\gamma_{n1}(x - h_2)] \sin(\alpha_n y) \qquad (3.152b)$$

Region 2:

$$E_y^{(2)} = \sum_{n=0}^{\infty} [S_{n2} \cos(\gamma_{n2}x) \cos(\alpha_n y) + S'_{n2} \sin(\gamma_{n2}x) \; \cos(\alpha_n y)] \qquad (3.152c)$$

$$H_y^{(2)} = \sum_{n=1}^{\infty} [M_{n2} \sin(\gamma_{n2}x) \sin(\alpha_n y) + M'_{n2} \cos(\gamma_{n2}x) \; \sin(\alpha_n y)] \qquad (3.152d)$$

Region 3:

$$E_y^{(3)} = \sum_{n=0}^{\infty} S_{n3} \sin[\gamma_{n1}(x + d + h_1)] \cos(\alpha_n y) \qquad (3.152e)$$

$$H_y^{(3)} = \sum_{n=1}^{\infty} M_{n3} \cos[\gamma_{n1}(x + d + h_1)] \sin(\alpha_n y) \qquad (3.152f)$$

where

$$S_{n1} = (-A_{n1}\, \gamma_{n1}\alpha_n - \omega\mu_0\beta\, B_{n1})/(\alpha_n^2 + \beta^2) \qquad (3.153a)$$

$$S_{n2} = (A_{n2}\, \gamma_{n2}\alpha_n - \omega\mu_0\beta\, B_{n2})/(\alpha_n^2 + \beta^2) \qquad (3.153b)$$

$$S_{n2}' = (-A_{n2}'\, \gamma_{n2}\alpha_n - \omega\mu_0\beta\, B_{n2}')/(\alpha_n^2 + \beta^2) \qquad (3.153c)$$

$$S_{n3} = (-A_{n3}\, \gamma_{n1}\alpha_n - \omega\mu_0\beta\, B_{n3})/(\alpha_n^2 + \beta^2) \qquad (3.153d)$$

$$M_{n1} = (\omega\epsilon_0\beta\, A_{n1} - \alpha_n\, \gamma_{n1}\, B_{n1})/(\alpha_n^2 + \beta^2) \qquad (3.153e)$$

$$M_{n2} = (\omega\epsilon_0\epsilon_r\beta A_{n2} + \alpha_n\, \gamma_{n2}\, B_{n2})/(\alpha_n^2 + \beta^2) \qquad (3.153f)$$

$$M_{n2}' = (\omega\epsilon_0\epsilon_r\beta\, A_{n2}' - \alpha_n\, \gamma_{n2}\, B_{n2}')/(\alpha_n^2 + \beta^2) \qquad (3.153g)$$

$$M_{n3} = (\omega\epsilon_0\beta\, A_{n3} - \alpha_n\, \gamma_{n1}\, B_{n3})/(\alpha_n^2 + \beta^2) \qquad (3.153h)$$

and

$$E_z^{(1)} = \sum_{n=1}^{\infty} C_{n1} \sin[\gamma_{n1}(x - h_2)] \sin(\alpha_n y) \qquad (3.154a)$$

$$H_z^{(1)} = \sum_{n=0}^{\infty} D_{n1} \cos[\gamma_{n1}(x - h_2)] \cos(\alpha_n y) \qquad (3.154b)$$

$$E_z^{(2)} = \sum_{n=1}^{\infty} [C_{n2} \cos(\gamma_{n2}x) \sin(\alpha_n y)$$
$$+ C_{n2}' \sin(\gamma_{n2}x) \sin(\alpha_n y)] \qquad (3.154c)$$

$$H_z^{(2)} = \sum_{n=0}^{\infty} [D_{n2} \sin(\gamma_{n2}x) \cos(\alpha_n y)$$

$$+ D_{n2}' \cos(\gamma_{n2}x) \cos(\alpha_n y)] \tag{3.154d}$$

$$E_z^{(3)} = \sum_{n=1}^{\infty} C_{n3} \sin[\gamma_{n1}(x + d + h_1)] \sin(\alpha_n y) \tag{3.154e}$$

$$H_z^{(3)} = \sum_{n=0}^{\infty} D_{n3} \cos[\gamma_{n1}(x + d + h_1)] \cos(\alpha_n y) \tag{3.154f}$$

where

$$C_{n1} = (j\beta \, \gamma_{n1} \, A_{n1} - j\omega\mu_0\alpha_n \, B_{n1})/(\alpha_n^2 + \beta^2) \tag{3.155a}$$

$$C_{n2} = (-j\beta \, \gamma_{n2} \, A_{n2} - j\omega\mu_0\alpha_n \, B_{n2})/(\alpha_n^2 + \beta^2) \tag{3.155b}$$

$$C_{n2}' = (j\beta \, \gamma_{n2} \, A_{n2}' - j\omega\mu_0\alpha_n \, B_{n2}')/(\alpha_n^2 + \beta^2) \tag{3.155c}$$

$$C_{n3} = (j\beta \, \gamma_{n1} \, A_{n3} - j\omega\mu_0\alpha_n \, B_{n3})/(\alpha_n^2 + \beta^2) \tag{3.155d}$$

$$D_{n1} = (-j\omega\epsilon_0\alpha_n \, A_{n1} - j\beta \, \gamma_{n1} \, B_{n1})/(\alpha_n^2 + \beta^2) \tag{3.155e}$$

$$D_{n2} = (-j\omega\epsilon_0\epsilon_r \, \alpha_n \, A_{n2} + j\beta \, \gamma_{n2} \, B_{n2})/(\alpha_n^2 + \beta^2) \tag{3.155f}$$

$$D_{n2}' = (-j\omega\epsilon_0\epsilon_r\alpha_n \, A_{n2}' - j\beta \, \gamma_{n2} \, B_{n2}')/(\alpha_n^2 + \beta^2) \tag{3.155g}$$

$$D_{n3} = (-j\omega\epsilon_0\alpha_n \, A_{n3} - j\beta \, \gamma_{n1} \, B_{n3})/(\alpha_n^2 + \beta^2) \tag{3.155h}$$

By writing the boundary conditions at $x = 0$ and $x = -d$, we have, at $x = 0$,

$$H_x^{(1)} = H_x^{(2)} \tag{3.156a}$$

$$E_y^{(1)} = E_y^{(2)} \tag{3.156b}$$

By substituting the field expressions in (3.156), we get

$$A_{n2} = A_{n1}\left(\frac{\gamma_{n1}}{\gamma_{n2}}\right)\sin(\gamma_{n1}\,h_2) \tag{3.157a}$$

$$B_{n2} = -B_{n1}\sin(\gamma_{n1}\,h_2) \tag{3.157b}$$

At $x = -d$,

$$E_y^{(3)} = E_y^{(2)} \tag{3.158a}$$

$$E_z^{(3)} = E_z^{(2)} \tag{3.158b}$$

$$H_y^{(3)} = H_y^{(2)} \tag{3.158c}$$

$$H_z^{(3)} = H_z^{(2)} \tag{3.158d}$$

By substituting the field expressions in (3.158) and solving, we get

$$A_{n3} = -\left[\frac{\gamma_{n2}}{\gamma_{n1}\sin(\gamma_{n1}h_1)}\right][A_{n2}\cos(\gamma_{n2}d) + A'_{n2}\sin(\gamma_{n2}d)] \tag{3.159a}$$

where

$$A'_{n2} = A_{n2}\,F_{n1} \tag{3.159b}$$

$$F_{n1} = -\frac{[\gamma_{n2}\cos(\gamma_{n2}d)\cos(\gamma_{n1}h_1) - \epsilon_r\gamma_{n1}\sin(\gamma_{n2}d)\sin(\gamma_{n1}h_1)]}{[\gamma_{n2}\sin(\gamma_{n2}d)\cos(\gamma_{n1}h_1) + \epsilon_r\gamma_{n1}\cos(\gamma_{n2}d)\sin(\gamma_{n1}h_1)]} \tag{3.159c}$$

and

$$B_{n3} = \left[\frac{\gamma_{n2}}{\gamma_{n1}\cos(\gamma_{n1}h_1)}\right][B_{n2}\sin(\gamma_{n2}d) + B'_{n2}\cos(\gamma_{n2}d)] \tag{3.159d}$$

where

$$B'_{n2} = B_{n2}\,F_{n2} \tag{3.159e}$$

$$F_{n2} = \frac{[\gamma_{n1}\cos(\gamma_{n2}d)\cos(\gamma_{n1}h_1) - \gamma_{n2}\sin(\gamma_{n2}d)\sin(\gamma_{n1}h_1)]}{[\gamma_{n1}\sin(\gamma_{n2}d)\cos(\gamma_{n1}h_1) + \gamma_{n2}\cos(\gamma_{n2}d)\sin(\gamma_{n1}h_1)]} \tag{3.159f}$$

Thus, all the constants are expressed in terms of A_{n1} and B_{n1}.

At $x = 0$,

$$E_y^{(1)} (y) = - \sum_{n=0}^{\infty} S_{n1} \sin(\gamma_{n1}h_2) \cos(\alpha_n y) \qquad (3.160a)$$

$$E_z^{(1)} (y) = - \sum_{n=1}^{\infty} C_{n1} \sin(\gamma_{n1}h_2) \sin(\alpha_n y) \qquad (3.160b)$$

By multiplying both sides by $\cos(\alpha_n y)$ and $\sin(\alpha_n y)$, respectively, and integrating from 0 to b, we have

$$L_{2n} = \int_0^b E_y^{(1)} (y)|_{x=0} \cos(\alpha_n y)dy = - \frac{b\delta}{2} S_{n1} \sin(\gamma_{n1}h_2),$$

$$\delta = \begin{cases} 2, n = 0 \\ 1, n \neq 0 \end{cases} \qquad (3.161a)$$

$$L_{1n} = \int_0^b E_z^{(1)} (y)|_{x=0} \sin(\alpha_n y)dy = - \frac{b}{2} C_{n1} \sin(\gamma_{n1}h_2) \qquad (3.161b)$$

By substituting for S_{n1} and C_{n1} from (3.153a) and (3.155a), we can express A_{n1} and B_{n1} in terms of L_{1n} and L_{2n} as follows:

$$A_{n1} = \frac{2}{b} \frac{(\alpha_n L_{2n}' + j\beta \ L_{1n})}{\gamma_{n1} \sin(\gamma_{n1}h_2)}, \quad L_{2n}' = L_{2n}/\delta \qquad (3.162a)$$

$$B_{n1} = \frac{2}{b} \frac{(j\beta \ L_{2n}' + \alpha_n L_{1n})}{j\omega\mu_0 \sin(\gamma_{n1}h_2)} \qquad (3.162b)$$

Furthermore, at $x = 0$,

$$H_y^{(1)} - H_y^{(2)} = I_z(y) \qquad (3.163a)$$

$$-H_z^{(1)} + H_z^{(2)} = I_y(y) \qquad (3.163b)$$

where $I_z(y)$ and $I_y(y)$ are the current densities on the fins at $x = 0$. By substituting expressions for $H_y^{(1)}$, $H_y^{(2)}$, $H_z^{(1)}$, and $H_z^{(2)}$ from (3.152) and (3.154) in (3.163), and after some algebraic manipulations, we get

$$\sum_{n=-\infty}^{\infty} G_{11} L_{2n} \cos(\alpha_n y) + \sum_{n=-\infty}^{\infty} G_{12} L_{1n} \cos(\alpha_n y) = b \ I_y(y) \qquad (3.164a)$$

$$\sum_{n=-\infty}^{\infty} G_{21} L_{2n} \sin(\alpha_n y) + \sum_{n=-\infty}^{\infty} G_{22} L_{1n} \sin(\alpha_n y) = b I_z(y) \qquad (3.164b)$$

where

$$
\begin{aligned}
G_{11} = {} & \frac{1}{(\alpha_n^2 + \beta^2)\sin(\gamma_{n1}h_2)}\left\{ \frac{j\omega\epsilon_0\alpha_n^2}{\gamma_{n1}} \right. \\
& \cdot \left[\cos(\gamma_{n1}h_2) - \epsilon_r F_{n1}\left(\frac{\gamma_{n1}}{\gamma_{n2}}\right)\sin(\gamma_{n1}h_2)\right] \\
& \left. + \frac{j\beta^2}{\omega\mu_0}\left[\gamma_{n1}\cos(\gamma_{n1}h_2) + \gamma_{n2}F_{n2}\sin(\gamma_{n1}h_2)\right]\right\}
\end{aligned}
\qquad (3.165a)
$$

$$
\begin{aligned}
G_{12} = -G_{21} = {} & \frac{1}{(\alpha_n^2 + \beta^2)\sin(\gamma_{n1}h_2)}\left\{ -\frac{\omega\epsilon_0\beta\alpha_n}{\gamma_{n1}} \right. \\
& \cdot \left[\cos(\gamma_{n1}h_2) - \epsilon_r F_{n1}\left(\frac{\gamma_{n1}}{\gamma_{n2}}\right)\sin(\gamma_{n1}h_2)\right] + \frac{\beta\alpha_n}{\omega\mu_0}\left[\gamma_{n1}\cos(\gamma_{n1}h_2)\right.\\
& \left.\left. + \gamma_{n2}F_{n2}\sin(\gamma_{n1}h_2)\right]\right\}
\end{aligned}
\qquad (3.165b)
$$

$$
\begin{aligned}
G_{22} = {} & \frac{1}{(\alpha_n^2 + \beta^2)\sin(\gamma_{n1}h_2)}\left\{ \frac{j\omega\epsilon_0\beta^2}{\gamma_{n1}} \right. \\
& \cdot \left[\cos(\gamma_{n1}h_2) - \epsilon_r F_{n1}\left(\frac{\gamma_{n1}}{\gamma_{n2}}\right)\sin(\gamma_{n1}h_2)\right] \\
& \left. + \frac{j\alpha_n^2}{\omega\mu_0}\left[\gamma_{n1}\cos(\gamma_{n1}h_2) + \gamma_{n2}F_{n2}\sin(\gamma_{n1}h_2)\right]\right\}
\end{aligned}
\qquad (3.165c)
$$

F_{n1} and F_{n2} are given by (3.159c) and (3.159f), respectively, and

$$L_{1n} = \int_s^{s+w} E_z(y)\sin(\alpha_n y)\,dy \qquad (3.166a)$$

$$L_{2n} = \int_s^{s+w} E_y(y)\cos(\alpha_n y)\,dy \qquad (3.166b)$$

3.8.3 Dispersion Equation

For the present problem, we choose the following basis functions:

$$E_y(y) = \sum_{m=0}^{M} c_m y^m \left[\left(\frac{w}{2}\right)^2 - y'^2\right]^{-1/2}, \quad s \leq y \leq s + w \qquad (3.167a)$$

$$E_z(y) = \sum_{m=1}^{M} d_m\, y^{m-1} \left[\left(\frac{w}{2} \right)^2 - y'^2 \right]^{1/2}, \quad s \leqslant y \leqslant s + w \qquad (3.167b)$$

By substituting (3.167) in (3.166), we get

$$L_{1n} = \int_{s}^{s+w} \sum_{m=1}^{M} d_m\, y^{m-1} \left[\left(\frac{w}{2} \right)^2 - y'^2 \right]^{1/2} \sin(\alpha_n y)\, dy$$

$$= \sum_{m=1}^{M} d_m\, L_{1n}^m \qquad (3.168a)$$

$$L_{2n} = \int_{s}^{s+w} \sum_{m=0}^{M} c_m\, y^{m} \left[\left(\frac{w}{2} \right)^2 - y'^2 \right]^{1/2} \cos(\alpha_n y)\, dy$$

$$= \sum_{m=0}^{M} c_m\, L_{2n}^m \qquad (3.168b)$$

where

$$y' = \left[y - \left(s + \frac{w}{2} \right) \right] \qquad (3.169)$$

By substituting (3.168) in (3.164), we get

$$\sum_{k=0}^{M} c_k \sum_{n=-\infty}^{\infty} G_{11}\, L_{2n}^k \cos(\alpha_n y)$$

$$+ \sum_{k=1}^{M} d_k \sum_{n=-\infty}^{\infty} G_{12}\, L_{1n}^k \cos(\alpha_n y) = b\, I_y(y) \qquad (3.170a)$$

$$\sum_{k=0}^{M} c_k \sum_{n=-\infty}^{\infty} G_{21}\, L_{2n}^k \sin(\alpha_n y)$$

$$+ \sum_{k=1}^{M} d_k \sum_{n=-\infty}^{\infty} G_{22}\, L_{1n}^k \sin(\alpha_n y) = b\, I_z(y) \qquad (3.170b)$$

By taking the inner product of (3.170a) with $E_y^m(y)$ and of (3.170b) with $E_z^m(y)$, and noting that $E_{y,z}$ and $I_{y,z}$ are nonzero in the complementary regions at $x = 0$, we get

$$\sum_{k=0}^{M} c_k \sum_{n=-\infty}^{\infty} G_{11}\, L_{2n}^m\, L_{2n}^k + \sum_{k=1}^{M} d_k \sum_{n=-\infty}^{\infty} G_{12}\, L_{2n}^m\, L_{1n}^k = 0,$$

$$m = 0, 1, \ldots, M \qquad (3.171a)$$

$$\sum_{k=0}^{M} c_k \sum_{n=-\infty}^{\infty} G_{21} \, L_{1n}^m \, L_{2n}^k + \sum_{k=1}^{M} d_k \sum_{n=-\infty}^{\infty} G_{22} \, L_{1n}^m \, L_{1n}^k = 0,$$

$$m = 1, 2, \ldots, M \qquad\qquad (3.171b)$$

Equation (3.171) is the required dispersion formula for determining the propagation constant β.

3.8.4 Application to a General Fin Line Consisting of Grooves and Finite Metalization Thickness

Consider a general fin line consisting of grooves and finite metalization thickness, as shown in Fig. 3.15. The solutions of (3.148a) for the various regions shown in Fig. 3.15 are

$$E_x^{(1)} = \sum_{n=1}^{\infty} A_{n1} \cos(\gamma_{n1} x) \sin(\alpha_{n1} y) \qquad\qquad (3.172a)$$

$$H_x^{(1)} = \sum_{n=0}^{\infty} B_{n1} \sin(\gamma_{n1} x) \cos(\alpha_{n1} y) \qquad\qquad (3.172b)$$

$$E_x^{(2)} = \sum_{n=1}^{\infty} \{A_{n2} \sin[\gamma_{n2}(x - a_1)] \sin[\alpha_{n2}(y - b_1)]$$
$$+ \, A_{n2}' \cos[\gamma_{n2}(x - a_1)] \sin[\alpha_{n2}(y - b_1)]\} \qquad\qquad (3.172c)$$

$$H_x^{(2)} = \sum_{n=0}^{\infty} \{B_{n2} \cos[\gamma_{n2}(x - a_1)] \cos[\alpha_{n2}(y - b_1)]$$
$$+ \, B_{n2}' \sin[\gamma_{n2}(x - a_1)] \cos[\alpha_{n2}(y - b_1)]\} \qquad\qquad (3.172d)$$

$$E_x^{(3)} = \sum_{n=1}^{\infty} \{A_{n3} \sin[\gamma_{n3}(x - a_2)] \sin[\alpha_{n3}(y - b_3)]$$
$$+ \, A_{n3}' \cos[\gamma_{n3}(x - a_2)] \sin[\alpha_{n3}(y - b_3)]\} \qquad\qquad (3.172e)$$

$$H_x^{(3)} = \sum_{n=0}^{\infty} \{B_{n3} \cos[\gamma_{n3}(x - a_2)] \cos[\alpha_{n3}(y - b_3)]$$
$$+ \, B_{n3}' \sin[\gamma_{n3}(x - a_2)] \cos[\alpha_{n3}(y - b_3)]\} \qquad\qquad (3.172f)$$

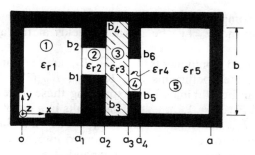

Fig. 3.15   Cross section of a generalized fin line with finite metalization thickness and grooves in the waveguide housing.

$$E_x^{(4)} = \sum_{n=1}^{\infty} \{A_{n4} \sin[\gamma_{n4}(x - a_3)] \sin[\alpha_{n4}(y - b_5)] + A_{n4}'$$

$$\cdot \cos[\gamma_{n4}(x - a_3)] \sin[\alpha_{n4}(y - b_5)]\} \qquad (3.172g)$$

$$H_x^{(4)} = \sum_{n=0}^{\infty} \{B_{n4} \cos[\gamma_{n4}(x - a_3)] \cos[\alpha_{n4}(y - b_5)] + B_{n4}'$$

$$\cdot \sin[\gamma_{n4}(x - a_3)] \cos[\alpha_{n4}(y - b_5)]\} \qquad (3.172h)$$

$$E_x^{(5)} = \sum_{n=1}^{\infty} A_{n5} \cos[\gamma_{n5}(x - a)] \sin(\alpha_{n5}y) \qquad (3.172i)$$

$$H_x^{(5)} = \sum_{n=0}^{\infty} B_{n5} \sin[\gamma_{n5}(x - a)] \cos(\alpha_{n5}y) \qquad (3.172j)$$

where

$$\alpha_{n1} = \alpha_{n5} = \frac{n\pi}{b}, \quad \alpha_{n2} = \frac{n\pi}{b_2 - b_1},$$

$$\alpha_{n3} = \frac{n\pi}{b_4 - b_3}, \quad \alpha_{n4} = \frac{n\pi}{b_6 - b_5} \qquad (3.173)$$

and

$$\gamma_{ni} = \sqrt{k_0^2 \epsilon_{ri} - \beta^2 - \alpha_{ni}^2}, \quad i = 1, \ldots, 5 \qquad (3.174)$$

The y- and z- components of the fields can now be obtained from (3.147).

Let $E_{ayi}(y)$ and $E_{azi}(y)$ be unknown fields at the aperture $x = a_i$, $i = 1, 2, 3, 4$.

After the field components E_y, H_y, E_z, and H_z are matched over the apertures, the coefficients A_{ni}, B_{ni}, A'_{nj}, B'_{nj} ($i = 1, \ldots, 5; j = 2, \ldots, 4$) can be eliminated by expressing these in terms of unknown fields E_{ayi} and E_{azi}, $i = 1, \ldots, 4$. This results in a set of coupled integral equations for E_{ayi} and E_{azi}, $i = 1, \ldots, 4$. The Ritz-Galerkin technique can now be used to solve this set of coupled integral equations. To this end, the unknown aperture fields are expanded as

$$E_{ayi}(y) = \sum_{m=0}^{N_i} C_m^{(i)} \cos \frac{m\pi}{d_i} (y - h_i) \tag{3.175a}$$

$$E_{azi}(y) = \sum_{m=1}^{N_i} D_m^{(i)} \sin \frac{m\pi}{d_i} (y - h_i) \tag{3.175b}$$

where

$$\begin{aligned} d_1 &= d_2 = b_2 - b_1, \; d_3 = d_4 = b_6 - b_5 \\ h_1 &= h_2 = b_1, \; h_3 = h_4 = b_5 \end{aligned} \tag{3.176}$$

By using (3.175) and (3.170), the integral equations are finally reduced to a set of eight homogeneous linear equations for C_m and D_m. These equations are written as

$$[G(k_0, \beta)] \, \mathbf{X} = 0 \tag{3.177}$$

where $\mathbf{X}$ is a column vector given by

$$\mathbf{X} = [\mathbf{C}^{(1)T} \, \mathbf{D}^{(1)T} \, \mathbf{C}^{(2)T} \, \mathbf{D}^{(2)T} \, \mathbf{C}^{(3)T} \, \mathbf{D}^{(3)T} \, \mathbf{C}^{(4)T} \, \mathbf{D}^{(4)T}]^T \tag{3.178}$$

The superscript T denotes transposition. The propagation constant is obtained from the eigenvalue equation:

$$\det[G(k_0, \beta)] = 0 \tag{3.179}$$

At cut-off, $\beta = 0$, the homogeneous equation (3.177) can be split into two decoupled equations of the form:

$$[G]_1 \, \mathbf{C} = 0, \; \mathbf{C} = [\mathbf{C}^{(1)T} \, \mathbf{C}^{(2)T} \, \mathbf{C}^{(3)T} \, \mathbf{C}^{(4)T}] \tag{3.180a}$$

$$[G]_2 \, \mathbf{D} = 0, \, \mathbf{D} = [\mathbf{D}^{(1)T} \, \mathbf{D}^{(2)T} \, \mathbf{D}^{(3)T} \, \mathbf{D}^{(4)T}] \qquad (3.180b)$$

where $[G]_1$ and $[G]_2$ are both $N \times N$ matrices, with $N = \Sigma_i(N_i + 1)$. The roots of the equations $\det[G]_1 = 0$ and $\det[G]_2 = 0$ correspond to the HE-mode and EH-mode cut-off, respectively.

REFERENCES

1. T. Itoh and R. Mittra, "A Technique for Computing Dispersion Characteristics of Shielded Microstrip Lines," *IEEE Trans. Microwave Theory Tech.*, Vol. MTT-22, pp. 896–898, Oct. 1974.

2. L.P. Schmidt and T. Itoh, "Spectral Domain Analysis of Dominant and Higher Order Modes in Fin-Lines," *IEEE Trans. Microwave Theory Tech.*, Vol. MTT-28, pp. 981–985, Sept. 1980.

3. J.B. Knorr and P.M. Shayda, "Millimeter Wave Fin-Line Characteristics," *IEEE Trans. Microwave Theory Tech.*, Vol. MTT-28, pp. 737–743, July 1980.

4. L.P. Schmidt and T. Itoh, "Characteristics of a Generalized Fin-Line for Millimeter Wave Integrated Circuits," *Int. J. of Infrared and Millimeter Waves*, Vol. 2, No. 3, pp. 427–436, 1981.

5. L.P. Schmidt, T. Itoh, and H. Hofmann, "Characteristics of Unilateral Fin-Line Structures with Arbitrarily Located Slots," *IEEE Trans. Microwave Theory Tech.*, Vol. MTT-29, pp. 352–355, April 1981.

6. H.C.C. Fernandes and A.J. Giarola, "Dispersion in Unilateral Fin-Lines with Two Dielectric Layers," *IEE Proc.*, Vol. 131, Pt. H, No. 3, pp. 139–142, June 1984.

7. J.B. Davies and D. Mirshekar-Syahkal, "Spectral Domain Solution of Arbitrary Coplanar Transmission Line with Multilayer Substrate," *IEEE Trans. Microwave Theory Tech.*, Vol. MTT-25, pp. 143–146, Feb. 1977.

8. D. Mirshekar-Syahkal and J.B. Davies, "An Accurate, Unified Solution to Various Fin-Line Structures, of Phase Constant, Characteristic Impedance, and Attenuation," *IEEE Trans. Microwave Theory Tech.*, Vol. MTT-30, pp. 1854–1861, Nov. 1982.

9. H. Hofmann, "Dispersion of Planar Waveguides for Millimeter-Wave Application," *Arch. Elek. Ubertragung*, Vol. 31, pp. 40–44, Jan. 1977.

10. J. Bornemann, "Rigorous Field Theory Analysis of Quasi-Planar Waveguides," *IEE Proc.*, Vol. 132, Pt. H, No. 1, pp. 1–6, Feb. 1985.

11. S.B. Worm and R. Pregla, "Hybrid-Mode Analysis of Arbitrary Shaped Planar Microwave Structures by the Method of Lines," *IEEE Trans. Microwave Theory Tech.*, Vol. MTT-32, pp. 191–196, Feb. 1984.

12. Y.C. Shih and W.J.R. Hoefer, "Dominant and Second-Order Mode Cutoff Frequencies in Fin-Lines Calculated with a Two-Dimensional TLM Program," *IEEE Trans. Microwave Theory Tech.*, Vol. MTT-28, pp. 1443–1448, Dec. 1980.

13. I. Stakgold, *Boundary Value Problems of Mathematical Physics*, Vol. 2, McGraw-Hill, New York, 1968.

14. J.W. Dettman, *Mathematical Methods in Physics and Engineering*, McGraw-Hill, New York, 1962.

15. M. Helard and J. Citerne, "Exact Calculations of Scattering Parameters of a Step Slot Width Discontinuity in a Unilateral Fin-Line," *Electron. Lett.*, Vol. 19, No. 14, pp. 537–539, July 1983.

16. H. Meinel and B. Rembold, "New Millimeter Wave Fin-Line Attenuators and Switches," *IEEE MTT-S Int. Microwave Symp. Digest*, 1979, pp. 249–252.

17. P.J. Meier, "Integrated Fin-Line Millimeter Components," *IEEE Trans. Microwave Theory Tech.*, Vol. MTT-22, pp. 1209–1216, Dec. 1974.

18. R. Jansen, "Unified User Oriented Computation of Shielded, Covered and Open Planar Microwave and Millimeter-Wave Transmission Line Characteristics," *Microwaves, Opt. Acoust.*, Vol. MOA-1, pp. 14–22, Jan. 1979.

APPENDIX 3-A
CHARACTERISTIC EQUATIONS FOR DETERMINING THE PROPAGATION CONSTANTS OF SPECIFIC FIN-LINE STRUCTURES

1. Unilateral Fin Line (Fig. 2.2(a))

Characteristic Equation

$$\sum_{m=0}^{M} P_{im}\,\zeta_m + \sum_{m=0}^{N} Q_{im}\,\xi_m = 0; \quad i = 0, 1, 2, \ldots, M \qquad (3\text{-A.1a})$$

$$\sum_{m=0}^{M} R_{im}\,\zeta_m + \sum_{m=0}^{N} S_{im}\,\xi_m = 0; \quad i = 0, 1, 2, \ldots, N \qquad (3\text{-A.1b})$$

where

$$P_{im} = \sum_{n=-\infty}^{\infty} \hat{f}^*_{xi}(\alpha_n)\,\hat{G}_{11}(\alpha_n, \beta)\hat{g}_{zm}(\alpha_n);$$

$$i = 0, 1, 2, \ldots, M \qquad (3\text{-A.2a})$$

$$Q_{im} = \sum_{n=-\infty}^{\infty} \hat{f}^*_{xi}(\alpha_n)\,\hat{G}_{12}(\alpha_n, \beta)\hat{f}_{xm}(\alpha_n);$$

$$i = 0, 1, 2, \ldots, M \qquad (3\text{-A.2b})$$

$$R_{im} = \sum_{n=-\infty}^{\infty} \hat{g}^*_{zi}(\alpha_n)\hat{G}_{21}(\alpha_n, \beta)\hat{g}_{zm}(\alpha_n);$$

$$i = 0, 1, 2, \ldots, N \qquad (3\text{-A.2c})$$

$$S_{im} = \sum_{n=-\infty}^{\infty} \hat{g}^*_{zi}(\alpha_n)\hat{G}_{22}(\alpha_n, \beta)\hat{f}_{xm}(\alpha_n);$$

$$i = 0, 1, 2, \ldots, N \qquad (3\text{-A.2d})$$

Dyadic Green's Functions

$$\hat{G}_{11}(\alpha_n, \beta) = -\frac{j\alpha_n\beta}{P_0}(P_1 \sinh \gamma d \cosh \gamma d$$
$$+ P_2 \sinh^2\gamma d + P_3) \tag{3-A.3a}$$

$$\hat{G}_{12}(\alpha_n, \beta) = -\frac{j}{P_0}(P_4 \sinh \gamma d \cosh \gamma d$$
$$+ P_5 \sinh^2\gamma d + P_6) \tag{3-A.3b}$$

$$\hat{G}_{21}(\alpha_n, \beta) = -\frac{j}{P_0}(P_7 \sinh \gamma d \cosh \gamma d$$
$$+ P_8 \sinh^2\gamma d + P_9) \tag{3-A.3c}$$

$$\hat{G}_{22}(\alpha_n, \beta) = \hat{G}_{11}(\alpha_n, \beta) \tag{3-A.3d}$$

where

$$P_1 = \gamma[k_0^2\gamma_0^2(\coth^2 \gamma_0 h_1 + \epsilon_r) + (k^2\gamma_0^2 + k_0^2\gamma^2)$$
$$\cdot \coth \gamma_0 h_1 \coth \gamma_0 h_2] \tag{3-A.4a}$$

$$P_2 = \gamma_0[(k^2\gamma_0^2 + k_0^2\gamma^2) \coth \gamma_0 h_1 + k_0^2\gamma^2$$
$$\cdot (\coth^2 \gamma_0 h_1 + \epsilon_r) \coth \gamma_0 h_2] \tag{3-A.4b}$$

$$P_3 = k^2\gamma_0\gamma^2(\coth \gamma_0 h_1 + \coth \gamma_0 h_2) \tag{3-A.4c}$$

$$P_4 = \gamma[k_0^2\gamma_0^2(k^2 - \beta^2)(\coth^2 \gamma_0 h_1 + \epsilon_r) + (k_0^2 - \beta^2)$$
$$\cdot (k^2\gamma_0^2 + k_0^2\gamma^2) \coth \gamma_0 h_1 \coth \gamma_0 h_2] \tag{3-A.4d}$$

$$P_5 = \gamma_0[k_0^2\gamma^2(k_0^2 - \beta^2)(\coth^2 \gamma_0 h_1 + \epsilon_r) \coth \gamma_0 h_2$$
$$+ (k^2 - \beta^2)(k^2\gamma_0^2 + k_0^2\gamma^2) \coth \gamma_0 h_1] \tag{3-A.4e}$$

$$P_6 = k^2\gamma_0\gamma^2(k_0^2 - \beta^2)(\coth \gamma_0 h_1 + \coth \gamma_0 h_2) \tag{3-A.4f}$$

$$P_7 = \gamma[k_0^2\gamma_0^2(k^2 - \alpha_n^2)(\coth^2 \gamma_0 h_1 + \epsilon_r) + (k_0^2 - \alpha_n^2)$$
$$\cdot (k^2\gamma_0^2 + k_0^2\gamma^2) \coth \gamma_0 h_1 \coth \gamma_0 h_2] \tag{3-A.4g}$$

$$P_8 = \gamma_0[(k^2 - \alpha_n^2)(k^2\gamma_0^2 + k_0^2\gamma^2) \coth \gamma_0 h_1$$
$$+ k_0^2\gamma^2(k_0^2 - \alpha_n^2)(\epsilon_r + \coth^2 \gamma_0 h_1) \coth \gamma_0 h_2] \qquad (3\text{-A.4h})$$

$$P_9 = k^2\gamma_0\gamma^2(k_0^2 - \alpha_n^2)(\coth \gamma_0 h_1 + \coth \gamma_0 h_2) \qquad (3\text{-A.4i})$$

$$P_0 = \omega\mu_0\gamma_0\gamma \ [(k_0^2\gamma^2 + k^2\gamma_0^2) \coth \gamma_0 h_1 \sinh \gamma d \cosh \gamma d$$
$$+ k_0^2\gamma_0\gamma (\coth^2 \gamma_0 h_1 + \epsilon_r)\sinh^2 \gamma d + k^2 \gamma_0\gamma] \qquad (3\text{-A.4j})$$

$$\gamma_0^2 = \alpha_n^2 + \beta^2 - k_0^2, \ \gamma^2 = \alpha_n^2 + \beta^2 - k^2,$$
$$k^2 = k_0^2\epsilon_r, \ k_0^2 = \omega^2\mu_0\epsilon_0 \qquad (3\text{-A.5a})$$

$$\alpha_n = n\pi/b; \quad n = 0, \pm 1, \pm 2, \ldots, \infty \qquad (3\text{-A.5b})$$

Basis Functions

Choose (3.58). Thus,

$$\hat{e}_x(\alpha_n) = \sum_{m=0}^{M} \xi_m \hat{f}_{xm}(\alpha_n) \qquad (3\text{-A.6a})$$

$$\hat{e}_z(\alpha_n) = \sum_{m=0}^{N} \zeta_m \hat{g}_{zm}(\alpha_n) \qquad (3\text{-A.6b})$$

where

$$\hat{f}_{xm}(\alpha_n) = \text{Re}\left\{\frac{\pi w}{4} e^{j\alpha_n(s+w/2)}\left[e^{jm\pi/2} J_0\left(\frac{1}{2}(\alpha_n w + m\pi)\right)\right.\right.$$
$$\left.\left. + e^{-jm\pi/2} J_0\left(\frac{1}{2}(\alpha_n w - m\pi)\right)\right]\right\} \qquad (3\text{-A.6c})$$

$$\hat{g}_{zm}(\alpha_n) = \text{Im}\left\{-\frac{j\pi w}{4} e^{j\alpha_n(s+w/2)}\left[e^{jm\pi/2} J_0\left(\frac{1}{2}(\alpha_n w + m\pi)\right)\right.\right.$$
$$\left.\left. - e^{-jm\pi/2} J_0\left(\frac{1}{2}(\alpha_n w - m\pi)\right)\right]\right\} \qquad (3\text{-A.6d})$$

2. Insulated Fin Line (Fig. 2.2(c))

Expressions for P_0–P_9 given in (3-A.4) are replaced by

$$P_1 = k_0^2 \gamma_0 \gamma (\coth^2 \gamma_0 h + \epsilon_r) \tag{3-A.7a}$$

$$P_2 = (k^2 \gamma_0^2 + k_0^2 \gamma^2) \coth \gamma_0 h \tag{3-A.7b}$$

$$P_3 = k^2 \gamma^2 \coth \gamma_0 h \tag{3-A.7c}$$

$$P_4 = k_0^2 \gamma_0 \gamma (k^2 - \beta^2)(\coth^2 \gamma_0 h + \epsilon_r) \tag{3-A.7d}$$

$$P_5 = (k^2 - \beta^2)(k^2 \gamma_0^2 + k_0^2 \gamma^2) \coth \gamma_0 h \tag{3-A.7e}$$

$$P_6 = k^2 \gamma^2 (k_0^2 - \beta^2) \coth \gamma_0 h \tag{3-A.7f}$$

$$P_7 = k_0^2 \gamma_0 \gamma (k^2 - \alpha_n^2)(\coth^2 \gamma_0 h + \epsilon_r) \tag{3-A.7g}$$

$$P_8 = (k^2 - \alpha_n^2)(k^2 \gamma_0^2 + k_0^2 \gamma^2) \coth \gamma_0 h \tag{3-A.7h}$$

$$P_9 = k^2 \gamma^2 (k_0^2 - \alpha_n^2) \coth \gamma_0 h \tag{3-A.7i}$$

$$P_0 = \omega \mu_0 \gamma [(k^2 \gamma_0^2 + k_0^2 \gamma^2) \coth \gamma_0 h \sinh \gamma d \cosh \gamma d$$
$$+ k_0^2 \gamma_0 \gamma (\coth^2 \gamma_0 h + \epsilon_r) \sinh^2 \gamma d + k^2 \gamma_0 \gamma] \tag{3-A.7j}$$

All other equations, (3-A.1) to (3-A.3), (3-A.5) and (3-A.6) of the unilateral fin line remain valid.

3. Bilateral Fin Line (Fig. 2.2(b))

Odd-Mode Excitation

The elements of dyadic Green's function are given by

$$\hat{G}_{11}(\alpha_n, \beta) = \frac{-j \alpha_n \beta}{\omega \mu_0 \gamma_0 \gamma} (\gamma_0 \coth \gamma d + \gamma \coth \gamma_0 h) \tag{3-A.8a}$$

$$\hat{G}_{12}(\alpha_n, \beta) = \frac{-j}{\omega \mu_0 \gamma_0 \gamma} [\gamma_0 (k^2 - \beta^2) \coth \gamma d$$
$$+ \gamma (k_0^2 - \beta^2) \coth \gamma_0 h] \tag{3-A.8b}$$

$$\hat{G}_{21}(\alpha_n, \beta) = \frac{-j}{\omega\mu_0\gamma_0\gamma}[\gamma_0(k^2 - \alpha_n^2) \coth \gamma d$$

$$+ \gamma(k_0^2 - \alpha_n^2)\coth \gamma_0 h] \qquad\qquad (3\text{-A.8c})$$

$$\hat{G}_{22}(\alpha_n, \beta) = \hat{G}_{11}(\alpha_n, \beta) \qquad\qquad (3\text{-A.8d})$$

Even-Mode Excitation

The elements of dyadic Green's function are the same as (3-A.8) when coth(γd) is replaced by tanh(γd).

All other equations (3-A.1) and (3-A.2), (3-A.5) and (3-A.6) of the unilateral fin line remain valid.

4. Double-Dielectric Bilateral Fin Line (with Fins Facing Each Other) (Fig. 2.4(b))

Odd-Mode Excitation

All the equations (3-A.1) to (3-A.6) of the unilateral fin line are valid.

Even-Mode Excitation

Replace coth($\gamma_0 h_2$) by tanh($\gamma_0 h_2$) in (3-A.4). All other equations (3-A.1) to (3-A.3) and (3-A.5) to (3-A.6) of the unilateral fin line remain valid.

5. Double-Dielectric Bilateral Fin Line (with Fins Facing Side Walls) (Fig. 2.4(c))

Odd-Mode Excitation

All the equations (3-A.1) to (3-A.6) of the unilateral fin line are valid.

Even-Mode Excitation

Replace coth($\gamma_0 h_1$) by tanh($\gamma_0 h_1$) in (3-A.4). All other equations (3-A.1) to (3-A.3) and (3-A.5) to (3-A.6) of the unilateral fin line remain valid.

6. Special Cases of Unilateral, Insulated, Bilateral, and Double-Dielectric Fin Lines (Figs. 2.2(a–c) and 2.4(b, c))

Slots Centered in the E-Plane ($b = w + 2s$)

In the aforementioned fin-line structures, if the slot is centered in the E-plane, the following changes need to be incorporated in the formulas for the characteristic equation.

In equations (3-A.5) and (3-A.6), consider even values of m and n, i.e.,

$$n = 0, \pm2, \pm4, \ldots \; ; m = 0, 2, 4, \ldots$$

Asymmetric Fin Lines (Fig. 2.6)

When the above-mentioned fin lines are in asymmetric configuration, simply set $s = 0$ in (3-A.6). All other equations remain valid.

7. Edge-Coupled Unilateral Fin Lines (Fig. 2.3(a))

Odd-Mode Excitation

All the equations (3-A.1) to (3-A.6) of the unilateral fin line are valid.

Even-Mode Excitation

For this case, equation (3-A.5b) is replaced by

$$\alpha_n = \left(n - \frac{1}{2}\right)\frac{\pi}{b}; \quad n = \pm1, \pm2, \pm3, \ldots$$

Furthermore, consider the imaginary part instead of the real part in (3-A.6c), and the real part instead of the imaginary part in (3-A.6d). All other equations (3-A.1) to (3-A.4) and (3-A.5a) remain valid.

8. Edge-Coupled Insulated Fin Line (Fig. 2.7(a))

Odd-Mode Excitation

Use the formulas derived for the insulated fin line.

Even-Mode Excitation

Use the formulas derived for the insulated fin line with the following changes: α_n given in (3-A.5b) is replaced by

$$\alpha_n = \left(n - \frac{1}{2}\right)\frac{\pi}{b}; n = \pm 1, \pm 2, \pm 3, \ldots$$

Furthermore, consider the imaginary part in (3-A.6c) and the real part in (3-A.6d).

9.   Edge-Coupled Bilateral Fin Line (Fig. 2.3(b))

Odd-Odd Mode Excitation

Use the formulas derived for the odd-mode excitation of a bilateral fin line.

Even-Odd Mode Excitation

Use the formulas derived for the even-mode excitation of a bilateral fin line.

Odd-Even Mode Excitation

Use the formulas derived for the odd-mode excitation of a bilateral fin line with the following changes: α_n given in (3-A.5b) gets replaced by

$$\alpha_n = \left(n - \frac{1}{2}\right)\frac{\pi}{b}; n = \pm 1, \pm 2, \pm 3, \ldots$$

Furthermore, consider the imaginary part in (3-A.6c) and the real part in (3-A.6d).

Even-Even Mode Excitation

Use the formulas derived for the even-mode excitation of a bilateral fin line with the same changes as indicated for the odd-even mode excitation.

Chapter 4
Unilateral and Insulated Fin-Line Characteristics

4.1 INTRODUCTION

The most important fin-line propagation parameters required in the design of millimeter-wave integrated circuits are the *normalized guide wavelength* and the *characteristic impedance*. Furthermore, in order to assess the single-mode operating bandwidth, it is necessary to have a knowledge of the higher order modes. This information is also useful for an exact characterization of various discontinuity structures.

The finite metalization thickness and mounting grooves in the fin-line housing appreciably alter the basic propagation characteristics, especially at higher millimeter-wave frequencies. For accurate circuit design, it is therefore desirable to study the effect of these parameters on the basic fin-line propagation parameters.

Conductor and dielectric losses are other important parameters of a fin line. Although these parameters do not directly enter the design equations, they are quite useful for estimating the *overall loss* of a component. The overall loss that may occur in a particular fin-line configuration can also be estimated by measuring the unloaded and loaded Q-factors.

In this chapter, we present the basic propagation parameters, normalized guide wavelength (λ/λ_0) and characteristic impedance (Z), of unilateral and insulated fin lines and their variants. Numerical computations are carried out by using Cohn's approximate method (Ch. 2) as well as the rigorous spectral domain technique (Ch. 3). Cohn's approximate method is computationally faster and gives reasonably accurate results for narrow slot widths, typically $w/d \leq 2$, $w/b \leq 0.15$, and $w \leq \lambda_0/4\sqrt{\epsilon_r}$ [1]. As mentioned earlier in Ch. 3, the accuracy of numerical results obtained by using spectral domain technique essentially depends on the accuracy with which the basis functions represent the true electric field distribution of the slot. For all the computations reported in this chapter using spectral domain technique, we use sinusoidal basis functions given in (3.53) for the centered slot and (3.58) for arbitrarily located slots.

Several graphs are plotted basically to explain the propagation characteristics as a function of various structural parameters and also to point out some special features. Sensitivity analysis of unilateral fin lines is carried out essentially to study the tolerance requirements on the waveguide walls, the dielectric constant, and the thickness of the substrate. We present attenuation characteristics in order to obtain some idea about the overall transmission loss in various fin-line configurations. Dispersion of higher order modes is studied to assess the single-mode operating bandwidth. Furthermore, for application in nonreciprocal and monolithic circuit devices, we present the characteristics of the unilateral fin line using ferrite as well as metal-insulator-semiconductor (MIS) substrates.

4.2 UNILATERAL FIN LINES

By using the formulas presented in Ch. 3, the normalized guide wavelength λ/λ_0 and characteristic impedance Z are evaluated for the unilateral fin line and its variants. In order to check the accuracy of the numerical results obtained using spectral domain formulas, λ/λ_0 and Z are computed by using different basis functions. These results are presented in Tables 4.1 and 4.2. While using the sinusoidal basis functions, only the transverse component of the electric field distribution is considered in the first-order solution ($N = M = 1$). For second-order ($N = M = 2$) and third-order ($N = M = 3$) solutions, we include both the transverse and longitudinal components. It was found numerically that about 300 spectral terms are adequate for accurate results.

By comparing the numerical results listed in Tables 4.1 and 4.2 for λ/λ_0 and Z, we can observe that, for small slot widths, all the distributions except $f_x(x) = 1$ yield fairly accurate results. For broader slot widths, sinusoidal basis functions with a single-term approximation ($N = M = 1$) result in large errors. The second-order ($N = M = 2$) and third-order ($N = M = 3$) solutions yield accurate results. It is interesting to note that a single-term approximate distribution, $f_x(x) = 1 + |2x/w|^3$, yields fairly accurate results for all slot widths. It is pertinent to point out here that, for $w/b = 1$, $f_x(x) = 1$ is the true representation of the electric field distribution. Hence, the computed results of Z and λ/λ_0 for $w/b = 1$ obtained by using $f_x(x) = 1$ are exact.

Table 4.1

COMPARISON OF COMPUTED RESULTS OF λ/λ_0 OF UNILATERAL FIN LINE (INSET TO FIG. 4.1) FOR DIFFERENT BASIS FUNCTIONS: Waveguide WR-28, Frequency = 34 GHz, h_2 = 3.556 mm, ϵ_r = 2.22, d = 0.254 mm

w/b	$f_x(x) = 1$ (Eq. (3.48a))	$f_x(x) = 1 + \left\|\frac{2x}{w}\right\|^3$ (Eq. (3.50a))	Sinusoidal basis functions (Eq. (3.53) with Eq. (3.41))		
			$N = M = 1$	$N = M = 2$	$N = M = 3$
0.02	0.871	0.8729	0.8740	0.8741	0.8741
0.05	0.896	0.8989	0.9009	0.9009	0.9009
0.10	0.927	0.9306	0.9331	0.9331	0.9331
0.20	0.974	0.9784	0.9806	0.9808	0.9808
0.30	1.012	1.0172	1.0184	1.0193	1.0193
0.50	1.0775	1.0839	1.0827	1.0861	1.0863
0.70	1.1350	1.1411	1.1349	1.1434	1.1440
0.90	1.1794	1.1800	1.1596	1.1813	1.1800
1.00	1.1897	1.1811	1.1328	1.1813	1.1867

Table 4.2

COMPARISON OF COMPUTED RESULTS OF $Z(\Omega)$ OF UNILATERAL FIN LINE (INSET TO FIG. 4.1) FOR DIFFERENT BASIS FUNCTIONS: Waveguide WR-28, Frequency = 34 GHz, $h_2 = 3.556$ mm, $\epsilon_r = 2.22$, $d = 0.254$ mm

w/b	$f_x(x) = 1$ (Eq. (3.48a))	$f_x(x) = 1 + \left\|\dfrac{2x}{w}\right\|^3$ (Eq. (3.50a))	Sinusoidal basis functions (Eq. (3.53) with Eq. (3.41))		
			$N = M = 1$	$N = M = 2$	$N = M = 3$
0.02	118.1	120.7	122.0	122.5	122.7
0.05	150.3	153.8	155.3	157.4	155.5
0.10	188.6	193.3	195.0	195.7	195.0
0.20	248.2	255.4	257.8	257.7	257.9
0.30	298.7	308.2	311.2	311.1	311.3
0.50	384.5	396.7	399.0	399.3	399.4
0.70	449.2	459.5	455.0	458.1	458.5
0.90	486.5	488.1	467.3	483.9	485.0
1.00	492.4	486.3	445.8	484.4	488.0

Table 4.3

COMPARISON OF COMPUTED RESULTS OF λ/λ_0 AND $Z(\Omega)$ OF UNILATERAL FIN LINE (INSET TO FIG. 4.1) USING SPECTRAL DOMAIN FORMULAS WITH COHN'S METHOD: Waveguide WR-28, Frequency = 34 GHz, h_2 = 3.556 mm, ϵ_r = 2.22, d = 0.254 mm

w(mm)	λ/λ_0			$Z(\Omega)$		
	Cohn	Spectral domain		Cohn	Spectral domain	
		$N = M = 1$	$N = M = 2$		$N = M = 1$	$N = M = 2$
0.05	0.8645	0.8667	0.8668	108.9	112.6	113.2
0.1	0.8799	0.8824	0.8824	129.0	133.1	133.4
0.2	0.9024	0.9055	0.9055	157.4	160.9	161.0
0.3	0.9206	0.9239	0.9239	180.0	183.6	183.6
0.4	0.9365	0.9399	0.9399	199.7	203.7	203.7
0.5	0.9511	0.9542	0.9542	217.9	222.2	222.2
1.0	1.0123	1.0117	1.0125	295.8	301.6	301.7
2.0	1.1165	1.1006	1.1052	419.4	420.5	421.2

The numerical results on λ/λ_0 and Z obtained using spectral domain formulas are compared with those obtained by Cohn's method in Table 4.3. We can see that Cohn's method yields fairly accurate results on λ/λ_0 for small slot widths, typically $w/b \leq 0.15$. Table 4.4 compares the numerical results on λ/λ_0 and Z obtained using spectral domain formulas with those obtained by modal analysis. We may observe that the agreement in the results is fairly good.

In this section, we present the propagation parameters of unilateral fin lines as a function of various structural parameters. All the computations reported here use Cohn's method for small slot widths ($w/b \leq 0.15$, $w/d \leq 2$, and $w \leq \lambda_0/4\sqrt{\epsilon_r}$) and spectral domain formulas with sinusoidal basis functions ($N = M = 3$) for broader slots.

Table 4.4

COMPARISON OF COMPUTED RESULTS OF λ/λ_0 AND $Z(\Omega)$ OF
UNILATERAL FIN LINE (INSET TO FIG. 4.1) USING
SPECTRAL DOMAIN FORMULAS WITH MODAL ANALYSIS:
Waveguide WR-28, Frequency = 34 GHz, h_2 = 3.556 mm, ϵ_r = 2.22,
d = 0.254 mm

w	Frequency (GHz)	Modal analysis		Spectral domain	
		λ/λ_0	$Z(\Omega)$	λ/λ_0	$Z(\Omega)$
0.5	26.0	1.0196	230.93	1.0200	228.3
0.5	30.0	0.9791	226.04	0.9794	223.4
0.5	35.0	0.9491	224.88	0.9494	222.3
0.5	40.0	0.9302	226.56	0.9304	223.9

4.2.1 Centered Slot

The variations of λ/λ_0 and Z for a unilateral fin line at Ka band with centered slots are plotted in Fig. 4.1 for d = 0.254 mm, and in Fig. 4.2 for d = 0.127 mm. In both of these figures, we have considered narrow slot widths. We may observe that λ/λ_0 decreases as the frequency increases. However, the value of Z first decreases and then increases, but the variation in Z is small. As d increases, with all other parameters fixed, both

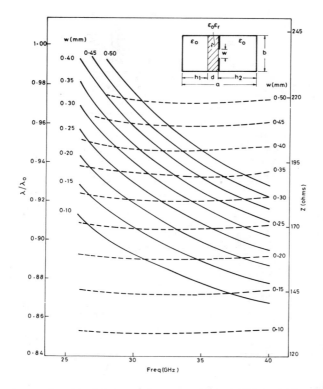

Fig. 4.1 Normalized guide wavelength λ/λ_0 and characteristic
impedance Z *versus* frequency of unilateral fin line:
$\epsilon_r = 2.22$ $d = 0.254$ mm
$h_1 = 3.302$ mm $h_2 = 3.556$ mm
———— λ/λ_0 ———— Z
waveguide = WR(28)

λ/λ_0 and Z decrease slightly. Furthermore, for a fixed frequency, as w
increases, both λ/λ_0 and Z increase. The lower limit for Z that can be
achieved with practically realizable slot widths is typically 100–120 ohms.
For practical applications, it is sometimes desirable to have lower impedance values. One simple way to achieve lower impedance is to increase
the dielectric constant of the substrate [2]. This approach is not practical

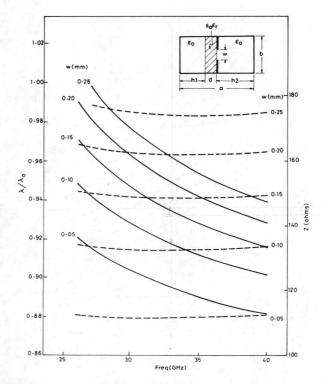

Fig. 4.2 Normalized guide wavelength λ/λ_0 and characteristic
impedance Z *versus* frequency of unilateral fin line:
    $\epsilon_r = 2.22$ $d = 0.127$ mm
    $h_1 = 3.429$ mm $h_2 = 3.556$ mm
    ——— λ/λ_0 ——— Z
    waveguide = WR(28)

because it makes the circuit size quite small.

Figures 4.3 to 4.5 show the variations of λ/λ_0 and Z for a unilateral fin line with a narrow centered slot for U, E, and W bands. These characteristics are similar to those plotted in Figs. 4.1 and 4.2.

The variations of λ/λ_0 and Z for a unilateral fin line at Ka band with a broader centered slot are plotted in Fig. 4.6. For moderate slot widths,

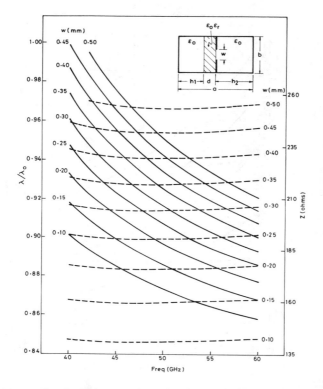

Fig. 4.3 Normalized guide wavelength λ/λ_0 and characteristic
impedance Z *versus* frequency of unilateral fin line:

$\epsilon_r = 2.22$	$d = 0.254$ mm
$h_1 = 2.1336$ mm	$h_2 = 2.3876$ mm
———— λ/λ_0	$---- Z$

waveguide = WR(19)

the trend in these characteristics is similar to that depicted in Figs. 4.1 and
4.2, while for broader slot widths approaching the full waveguide height,
Z decreases significantly with an increase in frequency. For $w = 3.556$
mm, the structure reduces to a slab loaded waveguide.

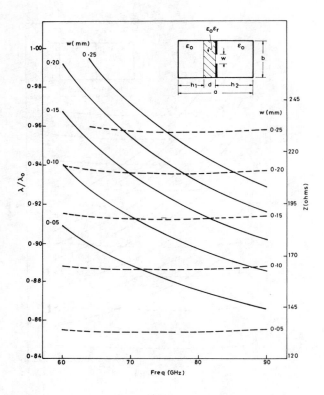

Fig. 4.4   Normalized guide wavelength λ/λ_0 and characteristic
impedance Z *versus* frequency of unilateral fin line:
$\epsilon_r = 2.22$ $d = 0.127$ mm
$h_1 = 1.4224$ mm $h_2 = 1.5494$ mm
———— λ/λ_0 —— — Z
waveguide = WR(12)

4.2.2   Centered Slot on Laterally Displaced Dielectric Substrate

The variations of λ/λ_0 and Z for a unilateral fin line with narrow centered
slots on a laterally displaced dielectric substrate are shown in Figs. 4.7 and
4.8. In comparing with Fig. 4.1, we can see that by laterally displacing the

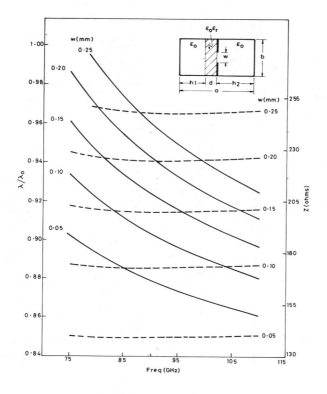

Fig. 4.5 Normalized guide wavelength λ/λ_0 and characteristic impedance Z *versus* frequency of unilateral fin line:
$\epsilon_r = 2.22$ $d = 0.127$ mm
$h_1 = 1.143$ mm $h_2 = 1.27$ mm
——— λ/λ_0 ——— Z
waveguide = WR(10)

dielectric substrate, λ/λ_0 increases marginally and the change in Z is also negligible. This is because, for narrow slot widths, the E-field is essentially concentrated across the slot, and the side walls do not have much influence

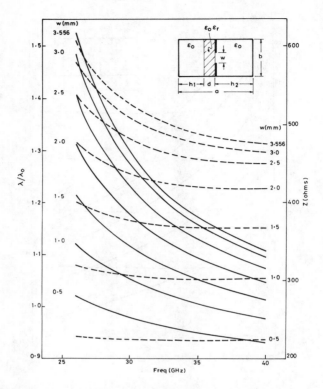

Fig. 4.6 Normalized guide wavelength λ/λ_0 and characteristic
impedance Z *versus* frequency of unilateral fin line with
broader slot:

$\epsilon_r = 2.22$	$d = 0.254$ mm
$h_1 = 3.302$ mm	$h_2 = 3.556$ mm
——— λ/λ_0	——— Z

waveguide $=$ WR(28)

for moderate displacement of the dielectric about the waveguide center.
As the slots are made broader, the guide wall that is closer to the substrate
begins to interact increasingly with the slot fields. This effect is depicted
in Figs. 4.9 and 4.10. We may observe that λ/λ_0 decreases as the frequency

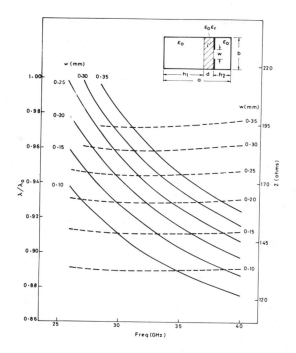

Fig. 4.7 Normalized guide wavelength λ/λ_0 and characteristic
impedance Z *versus* frequency of unilateral fin line with
laterally displaced dielectric substrate:

$\epsilon_r = 2.22$ $d = 0.254$ mm
$h_1 = 5.08$ mm $h_2 = 1.778$ mm
———— λ/λ_0 ———— Z
waveguide = WR(28)

is increased, or as w is decreased. For a fixed frequency, as w is increased,
Z first increases and then decreases. For a fixed value of w, as frequency
increases, Z first decreases and then increases. By comparing with Fig.
4.6, we can see that λ/λ_0 is higher for the case of a laterally displaced
dielectric substrate. Furthermore, for broader slots widths, Z decreases
significantly with lateral displacement of the dielectric substrate.

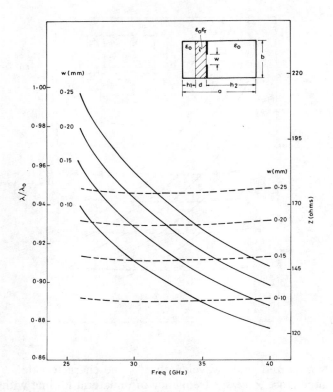

Fig. 4.8 Normalized guide wavelength λ/λ_0 and characteristic impedance Z *versus* frequency of unilateral fin line with laterally displaced dielectric substrate:

$\epsilon_r = 2.22$ $d = 0.254$ mm

$h_1 = 1.524$ mm $h_2 = 5.334$ mm

——— λ/λ_0 ——— Z

waveguide = WR(28)

4.2.3 Slot Displaced in Symmetric E-plane

The effect of displacing the slot in the E-plane is shown in Fig. 4.11. For a slot of fixed width w, the characteristics of λ/λ_0 and Z as a function of s are symmetrical about $s = (b - w)/2$. Hence, the plots are shown

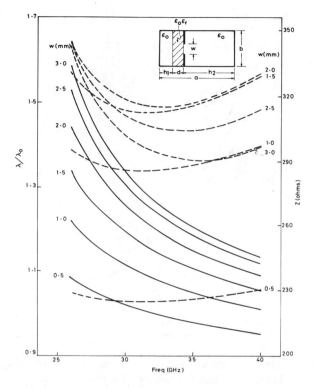

Fig. 4.9 Normalized guide wavelength λ/λ_0 and characteristic impedance Z *versus* frequency of unilateral fin line with broader slots and laterally displaced dielectric substrate:

$\epsilon_r = 2.22$ $d = 0.254$ mm

$h_2 = 5.334$ mm $h_1 = 1.524$ mm

——— λ/λ_0 — — — Z

waveguide $= $ WR(28)

only from $s = 0$ to $(b - w)/2$. As s is increased from 0 to $(b - w)/2$, λ/λ_0 first increases and then decreases, whereas Z increases and saturates near $(b - w)/2$. For a fixed value of s, both λ/λ_0 and Z increase as w is increased. The main feature to be observed is that lower impedances can be achieved by displacing the slot toward one of the side walls.

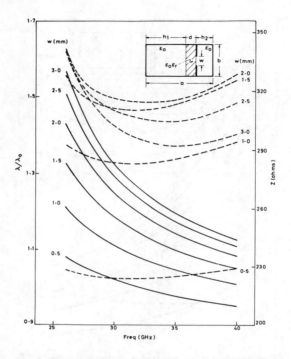

Fig. 4.10 Normalized guide wavelength λ/λ_0 and characteristic
            impedance Z *versus* frequency of unilateral fin line with
            broader slots and laterally displaced dielectric substrate:

$\epsilon_r = 2.22$ .... $d = 0.254$ mm

$h_1 = 5.08$ mm .... $h_2 = 1.778$ mm

——— λ/λ_0 .... — — — Z

waveguide = WR(28)

4.2.4 Sensitivity Analysis

The sensitivity analysis of a fin line is essential to establish tolerance
requirements on the waveguide housing and the dielectric substrate. The
variations of λ/λ_0 and Z as a function of the percentage change in the
waveguide dimensions, a and b, of a unilateral fin line are shown in Fig.

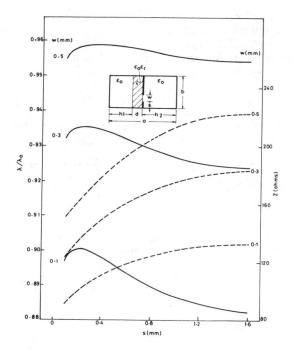

Fig. 4.11 Effect of displacing the slot on the normalized guide
wavelength λ/λ_0 and characteristic impedance Z:

$\epsilon_r = 2.22$ $d = 0.254$ mm
$h_1 = 3.302$ mm $h_2 = 3.556$ mm
waveguide = WR(28)   frequency = 34 GHz
————— λ/λ_0 – – – – Z

4.12. Similar variations as a function of the percentage change in relative
dielectric constant ϵ_r and substrate thickness d are shown in Fig. 4.13. For
the structural parameters considered in these figures, we can observe that
as the parameter a changes by $\pm\ 10\%$, λ/λ_0 changes by $\binom{-0.44}{+0.32}\%$ and Z
changes by $\binom{-2.16}{+1.78}\%$. Conversely, for a $\pm 10\%$ change in b, λ/λ_0 changes by
$\binom{-0.75}{+0.58}\%$, whereas Z changes by $\binom{-0.3}{+0.5}\%$. For a $\pm 10\%$ change in the substrate

thickness d, λ/λ_0 and Z change by $\binom{-0.67}{+0.61}\%$ and $\binom{-0.50}{+0.44}\%$, respectively. Also, if the relative dielectric constant ϵ_r changes by $\pm$ 10%, then λ/λ_0 changes by $\binom{-2.82}{+2.63}\%$, whereas Z changes by $\binom{-1.46}{+1.40}\%$. This study reveals that the tolerance requirements on parameters a and ϵ_r are more stringent than those on parameters b and d.

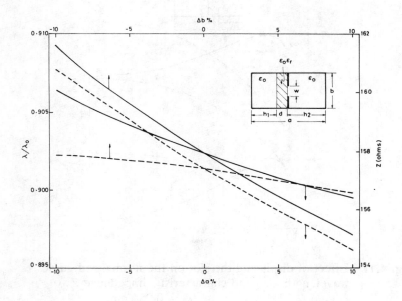

Fig. 4.12 Normalized guide wavelength λ/λ_0 and characteristic impedance Z *versus* percentage change in waveguide dimensions a and b:

$\epsilon_r = 2.22$	$d = 0.254$ mm
$w = 0.2$ mm	$h_2 = h_1 + d$
frequency = 34 GHz	waveguide = WR(28)
——— λ/λ_0	——— Z

4.2.5 Centered Slot with Periodic Stub Loading [3]

A unilateral fin line having a centered slot and periodic stub loading is shown in Fig. 4.14. This type of periodic stub loading is useful for many

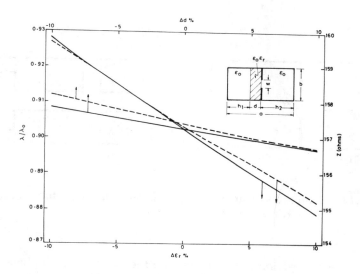

Fig. 4.13 Normalized guide wavelength λ/λ_0 and characteristic
impedance Z *versus* percentage change in substrate thickness
d and dielectric constant ϵ_r:

$\epsilon_r = 2.22$	$d = 0.254$ mm
$w = 0.2$ mm	$h_2 = h_1 + d$
frequency $= 34$ GHz	waveguide $=$ WR(28)
——— λ/λ_0	— — — Z

device applications, such as filters. Figure 4.15 shows the k_0-β diagram of
this configuration [3]. Because of the inductive reactance of the series stub,
the curve for the unilateral fin line without stubs is higher than that for
the same structure with a periodic stub. It is interesting to note that the
unilateral fin line with periodic stub loading exhibits stopband as well as
passband regions. For the dimensional parameters chosen in Fig. 4.15, the
first stopband region occurs in the frequency band $2.8 < k_0p < 2.931$, and
the first passband region occurs in the frequency band $1.038 < k_0p < 2.8$.

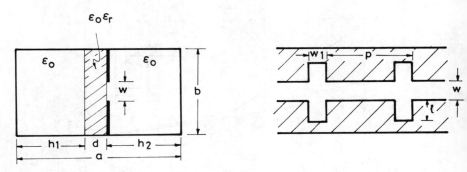

Fig. 4.14 Centered slot unilateral fin line with periodic stub loading
(after Kitazawa and Mittra [3]).

The effect of periodic stub loading on the normalized stopband width
$\Delta k / k_c$ is shown in Fig. 4.16 [3]. Here, Δk is the width of the stopband and
k_c is the center frequency. We may observe that as the stub length l or
stub width w_1 is increased, the stopband width increases. The increase in
stopband width with an increase in w_1, however, is relatively small.

4.2.6 Modal Spectrum

In order to assess the single-mode operating bandwidth, it is necessary
to study the higher order mode behavior. The higher order mode analysis
is also extremely useful for characterizing various discontinuity structures.

The dispersion characteristics of the dominant and higher order modes
in a unilateral fin line are plotted in Fig. 4.17 [4]. The dashed curves in
this figure are the dispersion characteristics of the higher order modes,
which are not excited by the incident H_{10} wave. It is observed that for all
the modes, λ_0/λ increases as the frequency increases. The first important
higher order mode is HE_3. It is pertinent to point out here that the modal
spectrum changes significantly with mounting groove depth (e) and
metalization thickness (t) [5–6]. Their effect on the dominant mode propagation parameters, and also on the operating bandwidth, is presented in
the following sections.

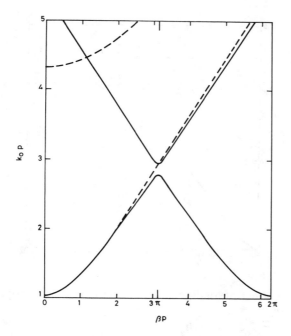

Fig. 4.15 The $k_0 - \beta$ diagram of unilateral fin line with periodic stub
loading:

——— uniform fin line	——— fin line with stubs
$\epsilon_r = 2.2$	$h_2 = 0.094$ in
$d = 0.005$ in	$h_1 = 0.089$ in
$w = 0.005$ in	$b = 0.094$ in
$w_1 = 0.02$ in	$l = 0.04$ in
$p = 0.12$ in	

(From Kitazawa and Mittra [3], Copyright © 1984 IEEE, reprinted with
permission.)

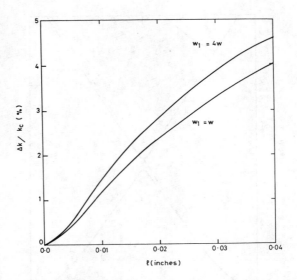

Fig. 4.16 The effect of loading stubs on the normalized stopband width
$\Delta k/k_c$:

$\epsilon_r = 2.2$ $h_2 = 0.094$ in
$d = 0.005$ in $h_1 = 0.089$ in
$w = 0.005$ in $b = 0.094$ in
$p = 0.12$ in

(From Kitazawa and Mittra [3], Copyright © 1984 IEEE, reprinted with permission.)

4.2.7 Effect of Finite Metalization Thickness [5–6]

The effect of finite metalization thickness (t) on the effective dielectric constant (ϵ_f) and the characteristic impedance (Z) of the dominant mode of a unilateral fin line with centered slot is shown in Fig. 4.18 [6]. The main feature to be observed is that Z decreases as t increases. In the lower frequency range (near the cut-off frequency), the fin line behaves as a ridged waveguide; therefore, as t is increased, the cut-off frequency is

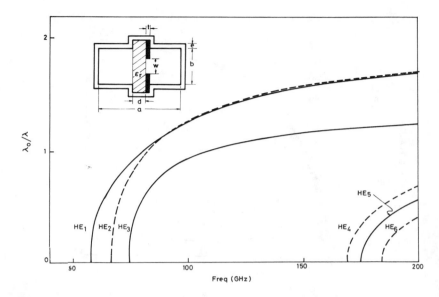

Fig. 4.17 Dispersion characteristics for the first six eigenmodes in a
unilateral fin line:

$w = 0.3$ mm $e = 0.5$ mm
$a = 1.65$ mm $b = a/2$
$d = 110$ μm $t = 5$ μm
$\epsilon_r = 3.75$
———— modes which are not excited by an
incident H_{10}–wave

(From Vahldieck [4], Copyright © 1984 IEEE, reprinted with permission.)

lowered. Alternatively, ϵ_f increases. However, in the higher frequency
range, the structure behaves as a slotline; thus, ϵ_f decreases as t is increased.
The effect of metalization thickness is higher at higher operating frequencies and for narrow slot widths [5–6]. It is interesting to note that for some
frequencies within this band, the effect of t on ϵ_f is negligible.

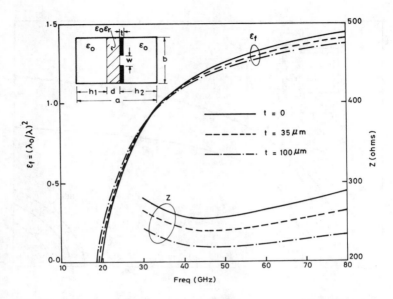

Fig. 4.18 Effect of finite metalization thickness on the propagation
characteristics of unilateral fin line:

$$\epsilon_r = 3.8 \qquad h_1 = 0.089 \text{ in}$$
$$d = 0.005 \text{ in} \qquad h_2 = 0.094 \text{ in}$$
$$b = 0.094 \text{ in} \qquad w/b = 0.2$$

(From Kitazawa and Mittra [6], Copyright © 1984 IEEE, reprinted with
permission.)

4.2.8 Effect of Mounting Grooves [4–5]

The influence of mounting grooves on the modal spectrum of a unilateral
fin line is shown in Fig. 4.19 [5]. For smaller groove depths, the dominant
mode is unaffected. However, as the groove depth increases, the dominant
mode interacts strongly with the next higher order mode, resulting in an
increase in the dominant mode propagation constant. In general, the cut-
off frequency of the higher order mode is slightly lowered, thereby resulting
in lower single-mode operating bandwidth [4]. These effects are more
pronounced at higher millimeter-wave frequencies, and they are functions
of frequency, dielectric constant, and substrate thickness.

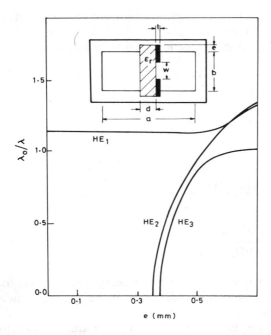

Fig. 4.19 Influence of the mounting grooves on the dominant and higher order modes in a unilateral fin line:

$a = 3.1$ mm	$b = a/2$
$t = 10$ μm	$w = 0.35$ mm
$d = 110$ μm	$\epsilon_r = 3.75$
frequency $= 80$ GHz	

(From Vahldieck and Hoefer [5], Copyright © 1985 IEEE, reprinted with permission.)

4.2.9 Magnetized Ferrite Substrate [7–9]

Nonreciprocal fin-line components are based on the properties of a ferrite substrate subjected to a magnetic field, or the gyroelectric properties of a semiconducting layer subjected to a magnetostatic field [7, 10]. In this section, we present the characteristics of a unilateral fin line with magnetized ferrite substrate.

Figure 4.20 shows the dispersion characteristics of a unilateral fin line with magnetized ferrite substrate [7]. The ferrite substrate is magnetized to saturation along the x-direction, giving rise to a dyadic permeability tensor [7]:

$$\overrightarrow{\mu} = \begin{bmatrix} \mu_0 & 0 & 0 \\ 0 & \mu & -jk \\ 0 & jk & \mu \end{bmatrix} \tag{4.1}$$

where

$$\frac{\mu}{\mu_0} = \frac{\omega^2 - \gamma H_0(\gamma H_0 + \gamma \cdot 4\pi M_s)}{\omega^2 - (\gamma H_0)^2} \tag{4.2a}$$

$$\frac{k}{\mu_0} = \frac{|\gamma| \, 4\pi M_s \cdot \omega}{\omega^2 - (\gamma H_0)^2} \tag{4.2b}$$

where μ_0 is the permeability of free space, γ is the gyromagnetic ratio, ω is the operating frequency in radians, H_0 is the applied dc field, and M_s is the magnetization.

We may observe from Fig. 4.20 that as frequency increases, λ_0/λ increases for both the forward and backward directions of propagation. Over the complete frequency range being considered, λ_0/λ for the two directions of propagation are different, thereby giving rise to nonreciprocal characteristics.

It is interesting to note that the nonreciprocity increases as the thickness of the ferrite slab is increased. However, for practical applications, the nonreciprocal characteristics exhibited by the structure shown in Fig. 4.20 are not adequate. A solution for this problem is to use an additional dielectric spacer between the fin and the ferrite substrate as shown in Fig. 4.21 [8–9].

4.2.10 Metal-Insulator-Semiconductor Substrate [11]

A typical MIS substrate in a unilateral fin line is shown by Fig. 4.22. In this structure, depending on the resistivity, thickness of the substrate,

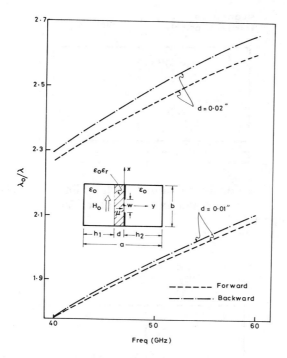

Fig. 4.20 Dispersion characteristics of unilateral fin line with magnetized ferrite substrate:

$\epsilon_r = 12.5$ $4\pi M_s = 5000$ Gauss
$H_0 = 500$ oe $h_2 = b = 0.094$ in
$h_1 = 0.094$ in $- d$ $b/w = 2$

(From Hayashi and Mittra [7], Copyright © 1983 IEEE, reprinted with permission.)

and operating frequency, several modes can propagate. Of particular interest is the slow-wave mode, which is useful for monolithic integrated circuit technology. In practice, it is necessary to choose optimum dimensions so as to identify a useful slot mode range. This range is characterized by minimum attenuation and maximum slow-wave factor. Typical characteristics of the MIS unilateral fin line are available in the literature [11].

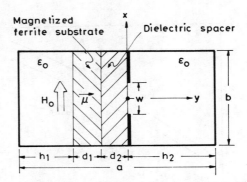

Fig. 4.21 Cross-sectional view of unilateral fin line with magnetized ferrite substrate and dielectric spacer (after Beyer and Solbach [8]).

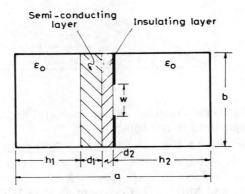

Fig. 4.22 Cross-sectional view of unilateral fin line formed on metal-insulator-semiconductor substrate (after Abdel Azeim *et al.* [11]).

4.2.11 Slot Coupled to Strip-Conductors [12–13]

Several practical integrated circuit components, including filters and directional couplers, invariably require coupling of the slot to single or coupled strip conductors. Typical structures that use strip-slot combinations and their dispersion characteristics are shown in Figs. 4.23 and 4.24 [12].

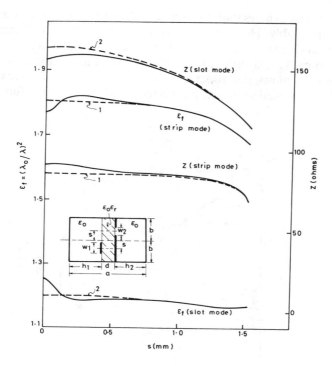

Fig. 4.23 Dispersion and characteristic impedance of unilateral fin line
with slot coupled to a single strip conductor:

$\epsilon_r = 2.2$ $d = 0.254$ mm
$a = 4b = 7.112$ mm   frequency $= 33$ GHz
$w_1 = 0.3$ mm $w_2 = 0.2$ mm
1: $w_2 = 0$ 2: $w_1 = 0$

(From Schmidt [12], first presented at the 11th European Microwave Conference, reprinted with permission.)

The structure of Fig. 4.23 incorporates a single strip conductor. Two
fundamental modes are possible—namely, the slot mode and the strip
mode. Superimposed on this graph are the dispersion characteristics of an
isolated slot ($w_1 = 0$) and an isolated strip with a ground plane ($w_2 = 0$).
A comparison of the dispersion characteristics of the slot mode with those

of an isolated slot shows that, for smaller values of s, the two characteristics deviate appreciably. However, for larger values of s, the two characteristics merge. A similar trend can be seen between the dispersion characteristics of the strip mode and those of an isolated strip with a ground plane.

Figure 4.24 shows the dispersion characteristics of a unilateral fin line with the slot coupled to two strip conductors. There are three fundamental

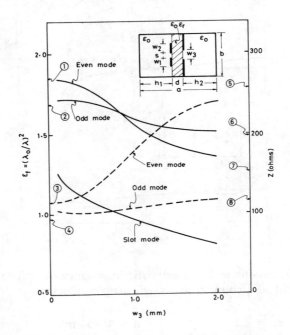

Fig. 4.24   Dispersion and characteristic impedance of unilateral fin line with slot coupled to a pair of strip conductors:

$\epsilon_r = 2.22$ $d = 0.254$ mm
$a = 2b = 7.112$ mm $w_1 = w_2 = 0.2$ mm
$s = 0.4$ mm   frequency $= 33$ GHz
① . . . ④: $w_3 = 0$ ⑤ . . . ⑧: $w_3 = b$
———— ϵ_f — — — Z

(From Schmidt [12], first presented at the 11th European Microwave Conference, reprinted with permission.)

modes possible. These are the slot mode, and the even- and odd-strip modes. It is interesting to note that in this structure the propagation constants of the even- and odd-strip modes can be equalized by varying the slot width w_3. The structure, therefore, is very useful for high-directivity coupler applications. The effective dielectric constant for the slot mode is lower than the values for the even- and odd-strip modes.

In addition to the aforementioned strip-slot configurations, several other practical structures are also reported in the literature [13].

4.2.12 Conductor and Dielectric Losses [14]

The variations of the attenuation constant in the conductor (α_c) and in the dielectric (α_d) of a unilateral fin line as a function of normalized slot width (w/b) are depicted in Fig. 4.25 [14]. As expected, both α_c and α_d decrease with an increase in w/b. Furthermore, the dielectric loss is very small as compared with the conductor loss. The variations of conductor and dielectric losses as a function of frequency are available in the literature [14].

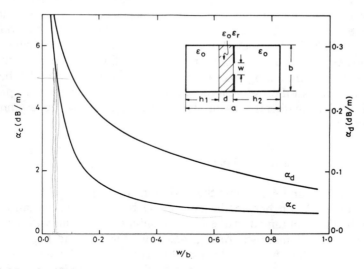

Fig. 4.25 Conductor loss (α_c) and dielectric loss (α_d) of a unilateral fin line with centered dielectric:

$\epsilon_r = 2.22$ $\tan \delta_i = 2 \times 10^{-4}$
$\rho = 3 \times 10^{-8}$ Ω.m $d = 0.127$ mm
frequency $= 40$ GHz

(From Syahkal and Davies [14], Copyright © 1982 IEEE, reprinted with permission.)

4.2.13 Coupling to a Dielectric Resonator [15]

Dielectric resonators coupled to fin lines are useful in the design of stabilized fin-line oscillators and tunable filters. Theoretical and experimental studies of a cylindrical dielectric resonator coupled to a unilateral fin line at Ka band have been reported by Hernandez-Gil and Perez [15]. It has been pointed out that by varying the spacing between the resonator and the substrate, the external Q-factor of the resonator can be varied from 10 to 10^4. Furthermore, the coupling increases as the resonator is moved closer to the fin-line slot as well as with an increase in the slot width.

4.3 ASYMMETRIC UNILATERAL FIN LINES

As pointed out in Sec. 4.2.1, the obtainable lower limit for the characteristic impedance Z of practically realizable slot widths in a unilateral fin line with centered slot is typically on the order of 100 ohms. One way of lowering the impedance is by lateral displacement of the dielectric substrate. However, as discussed in Sec. 4.2.2, substantial reduction in Z can occur only for broader slot widths. Another way of realizing lower impedances is to use an asymmetric unilateral fin line. This structure is also useful for mounting packaged active devices because the bottom shielding wall can then serve as a heat sink. In the following, we present the dispersion characteristics of the dominant mode of an asymmetric unilateral fin line.

4.3.1 Single Fin in the E-plane

Figures 4.26 and 4.27 show the variations of λ/λ_0 and Z for an asymmetric unilateral fin line in the Ka and U bands. These variations are similar to those obtained in the case of unilateral fin line with centered slot (Fig. 4.1). Comparison of Fig. 4.26 with Fig. 4.1 and Fig. 4.27 with Fig. 4.3 shows that, for a fixed value of w, considerably lower impedances are obtained in the case of asymmetric fin lines. Equivalently, low impedances can be realized in the asymmetric unilateral fin-line configuration with more convenient slot widths than in a unilateral fin line with centered slot.

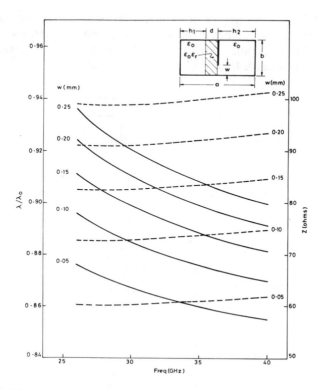

Fig. 4.26 Normalized guide wavelength λ/λ_0 and characteristic impedance Z *versus* frequency of asymmetric unilateral fin line:

$\epsilon_r = 2.22$ $d = 0.254$ mm
$h_1 = 3.302$ mm $h_2 = 3.556$ mm
——— λ/λ_0 ——— Z
waveguide = WR(28)

4.3.2   Single Fin on Laterally Displaced Dielectric Substrate

The variations of λ/λ_0 and Z for an asymmetric unilateral fin line with narrow slot and laterally displaced dielectric substrate are plotted in Figs.

4.28 and 4.29. By comparing with Fig. 4.26, we can see that by lateral displacement of the dielectric substrate, λ/λ_0 slightly increases, but the change in Z is negligible. For the same location of the substrate, if the slot width is increased, then Z changes considerably.

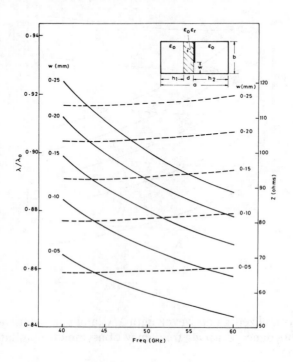

Fig. 4.27 Normalized guide wavelength λ/λ_0 and characteristic impedance Z *versus* frequency of asymmetric unilateral fin line:

$\epsilon_r = 2.22$	$d = 0.254$ mm
$h_1 = 2.1336$ mm	$h_2 = 2.3876$ mm
——— λ/λ_0	——— Z

waveguide = WR(19)

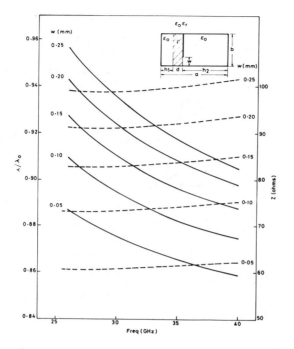

Fig. 4.28 Dispersion and characteristic impedance of asymmetric
unilateral fin line with laterally displaced dielectric substrate:

ϵ_r = 2.22 d = 0.254 mm

h_1 = 1.524 mm h_2 = 5.334 mm

———— λ/λ_0 – – – – Z

waveguide = WR(28)

4.4 INSULATED FIN LINES

In the insulated fin line, the fins are insulated at dc by an additional
dielectric substrate, thereby allowing bias to be applied to active circuit
components. As well as lowering the Q, the additional dielectric substrate
used for insulating the fins alters the basic propagation characteristics
considerably, and thus its effect must be taken into account while designing
a circuit component [16].

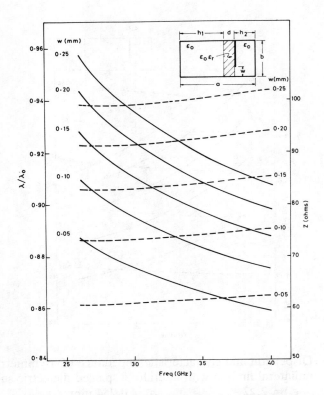

Fig. 4.29 Dispersion and characteristic impedance of asymmetric
unilateral fin line with laterally displaced dielectric substrate:

$\epsilon_r = 2.22$ $d = 0.254$ mm

$h_1 = 5.08$ mm $h_2 = 1.778$ mm

————— λ/λ_0 – – – – Z

waveguide = WR(28)

In the following, we present the dispersion characteristics of insulated
fin lines for the dominant and higher order modes. The effect of displacing
the slot in the symmetric E-plane is also considered.

4.4.1 Centered Slot

The variations of λ/λ_0 and Z for an insulated fin line with centered slots
are plotted in Figs. 4.30 and 4.31 for Ka and W bands, respectively. In
both graphs, narrow slot widths are considered. The variations are similar

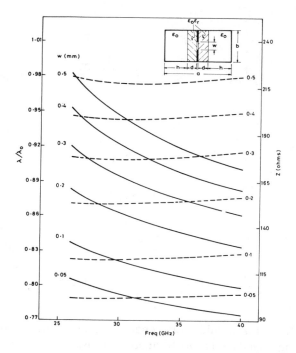

Fig. 4.30 Normalized guide wavelength λ/λ_0 and characteristic impedance Z *versus* frequency of insulated fin line with centered slot:

$\epsilon_r = 2.22$ $d = 0.127$ mm
$h = 3.429$ mm waveguide $=$ WR(28)
———— λ/λ_0 –––– Z

to those obtained in the case of a unilateral fin line. Comparison of Fig. 4.30 with Fig. 4.1 shows that, for a fixed slot width w, λ/λ_0 in the case of insulated fin line is slightly lower, and the change in Z is negligibly small. For broader slot widths, a significant change in both λ/λ_0 and Z is expected.

4.4.2 Slot Displaced in Symmetric E-plane

The effect of displacing the slot in the E-plane is shown in Fig. 4.32. As s increases from 0 to $(b - w)/2$, λ/λ_0 decreases and Z increases. Lower impedances are therefore possible by displacing the slot toward one of the

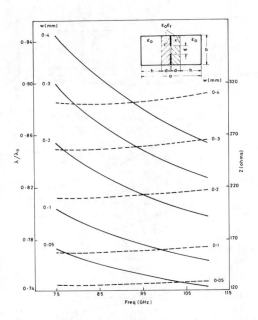

Fig. 4.31 Normalized guide wavelength λ/λ_0 and characteristic
impedance Z *versus* frequency of insulated fin line with
centered slot:

  $\epsilon_r = 2.22$ $d = 0.127$ mm
  $h = 1.143$ mm   waveguide = WR(10)
  ———— λ/λ_0 ——— Z

side walls. For a fixed value of s, λ/λ_0 decreases and Z increases as the
frequency is increased. The variations of λ/λ_0 and Z as a function of s are
symmetric about $s = (b - w)/2$.

4.4.3 Modal Spectrum [4]

The dispersion characteristics of the dominant and higher order modes
in an insulated fin line are shown in Fig. 4.33 [4]. The dashed curves in
this figure show the dispersion results of the higher order modes, which
are not excited by the incident hollow waveguide modes. We can see that
for all the modes, λ_0/λ increases as frequency increases. The important
higher order mode is HE_4. The modal bandwidth in the insulated fin line

decreases faster with an increase in the groove depth e. This is because of the strong dependence of the HE_4 mode on the groove depth.

It is worth mentioning here that the modal spectrum changes significantly with the mounting groove depth (e) as well as the finite metalization thickness (t). The effect of both these parameters should be taken into account for practical circuit components.

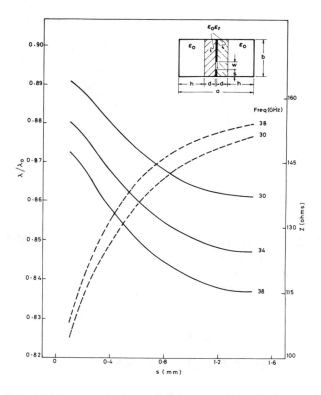

Fig. 4.32 Dispersion and characteristic impedance of insulated fin line with slot displaced in symmetric E-plane:

$\epsilon_r = 2.22$ $d = 0.127$ mm
$h = 3.429$ mm $w = 0.2$ mm
———— λ/λ_0 ———— Z
waveguide = WR(28)

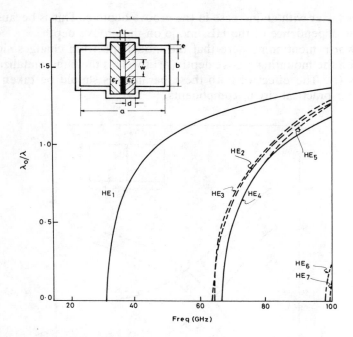

Fig. 4.33 Dispersion characteristics of the dominant and higher order
modes of an insulated fin line:

$a = 3.1$ mm $b = a/2$,
$d = 220$ μm $w = 0.6$ mm
$t = 5$ μm $e = 0.5$ mm
$\epsilon_r = 3.75$ ——— non-excited modes

(From Vahldieck [4], Copyright © 1984 IEEE, reprinted with permission.)

4.5 EDGE-COUPLED UNILATERAL FIN LINES

Edge-coupled unilateral fin lines are commonly used in directional couplers and balanced mixers. These fin lines are characterized in terms of
the dominant even- and odd-mode guide wavelengths and characteristic
impedances. In addition, higher order modes, which can be excited, must
be analyzed to determine the single-mode bandwidth. In order to have
additional flexibility in circuit design, more general types of edge-coupled
unilateral fin lines, which include slot displaced in symmetric E-plane and
multislot fin line, need to be considered.

In the following sections, we shall present the dispersion characteristics
of the dominant as well as higher order modes of the edge-coupled unilateral fin lines. Conductor and dielectric loss characteristics, which should
be useful for estimating the circuit losses in a component, are also presented.

4.5.1 Equal-Width Slots in Symmetric E-plane

The variations of λ/λ_0 and Z *versus* frequency for the dominant even- and odd-modes of an edge-coupled unilateral fin line with symmetrically located slots are shown in Figs. 4.34 and 4.35, respectively. For a fixed frequency, the characteristics as a function of s are plotted in Fig. 4.36. We can see that for fixed values of w and s, as frequency increases, λ/λ_0 decreases for the odd-mode, whereas the variation is negligibly small for the even-mode. For a fixed frequency and slot width, as s increases, λ/λ_0 increases and Z decreases for the even-mode. For the odd-mode, the curves for λ/λ_0 and Z are symmetric about $2s = (b/2 - w)$.

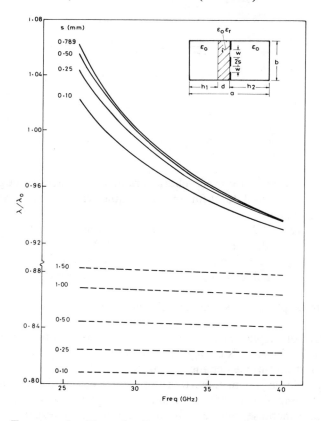

Fig. 4.34 Even- and odd-mode dispersion of edge-coupled unilateral fin line with equal width slots in symmetric E-plane:

$\epsilon_r = 2.22$	$d = 0.254$ mm
$w = 0.2$ mm	$h_1 = 3.302$ mm
$h_2 = 3.556$ mm	——— odd-mode
waveguide = WR(28)	– – – even-mode

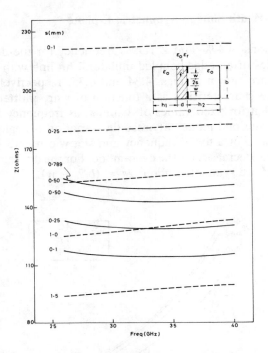

Fig. 4.35   Even- and odd-mode characteristic impedances of edge-
coupled unilateral fin line with equal width slots in symmetric
E-plane:

$\epsilon_r = 2.22$	$d = 0.254$ mm
$w = 0.2$ mm	$h_1 = 3.302$ mm
$h_2 = 3.556$ mm	———— odd-mode
waveguide = WR(28)	———— even-mode

4.5.2   Slots Displaced in Symmetric E-plane [17]

The effect of displacing the slots in the E-plane is shown in Fig. 4.37
[17]. As one of the slots is brought closer to the shielding wall, ϵ_f for both
the even- and odd-modes changes slightly, but the characteristic impedances show a larger change. Furthermore, the even-mode and odd-mode
characteristic impedances of slot 1 and the odd-mode characteristic impedance of slot 2 increase, whereas the even-mode characteristic impedance
of slot 2 decreases as s_1 is increased from a small value. For large values
of s_1 approaching 1.6, the characteristic impedances of slots 1 and 2 approach the same value. This is to be expected because $s_1 = 1.618$ corresponds to the case of an edge-coupled unilateral fin line with symmetrically
located slots.

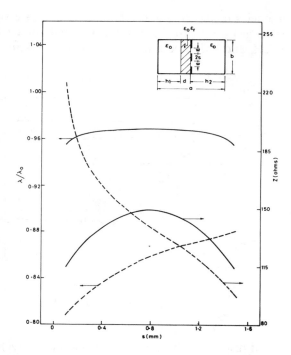

Fig. 4.36 Even- and odd-mode normalized guide wavelengths and characteristic impedances of edge-coupled unilateral fin line with equal width slots in symmetric E-plane:

$\epsilon_r = 2.22$ $d = 0.254$ mm
$h_1 = 3.302$ mm $h_2 = 3.556$ mm
$w = 0.2$ mm   frequency $= 34$ GHz
———— odd-mode   ———— even-mode
waveguide $=$ WR(28)

4.5.3 Modal Spectrum [18]

The dispersion characteristics of the dominant and higher order modes in an edge-coupled unilateral fin line with symmetrically located slots are shown in Fig. 4.38(a) [18]. The dashed curves in this figure are the dispersion characteristics for the case of zero groove depth ($e = 0$). For an incident TE_{10} wave, the dominant and first higher order modes are HE_1 and HE_3, respectively, whereas for an incident TE_{01} wave, the dominant and first higher order modes are EH_0 and HE_2, respectively. Figure 4.38(b) shows the cut-off frequency *versus* the groove depth of the hybrid modes in an edge-coupled unilateral fin line. We may observe that the cut-off frequency of the HE_1 mode is insensitive to the groove depth. However, the cut-off frequencies of the HE_2 and HE_3 modes decrease significantly with an increase in groove depth. Therefore, the single-mode bandwidth of the dominant EH_0 and HE_1 modes reduces significantly with an increase in the groove depth.

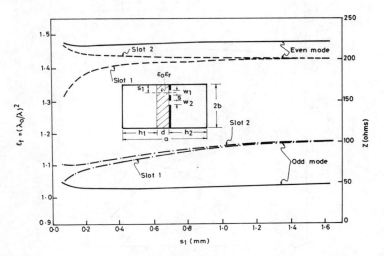

Fig. 4.37   Effect of displacing the slots in E-plane on the even- and odd-mode effective dielectric constants and characteristic impedances:

$h_1 = h_2 = 3.4935$ mm $s = 0.2$ mm
$w_1 = w_2 = 0.1$ mm $d = 0.125$ mm
$\epsilon_r = 2.2$ frequency = 33 GHZ
——— ϵ_f waveguide = WR(28)
———
—·—·— } Z

(From Schmidt *et al.* [17], Copyright © 1980 IEEE, reprinted with permission.)

4.5.4   Conductor and Dielectric Losses [14]

The variations of the conductor loss (α_c) and the dielectric loss (α_d) for the even-mode and odd-mode of an edge-coupled unilateral fin line with symmetrically located slots are shown in Fig. 4.39(a) and (b), respectively [14]. The dashed curve in this figure shows the variations of α_c and α_d for a unilateral fin line with slot width of $2w$. As expected, the conductor loss is higher than the dielectric loss. Both α_c and α_d are higher for the even-mode as compared with the odd-mode case. Further, for a fixed value of

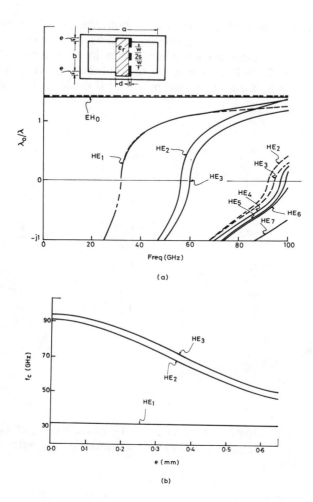

Fig. 4.38   (a) Dispersion characteristics for the dominant and higher
order modes in an edge-coupled unilateral fin line:

$a = 2b = 3.1$ mm $d = 220$ μm
$t = 5$ μm $s = 0.1$ mm
$w = 0.2$ mm $\epsilon_r = 3.75$
$————\, e = 0$ $———— \, e = 0.5$ mm

(b) Influence of waveguide groove depth on higher order
mode cut-off frequencies.

(From Bornemann [18], *IEE Proc.*, Pt. H, 1985, Vol. 132, pp. 1–6, reprinted with permission of IEE.)

s, as w increases, α_c and α_d decrease for both the even- and odd-modes of excitation. Conversely, as s increases, for a fixed value of w, α_c and α_d decrease for the even-mode case, whereas they increase for the odd-mode case. In the limit $2s \to 0$, α_c and α_d for the odd-mode excitation approach the values obtained for a unilateral fin line of slot width equal to $2w$.

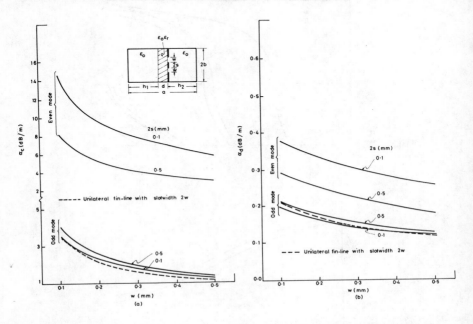

Fig. 4.39   (a) Conductor loss α_c and (b) dielectric loss α_d of even- and odd-modes of edge-coupled unilateral fin line with centered dielectric:

$d = 0.127$ mm $\epsilon_r = 2.22$
$\tan \delta_i = 2 \times 10^{-4}$ $\rho = 3 \times 10^{-8}$ Ω.m
frequency = 27 GHz   waveguide = WR(28)

(From Syahkal and Davies [14], Copyright © 1982 IEEE, reprinted with permission.)

REFERENCES

1. R.N. Simons, "Analysis of Millimeter-Wave Integrated Fin-Line," *IEE Proc.*, Vol. 130, Pt. H, No. 2, pp. 166–169, March 1983.
2. J.B. Knorr and P.M. Shayda, "Millimeter-Wave Fin-Line Characteristics," *IEEE Trans. Microwave Theory Tech.*, Vol. MTT-28, pp. 737–743, July 1980.

3. T. Kitazawa and R. Mittra, "An Investigation of Strip Lines and Fin-Lines with Periodic Stubs," *IEEE Trans. Microwave Theory Tech.*, Vol. MTT-32, pp. 684–688, July 1984.
4. R. Vahldieck, "Accurate Hybrid-Mode Analysis of Various Fin-Line Configurations including Multilayered Dielectrics, Finite Metallization Thickness and Substrate Holding Grooves," *IEEE Trans. Microwave Theory Tech.*, Vol. MTT-32, pp. 1454–1460, Nov. 1984.
5. R. Vahldieck and W.J.R. Hoefer, "The Influence of Metallization Thickness and Mounting Grooves on the Characteristics of Fin-Lines," *IEEE MTT-S Int. Microwave Symp. Digest*, 1985, pp. 143–144.
6. T. Kitazawa and R. Mittra, "Analysis of Fin-Line with Finite Metalization Thickness," *IEEE Trans. Microwave Theory Tech.*, Vol. MTT-32, pp. 1484–1487, Nov. 1984.
7. Y. Hayashi and R. Mittra, "An Analytical Investigation of Fin-Lines with Magnetized Ferrite Substrate," *IEEE Trans. Microwave Theory Tech.*, Vol. MTT-31, pp. 495–498, June 1983.
8. A. Beyer and K. Solbach, "A New Fin-Line Ferrite Isolator for Integrated Millimeter-Wave Circuits," *IEEE Trans. Microwave Theory Tech.*, Vol. MTT-29, pp. 1344–1348, Dec. 1981.
9. W. Zieniutycz, "Nonreciprocal Phase Shift in Fin-Line with Layered Substrate Containing Magnetised Ferrite," *Electron. Lett.*, Vol. 20, No. 4, pp. 183–185, Feb. 1984.
10. S. Tedjini and E. Pic, "Investigation of Nonreciprocal Fin-Line Devices," *IEE Proc.*, Vol. 131, Pt. H, No. 1, pp. 61–63, Feb. 1984.
11. A. Abdel Azeim, H. El Hennawy, and S. Mahrous, "Analysis of Fin-Lines on Semiconductor Substrate," *14th Eur. Microwave Conf. Digest*, 1984, pp. 346–351.
12. L.P. Schmidt, "A Comprehensive Analysis of Quasi-Planar Waveguides for Millimeter-Wave Application," *11th Eur. Microwave Conf. Digest*, 1981, pp. 315–320.
13. L.P. Schmidt and T. Itoh, "Characteristics of a Generalized Fin-Line for Millimeter-Wave Integrated Circuits," *Int. J. Infrared Millimeter Waves*, Vol. 2, No. 3, pp. 427–436, 1981.
14. D. Mirshekar-Syahkal and J.B. Davies, "An Accurate, Unified Solution to Various Fin-Line Structures, of Phase Constant, Characteristic Impedance and Attenuation," *IEEE Trans. Microwave Theory Tech.*, Vol. MTT-30, pp. 1854–1861, Nov. 1982.
15. F. Hernandez-Gil and J. Perez, "Analysis of the Coupling Coefficient between a Cylindrical Dielectric Resonator and a Fin-Line," *IEEE MTT-S Int. Microwave Symp. Digest*, 1986, pp. 221–224.
16. P.J. Meier, "Equivalent Relative Permittivity and Unloaded Q Fac-

tor of Integrated Fin-Line," *Electron. Lett.*, Vol. 9, No. 7, pp. 162–163, April 1973.

17. L.P. Schmidt, T. Itoh, and H. Hofmann, "Characteristics of Unilateral Fin-Line Structures with Arbitrarily Located Slots," *IEEE MTT-S Int Microwave Symp. Digest,* 1980, pp. 255–257.

18. J. Bornemann, "Rigorous Field Theory Analysis of Quasi-Planar Waveguides," *IEE Proc.*, Vol. 132, Pt. H, No. 1, pp. 1–6, Feb. 1985.

Chapter 5
Bilateral, Antipodal, and Double-Dielectric Fin-Line Characteristics

5.1 INTRODUCTION

In Ch. 4, we presented detailed dispersion characteristics of unilateral fin line, insulated fin line, and their variants. Two other basic fin-line structures commonly used in practical millimeter-wave integrated circuits are the *bilateral fin line* and the *antipodal fin line*. Both of these structures offer some specific advantages over the unilateral and insulated fin lines. For example, the bilateral fin line offers higher Q than the insulated fin line, thereby making it more suitable for filter applications [1]. As compared with the unilateral fin line, the bilateral fin line offers a larger single-mode bandwidth [2]. The antipodal fin-line structure (fins overlapping) is useful for realizing extremely low impedances [3].

One of the potentially useful structures among the variants of the basic fin lines is the double-dielectric bilateral fin line. This structure offers additional flexibility in circuit design because the propagation parameters can be controlled by varying the airgap. The double-dielectric bilateral fin line is a more general fin-line structure, and can be used to construct filters and other double planar circuits [4].

In this chapter, we present the normalized guide wavelength λ/λ_0 and the characteristic impedance Z of bilateral, antipodal, and double-dielectric fin lines and their variants. Cohn's approximate method is used to compute the dispersion results for extremely narrow slot widths. For broader slot widths, both the spectral domain method and modal analysis are used for numerical computations. Some representative graphs are presented, basically to explain the propagation characteristics as a function of various structural parameters. In addition, some special features of these fin lines are pointed out.

5.2 BILATERAL FIN LINES

A symmetric bilateral fin line can support two orthogonal modes—namely, the even-mode and the odd-mode. For all practical purposes, it is the even-mode that is important because this is the mode which becomes excited by the incident H_{10} mode of the hollow rectangular waveguide. In this section, we present dispersion characteristics of the dominant mode of a bilateral fin line as a function of various structural parameters. In addition, dispersion of higher order modes is studied to assess the single-mode operating bandwidth. Sensitivity analysis is carried out to study the tolerance requirements on the waveguide walls, and dielectric constant and thickness of the substrate. Attenuation characteristics are presented for comparison with other basic fin-line configurations. For application in nonreciprocal components, we have included the characteristics of bilateral fin lines with anisotropic (ferrite or semiconductor) substrates. We will study the effect of finite metalization thickness as well as that of the mounting grooves on the dispersion. Lastly, we shall present the dispersion characteristics of a bilateral fin line coupled through a strip conductor.

5.2.1 Centered Slots

Figures 5.1 to 5.4 show the characteristics of λ/λ_0 and Z for the dominant mode of a bilateral fin line with centered slots at Ka, U, E, and W bands, respectively. In all of these cases, we can see that λ/λ_0 decreases as the frequency increases. The general trend in the impedance curves is that the value of Z first decreases and then increases, while the variation over a given band remains quite small. For a fixed frequency, as w increases, both λ/λ_0 and Z increase. We may note that the bilateral fin-line impedance plots refer to one slot only. The total impedance would be half of the reported value for a single slot. A comparison of the dispersion characteristics of a bilateral fin line (Fig. 5.1) with those of a corresponding unilateral fin line (Fig. 4.1) shows that for fixed w and fixed frequency, both λ/λ_0 and Z (with impedance represented in the graph being halved) are lower in the case of a bilateral fin line.

5.2.2 Slots Displaced in E-plane

Figure 5.5 shows the effect of displacing the slots in the E-plane from their center position. The variations of λ/λ_0 and Z are plotted for s ranging

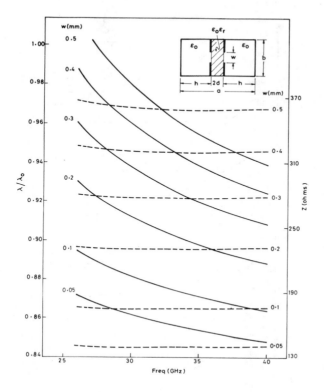

Fig. 5.1 Normalized guide wavelength λ/λ_0 and characteristic
impedance Z *versus* frequency of bilateral fin line:
waveguide = WR(28) $\epsilon_r = 2.22$
$d = 0.127$ mm $h = 3.429$ mm
———— λ/λ_0 ———— Z

from 0 to $(b - w)/2$ only, because the curves are symmetric about $s = (b - w)/2$. It is evident that as the two slots are displaced from their center position toward either the top or bottom wall, λ/λ_0 increases and Z decreases. As in the case of the unilateral fin line, the bilateral fin line also offers the possibility of realizing lower impedances by displacing the slots in the E-plane.

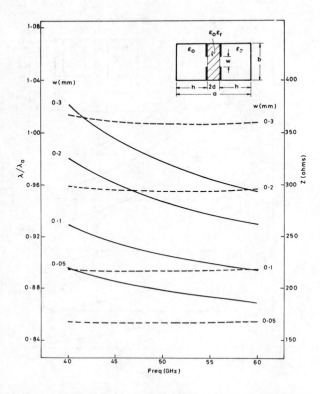

Fig. 5.2   Normalized guide wavelength λ/λ_0 and characteristic
impedance Z *versus* frequency of bilateral fin line:
waveguide = WR(19) $\epsilon_r = 2.22$
$d = 0.0635$ mm $h = 2.3241$ mm
————— λ/λ_0 ————— Z

5.2.3   Sensitivity Analysis

Typical results of the sensitivity analysis of a bilateral fin line are illustrated in Figs. 5.6 and 5.7. The variations of λ/λ_0 and Z, as a function of
percentage change in the waveguide dimensions, a and b, are shown in
Fig. 5.6, and the variations as a function of percentage change in ϵ_r and
d are shown in Fig. 5.7. For the structural parameters considered in these

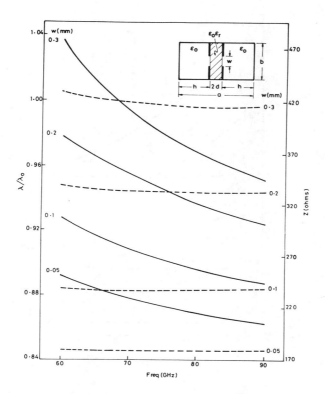

Fig. 5.3 Normalized guide wavelength λ/λ_0 and characteristic
impedance Z *versus* frequency of bilateral fin line:
    waveguide = WR(12) ϵ_r = 2.22
    d = 0.0635 mm h = 1.4859 mm
    —————— λ/λ_0 ————— Z

figures, we can observe that as the parameter a changes by $\pm 10\%$, λ/λ_0
changes by $\binom{-0.35}{+0.25}\%$ and Z changes by $\binom{-1.65}{+1.39}\%$. On the other hand, for a
$\pm 10\%$ change in b, λ/λ_0 changes by $\binom{-0.5}{+0.4}\%$, whereas Z changes by
$\binom{-0.35}{+0.43}\%$. For a $\pm 10\%$ change in the substrate thickness d, λ/λ_0 and Z

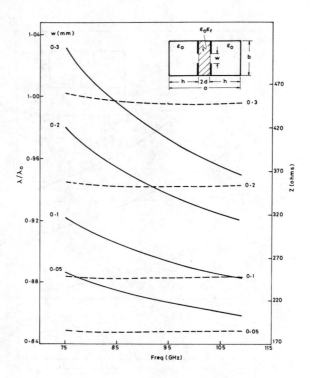

Fig. 5.4   Normalized guide wavelength λ/λ_0 and characteristic
impedance Z *versus* frequency of bilateral fin line:
  waveguide = WR(10) $\epsilon_r = 2.22$
  $d = 0.0635$ mm $h = 1.2065$ mm
  ——— λ/λ_0 ——— Z

change by $\binom{-0.8}{+0.7}\%$ and $\binom{-2.44}{+2.20}\%$, respectively. Furthermore, if the relative
dielectric constant ϵ_r changes by $\pm 10\%$, λ/λ_0 changes by $\binom{-2.66}{+2.50}\%$, whereas
Z changes by $\mp 1.6\%$. The sensitivity analysis reveals that the tolerance
requirements on the parameters a, d, and ϵ_r are more stringent than those
on parameter b.

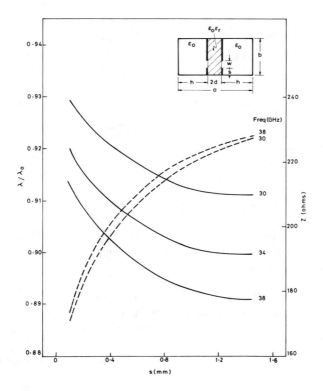

Fig. 5.5   Effect of displacing the slot on the normalized guide
wavelength λ/λ_0 and characteristic impedance Z:

$\epsilon_r = 2.22$ $d = 0.127$ mm
$h = 3.429$ mm $w = 0.2$ mm
———— λ/λ_0 ———— Z
waveguide = WR(28)

5.2.4   Modal Spectrum

The dispersion and the characteristic impedance of the dominant and
first higher order mode in a bilateral fin line are plotted in Fig. 5.8 [5].
The curves marked DM' in this figure are the dispersion characteristics

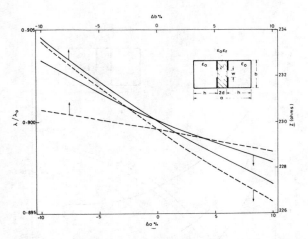

Fig. 5.6   Normalized guide wavelength λ/λ_0 and characteristic
impedance Z *versus* percentage change in waveguide
dimensions a and b:

$\epsilon_r = 2.22$	$d = 0.127$ mm
$h = 3.429$ mm	$w = 0.2$ mm
frequency $= 34$ GHz	waveguide $=$ WR(28)
——— λ/λ_0	——— Z

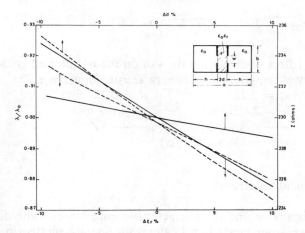

Fig. 5.7   Normalized guide wavelength λ/λ_0 and characteristic
impedance Z *versus* percentage change in substrate thickness
d and dielectric constant ϵ_r:

$\epsilon_r = 2.22$	$d = 0.127$ mm
$h = 3.429$ mm	$w = 0.2$ mm
frequency $= 34$ GHz	waveguide $=$ WR(28)
——— λ/λ_0	——— Z

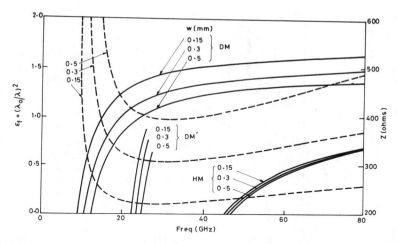

Fig. 5.8 Dispersion characteristics of the dominant and higher order modes in a bilateral fin line:

$\epsilon_r = 3.75$ $2d = 0.125$ mm
$h = 3.4935$ mm   waveguide = WR(28)
——— ϵ_f ——— Z
DM = dominant even-mode   DM' = dominant odd-mode
HM = first higher order even-mode

(From Schmidt and Itoh [5], Copyright © 1980 IEEE, reprinted with permission.)

for the structure with electric wall symmetry (odd-mode excitation). For a fixed value of w, we can observe that the effective dielectric constant (ϵ_f) increases as the frequency increases, whereas the impedance (Z) first decreases and then increases. It is interesting to note that the impedance characteristics show a broad minimum. For a fixed value of frequency, as w increases, ϵ_f decreases and Z increases. It may be mentioned here that the modal spectrum changes significantly with a change in the structural parameters. In the following, we present the effect of finite metalization thickness (t) and the groove depth (e) on the dominant mode propagation parameters as well as the operating bandwidth.

5.2.5 Effect of Finite Metalization Thickness [6, 7]

Figure 5.9 shows the effect of finite metalization thickness (t) on ϵ_f and Z for the dominant mode of a bilateral fin line with centered slot. The effect is similar to that observed in the case of a unilateral fin line (Fig.

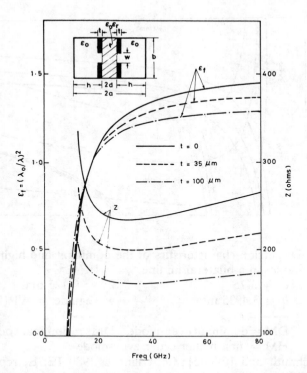

Fig. 5.9 Effect of finite metalization thickness on the propagation
characteristics of bilateral fin line:

$\epsilon_r = 3.0$ $w = 0.15$ mm
$b = 3.56$ mm $h = 3.4925$ mm
$d = 0.0625$ mm

(From Kitazawa and Mittra [6], Copyright © 1984 IEEE, reprinted with
permission.)

4.18) [6]. The variations of normalized cut-off wavelength (λ_c/a) *versus*
normalized slot width (w/b) of a bilateral fin line for two different values
of t/a and d/a are plotted in Fig. 5.10 [7]. We can see that the cut-off
wavelength decreases as w/b is increased. For large values of d/a (0.25),

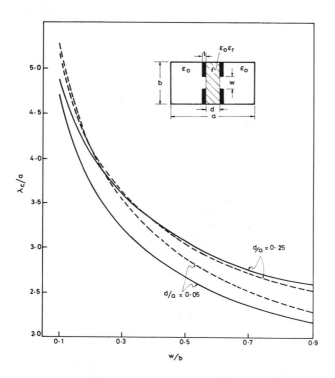

Fig. 5.10 Cut-off characteristics of the lowest order hybrid mode in a bilateral fin line:
$$b/a = 0.5$$
$$\epsilon_r = 2.32$$
——— $t/a = 0.05$
——— $t/a = 0.1$
(From Saha and Mazumder [7], reprinted with permission of IETE.)

as t/a is increased from 0.05 to 0.1, λ_c/a increases for $w/b \leqslant 0.4$ and decreases for $w/b \geqslant 0.4$. On the other hand, for small values of $d/a(0.05)$, as t/a is increased from 0.05 to 0.1, λ_c/a increases for all the values of w. For a fixed value of t/a, the variations of λ_c/a *versus* w/b having d/a as a parameter for a bilateral fin line with inverted dielectric are shown in Fig. 5.11 [7]. We may observe that as w/b or d/a increases, λ_c/a decreases.

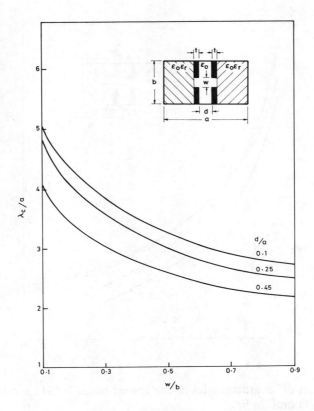

Fig. 5.11 Cut-off characteristics of the lowest order hybrid mode in a
bilateral fin line with inverted dielectric:

$b/a = 0.5$

$\epsilon_r = 2.32$

$t/a = 0.05$

(From Saha and Mazumder [7], reprinted with permission of IETE.)

5.2.6 Effect of Mounting Grooves [2, 8]

As pointed out in Sec. 4.2.8 in the case of a unilateral fin line, the
dominant mode is unaffected by small grooves in the housing, but as the
groove depth is increased, the dominant mode interacts increasingly with
the higher order modes, thus causing a significant change in the propagation
characteristics. In the case of a symmetrical bilateral fin line, it is known
that the dominant mode is insensitive to the groove depth [2]. The influence

of mounting grooves on the modal bandwidth of a bilateral fin line can be seen from Fig. 5.12 [2], wherein the ratio $\lambda_{c1}/\lambda_{c2}$ is plotted as a function of groove depth (e). For the sake of comparison, variations of $\lambda_{c1}/\lambda_{c2}$ for an insulated fin line and a unilateral fin line are superimposed on this graph. We can see that for a fixed slot width and for groove depths up to 0.5 mm, the bilateral fin line provides the highest single-mode (monomode) bandwidth. Moreover, this bandwidth is insensitive to groove depth. The insulated fin line provides a larger monomode bandwidth than the unilateral fin line for smaller groove depths, but it also shows a stronger dependence on the groove depth.

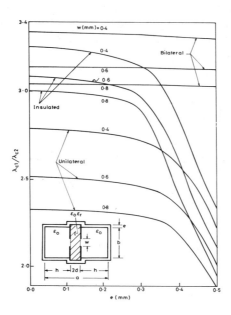

Fig. 5.12 Monomode bandwidth for a bilateral (inset in Fig. 5.12), unilateral (inset in Fig. 4.19) and insulated fin line (inset in Fig. 4.33) with several slot widths:

$a = 3.1$ mm $b = a/2$

$\epsilon_r = 3.0$ $t = 70$ μm

$d = 50$ μm (for unilateral and bilateral fin line)

$d = 25$ μm (for insulated fin line)

λ_{c1} = cut off wavelength of the dominant mode

λ_{c2} = cut off wavelength of the next higher order mode excited by H_{10}-incident wave

(From Vahldieck [2], Copyright © 1984 IEEE, reprinted with permission.)

5.2.7   Semiconductor Substrates [9–10]

A bilateral fin line using a semiconductor layer as an anisotropic media exhibits nonreciprocal attenuation characteristics. Fin-line isolators are therefore possible using a bilateral fin line with a semiconducting layer (see inset to Fig. 5.13). The commonly used semiconducting layers are GaAs and InSb. Of the two, InSb is reported to be more suitable than GaAs, especially at room temperatures [10].

The forward (α^+) and backward (α^-) attenuation constants of a bilateral fin line with a semiconductor layer are plotted as a function of d_1/b in Fig. 5.13 [9]. As d_1/b increases both α^+ and α^- increase. For $d_1/b = 0.6$, the values of α^+ and α^- are 35 Np/m and 195 Np/m, respectively [9]. In order to achieve lower losses and higher isolation, the optimization of semiconductor layer height, slot width, and other structural parameters is essential.

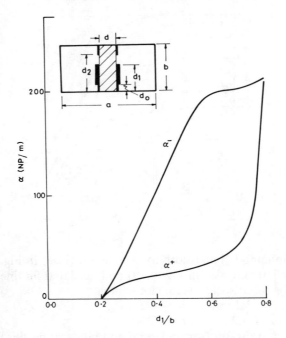

Fig. 5.13   Forward (α^+) and backward (α^-) attenuation *versus* the semiconductor position:

$B_0 = 0.8T$ $\qquad\qquad$ $d_0 = 0.2b$

$d_2 = 0.8b$ $\qquad\qquad$ $d = 0.125$ mm

frequency = 36 GHz $\quad$ waveguide = WR(28)

InSb semiconducting layer (2×1 μm, $\epsilon_r = 5.5$)

(From Tedjini and Pic [9], *IEE Proc.*, Pt. H, 1984, Vol. 131, pp. 61–63, reprinted with permission of IEE.)

5.2.8   Coupling through a Strip Conductor [11]

Integrated directional couplers in bilateral fin line sometimes require coupling through a strip conductor. The cross-sectional view of such a bilateral fin line coupled through a strip conductor and its dispersion characteristics are shown in Fig. 5.14 [11]. The solid curves in this figure are for magnetic wall symmetry at $a/2$, and the dotted curves are for electric wall symmetry at $a/2$. We may observe that the ratio λ_0/λ increases as the frequency is increased. For the EH_0 mode, λ_0/λ is virtually insensitive to frequency variation. This structure can be conveniently used for designing directional couplers below HE_1 cut-off [11].

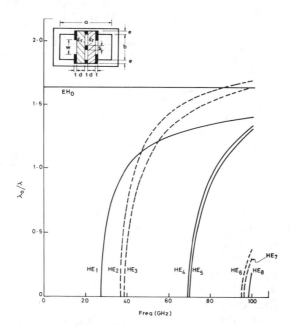

Fig. 5.14   Dispersion characteristics of the first nine propagating hybrid eigenmodes on a bilateral fin line coupled through a strip conductor:

$\epsilon_r = 3.75$ $d = 220 \ \mu m$
$t = 5 \ \mu m$ $s = 0.2 \ mm$
$w = 0.6 \ mm$ $e = 0.5 \ mm$
$a = 2b = 3.1 \ mm$
——— magnetic wall at $a/2$
– – – electric wall at $a/2$

(From Bornemann [11], *IEE Proc.*, Pt. H, 1985, Vol. 132, pp. 1–6, reprinted with permission of IEE.)

5.2.9   Conductor and Dielectric Losses [12]

Figure 5.15 shows the variations of the conductor loss (α_c) and dielectric loss (α_d) of a bilateral fin line as a function of normalized slot width (w/b). The variations are similar to those obtained in the case of a unilateral fin line (Fig. 4.25). A comparison with Fig. 4.25 shows that the bilateral fin line exhibits slightly lower dielectric loss, whereas the conductor loss is nearly the same in both cases.

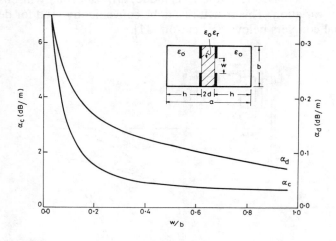

Fig. 5.15 Conductor loss (α_c) and dielectric loss (α_d) of a bilateral fin line with centered dielectric:

$\epsilon_r = 2.22$
$\tan \delta_i = 2 \times 10^{-4}$
$\rho = 3 \times 10^{-8}$ Ω.m
$d = 0.127$ mm
frequency = 40 GHz

(From Syahkal and Davies [12], Copyright © 1982 IEEE, reprinted with permission.)

5.3   ASYMMETRIC BILATERAL FIN LINES

As pointed out in Sec. 4.3, one easy way to realize lower impedances is to use asymmetric version of the basic fin-line configuration. Figure 5.16 shows the variations of normalized cut-off wavelength (λ_c/a) as a function of normalized slot width (w/b) for an asymmetric bilateral fin line [7]. We may observe that cut-off wavelength decreases as w/b is increased. For larger values of d/a (0.25), as t/a is varied from 0.05 to 0.1, λ_c/a increases for $w/b \lesssim 0.2$ and decreases for $w/b \gtrsim 0.2$. For small values of d/a (0.05), λ_c/a increases for all the values of w as t/a is increased. As compared with the bilateral fin line (Fig. 5.10), the asymmetric bilateral fin line exhibits a higher cut-off wavelength. Figure 5.17 shows the variations of λ_c/a *versus* w/b having d/a as a parameter for an asymmetric bilateral fin line with inverted dielectric [7]. The variations are similar to those reported in Fig. 5.11.

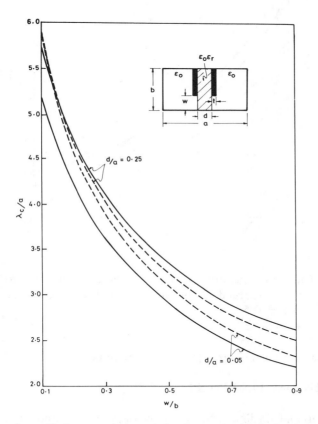

Fig. 5.16 Cut-off characteristics of the lowest order hybrid mode in an asymmetric bilateral fin line:

    $b/a = 0.5$
    $\epsilon_r = 2.32$
    ——— $t/a = 0.05$
    — — — $t/a = 0.1$

(From Saha and Mazumder [7], reprinted with permission of IETE.)

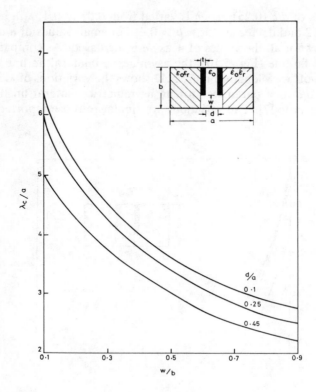

Fig. 5.17 Cut-off characteristics of the lowest order hybrid mode in an
asymmetric bilateral fin line with inverted dielectric:
$b/a = 0.5$
$\epsilon_r = 2.32$
$t/a = 0.05$
(From Saha and Mazumder [7], reprinted with permission of IETE.)

5.4 ANTIPODAL FIN LINES [3, 12, 13]

The antipodal fin line with either overlapping or nonoverlapping fins
finds application in practical integrated circuits [13]. Figure 5.18 shows the
basis structure as well as the variation of normalized guide wavelength
(λ/λ_0) as a function of slot width (w) for two different frequencies. The
dashed curve in this figure shows the variation of λ/λ_0 for a unilateral fin
line. We may observe that as w increases, λ/λ_0 increases for the structure
with nonoverlapping fins $(w > 0)$, whereas it decreases in the case of
overlapping fins $(w < 0)$. For a fixed value of $|w|$, as the frequency is

increased from 27 to 40 GHz, λ/λ_0 decreases for both cases, but the change observed in the case of overlapping fins is small. For a fixed frequency, the variations in Z as a function of slot width w are similar to those obtained for λ/λ_0. However, for a fixed value of w, as the frequency is increased, Z decreases in the case of nonoverlapping fins, whereas it increases in the case of overlapping fins. The change in Z in the latter case is negligible as the frequency is increased. For $w > 0$, the behavior of the antipodal fin line is similar to that of a unilateral fin line. Conversely, for $w < 0$, it behaves like a parallel-plate waveguide supporting the TEM mode [12]. The impedance variations of the antipodal fin line discussed above are not plotted here. These are available in the literature [12]. It is interesting to note that a wide range of characteristic impedances (10–500 ohms) can be achieved by using this structure.

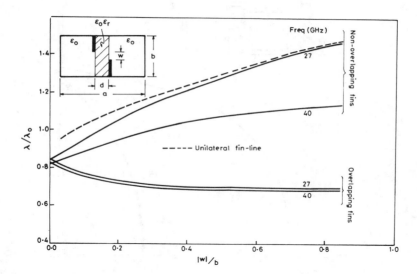

Fig. 5.18   Normalized guide wavelength λ/λ_0 of the dominant mode of an antipodal fin line as a function of slot width for two different frequencies:
$d = 0.127$ mm
$\epsilon_r = 2.22$
$\tan \delta_i = 2 \times 10^{-4}$
$\rho = 3 \times 10^{-8}$ Ω.m

(From Syahkal and Davies [12], Copyright © IEEE, reprinted with permission.)

The dispersion characteristics of the dominant and higher order modes in an antipodal fin line are plotted in Fig. 5.19. As the frequency increases, λ_0/λ increases for all the modes. Due to the asymmetrical nature of the antipodal fin line, all higher order modes can become excited. This is unlike the symmetrical unilateral and bilateral fin lines, where only a limited number of higher order modes become excited [2]. As discussed earlier with reference to the unilateral and bilateral fin lines, the groove depth as well as the finite metalization thickness significantly influence the propagation characteristics of both the dominant and higher order modes. Hence, their effect must be taken into account for accurate circuit design.

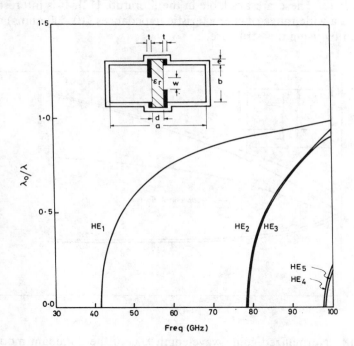

Fig. 5.19 Dispersion characteristics of the first five eigenmodes in an antipodal fin line:

$a = 3.1$ mm $b = a/2$
$d = 50$ μm $\epsilon_r = 3.0$
$t = 10.0$ μm $w = 0.8$ mm
$e = 0.5$ mm

(From Vahldieck [2], Copyright © 1984 IEEE reprinted with permission.)

The variations of normalized cut-off wavelength (λ_c/a) of the dominant mode *versus* normalized slot width (w/b) for an antipodal fin line (fins overlapping) are plotted in Fig. 5.20 [7] for two different values of t/a and d/a. We can see that as w/b increases, λ_c/a decreases. For small values of d/a (0.05), as t/a is increased from 0.05 to 0.1, λ_c/a decreases for $w/b \leqslant$ 0.6 and increases for $w/b \geqslant 0.6$. For a larger value of d/a (0.25), the trend is reversed. For $w/b \leqslant 0.6$, the curves for $d/a = 0.25$ lie below the curves for $d/a = 0.05$; and for $w/b \geqslant 0.6$, the trend is reversed. As compared with the bilateral fin line (Fig. 5.10), values of λ_c/a obtained in the present structure are much higher.

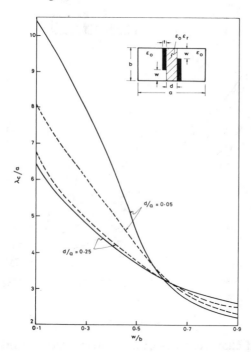

Fig. 5.20   Cut-off characteristics of the lowest order hybrid mode in an antipodal fin line:

$\quad\quad b/a = 0.5$

$\quad\quad \epsilon_r = 2.32$

$\quad\quad$————— $t/a = 0.05$

$\quad\quad$– – – – – $t/a = 0.1$

(From Saha and Mazumder [7], reprinted with permission of IETE.)

The variations of λ_c/a for an antipodal fin line with inverted dielectric (fins overlapping) *versus* w/b having d/a as a parameter are shown in Fig. 5.21 [7]. The variations are similar to those obtained in the case of a bilateral fin line (Fig. 5.11), except that the values of λ_c/a in the present structure are higher.

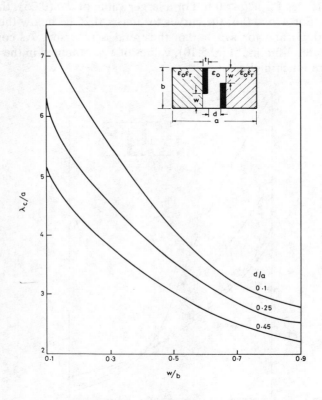

Fig. 5.21 Cut-off characteristics of the lowest order hybrid mode in an antipodal fin line with inverted dielectric:
$b/a = 0.5$
$\epsilon_r = 2.32$
$t/a = 0.05$
(From Saha and Mazumder [7], reprinted with permission of IETE.)

5.5 DOUBLE-DIELECTRIC BILATERAL FIN LINES

One of the potentially useful structures among the variants of the basic fin line is the double-dielectric bilateral fin line with an intervening air gap between the two symmetrically positioned substrates [4]. A distinct advantage of this structure is that the propagation characteristics can be varied by varying the air gap width, thereby providing more flexibility in practical circuit design. In the following, we present the dispersion characteristics of double-dielectric bilateral fin lines for two cases: (1) fins facing each other, and (2) fins facing side walls. The impedance results presented in the following sections are for half the structure. For the full structure, the impedance would be one-half of the reported value.

5.5.1 Fins Facing Each Other

The even-mode characteristic impedance Z and the normalized guide wavelength λ/λ_0 of the double-dielectric bilateral fin line (with fins facing each other) as a function of frequency are shown in Fig. 5.22. The nature of the curves is similar to that of a unilateral fin line (Fig. 4.6). However, the values of Z and λ/λ_0 for the double-dielectric bilateral fin line (with impedance represented in the graph being halved) are found to be lower than those for a unilateral fin line having the same parameters ($2a$, b, ϵ_r, d, w/b), but with centered fins.

The odd-mode characteristic impedance Z and the normalized guide wavelength λ/λ_0 of the aforementioned structure, for fixed air gap $2h_2 = 2$ mm, as a function of frequency are plotted in Fig. 5.23. A distinct feature to be observed is the cut-off nature of the odd-mode. For a fixed air gap, the cut-off frequency increases with an increase in the slot width. Furthermore, if the air gap is reduced in this structure, then the range of w/b over which the odd-mode propagation can be supported is reduced.

The effect of varying the air gap on Z and λ/λ_0 is depicted in Fig. 5.24 for the even-mode, and in Fig. 5.25 for the odd-mode. In the case of even-mode propagation, λ/λ_0 starts from a small value for a small air gap and increases with an increase in h_2. Conversely, Z starts from a large value and decreases as h_2 is increased. As expected, both curves tend to flatten over a small range of h_2 around 1.778 mm (about the plane, midway between the end wall and the guide center). There is a sharp increase in

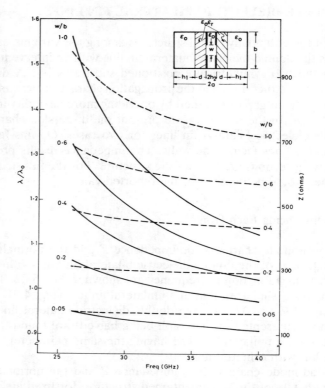

Fig. 5.22 Normalized guide wavelength λ/λ_0 and characteristic
impedance Z *versus* frequency of double-dielectric bilateral
fin line (fins facing each other) for even-mode:

$\epsilon_r = 2.22$	$d = 0.127$ mm
$h_2 = 1$ mm	$h_1 = a - d - h_2$
—— λ/λ_0	- - - Z

waveguide = WR(28)

λ/λ_0 and a sharp decrease in Z as the substrates are moved closer to the
two end walls (h_2 greater than about 3 mm).

In the case of odd-mode propagation, both Z and λ/λ_0 assume large
values for small values of the air gap, and decrease as h_2 is increased. As
in the case of even-mode propagation, the two curves tend to flatten for

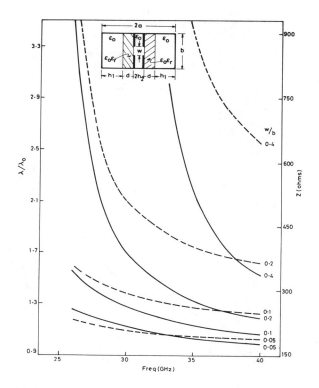

Fig. 5.23 Normalized guide wavelength λ/λ_0 and characteristic impedance Z *versus* frequency of double-dielectric bilateral fin line (fins facing each other) for odd-mode:

$\epsilon_r = 2.22$	$d = 0.127$ mm
$h_2 = 1$ mm	$h_1 = a - d - h_2$
—— λ/λ_0	———— Z
waveguide = WR(28)	

values of h_2 around 1.778 mm. Beyond $h_2 = 1.778$ mm, the impedance first increases and then decreases as the substrates approach the end walls. The curve for λ/λ_0 is nearly symmetrical about $h_2 = 1.778$ mm. Because the fins are backed by a dielectric substrate on only one side, a slight asymmetry, as can be observed in the curve, is to be expected.

258   DESIGN & ANALYSIS OF FIN LINES

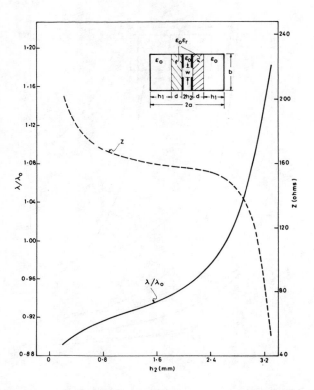

Fig. 5.24 Effect of varying the air gap on the even-mode normalized
guide wavelength λ/λ_0 and characteristic impedance Z:

$d = 0.127$ mm	$\epsilon_r = 2.22$
$w/b = 0.05$	$h_1 = a - d - h_2$
frequency $= 34$ GHz	waveguide $=$ WR(28)

5.5.2 Fins Facing the Side Walls

The characteristic impedance Z and the normalized guide wavelength
λ/λ_0, of the even- and odd-modes for a double-dielectric bilateral fin line
(with fins facing the side walls) as a function of frequency are depicted in
Figs. 5.26 and 5.27, respectively. The nature of the curves is similar to
that of a double-dielectric bilateral fin line with fins facing each other.

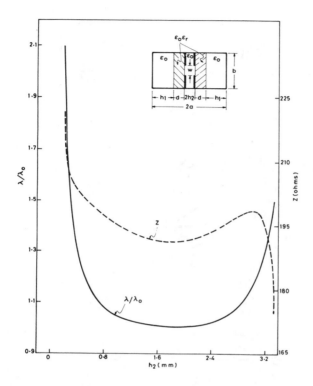

Fig. 5.25   Effect of varying the air gap on the odd-mode normalized guide wavelength λ/λ_0 and characteristic impedance Z:

$d = 0.127$ mm $\epsilon_r = 2.22$

$w/b = 0.05$ $h_1 = a - d - h_2$

frequency $= 34$ GHz   waveguide $=$ WR(28)

The effect of varying the air gap on Z and λ/λ_0 is shown in Fig. 5.28 for even-mode propagation. The characteristics are similar to those plotted in Fig. 5.24 for the structure with fins facing each other. The odd-mode characteristics as a function of air gap for the present structure are also similar to those in Fig. 5.25 for the structure with fins facing each other.

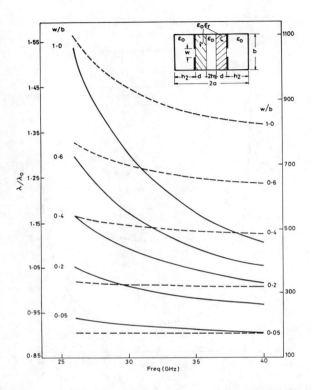

Fig. 5.26 Normalized guide wavelength λ/λ_0 and characteristic impedance Z *versus* frequency of double-dielectric bilateral fin line (fins facing side walls) for even-mode:

$\epsilon_r = 2.22$ $d = 0.127$ mm

$h_2 = 1$ mm $h_1 = a - d - h_2$

────── λ/λ_0 ────── Z

waveguide = WR(28)

5.6 EDGE-COUPLED BILATERAL FIN LINE

As discussed in Ch. 2, an edge-coupled bilateral fin line (see inset in Fig. 5.29) can support four propagating modes. These are the even-even, even-odd, odd-even, and odd-odd modes. The latter two are quasi-TEM modes, which are not normally excited in practice.

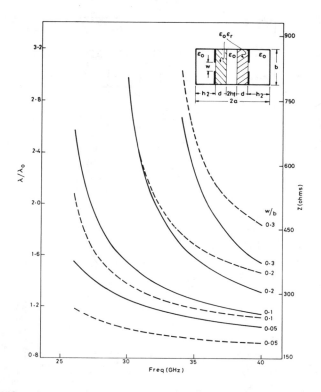

Fig. 5.27 Normalized guide wavelength λ/λ_0 and characteristic impedance Z *versus* frequency of double-dielectric bilateral fin line (fins facing side walls) for odd-mode:

$\epsilon_r = 2.22$	$d = 0.127$ mm
$h_2 = 1$ mm	$h_1 = a - d - h_2$
——— λ/λ_0	———— Z
waveguide = WR(28)	

The variations of λ/λ_0 and Z as a function of a/λ_0 are illustrated in Figs. 5.29 and 5.30, respectively [14]. For a fixed value of a/λ_0, as $w/2b$ is increased, λ/λ_0 and Z for both the even-even and even-odd modes increase. For a fixed value of $w/2b$, as a/λ_0 is increased, λ/λ_0 and Z for the even-even mode increase. However, λ/λ_0 for the even-odd mode decreases, whereas Z first decreases and then increases as a/λ_0 is increased.

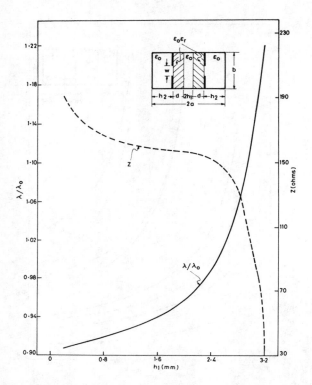

Fig. 5.28 Effect of varying the air gap on the even-mode normalized guide wavelength λ/λ_0 and characteristic impedance Z:

$d = 0.127$ mm	$\epsilon_r = 2.22$
$w/b = 0.05$	$h_1 = a - d - h_2$
———— λ/λ_0	———— Z
frequency = 34 GHz	waveguide = WR(28)

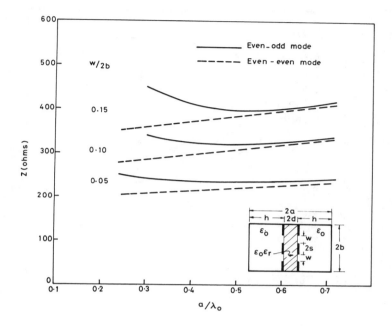

Fig. 5.29 Normalized guide wavelength λ/λ_0 *versus* normalized
frequency a/λ_0 of edge-coupled bilateral fin line:
$s/d = 0.1$
$d/a = 0.03515$
$\epsilon_r = 2.22$
waveguide $=$ WR(28)
(From Sharma and Hoefer [14], Copyright © 1983 IEEE, reprinted with
permission.)

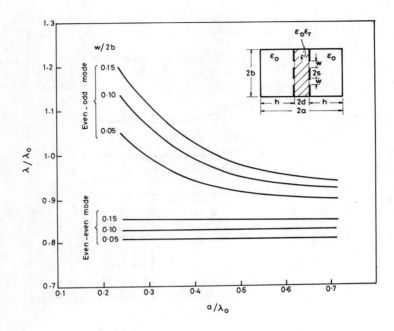

Fig. 5.30 Characteristic impedance Z *versus* normalized frequency a/λ_0
of edge-coupled bilateral fin line:
$s/d = 0.1$
$d/a = 0.03515$
$\epsilon_r = 2.22$
waveguide $=$ WR(28)
(From Sharma and Hoefer [14], Copyright © 1983 IEEE, reprinted with
permission.)

REFERENCES

1. P.J. Meier, "Equivalent Relative Permittivity and Unloaded Q Factor of Integrated Fin-Line," *Electron. Lett.*, Vol. 9, No. 7, pp. 162–163, April 1973.

2. R. Vahldieck, "Accurate Hybrid-Mode Analysis of Various Fin-Line Configurations including Multilayered Dielectrics, Finite Metallization Thickness and Substrate Holding Grooves," *IEEE Trans. Microwave Theory Tech.*, Vol. MTT-32, pp. 1454–1460, Nov. 1984.

3. H. Hofmann, "Calculation of Quasi-Planar Lines for mm-wave Application," *IEEE MTT-S Int. Microwave Symp. Digest*, 1977, pp. 381–384.

4. P. Nagpal, "Analysis of Double-Dielectric Fin-Line and Development of Fin-Line Filters and Couplers," Master's of Technology Thesis, Dept. of Electrical Engineering, Indian Institute of Technology, New Delhi, July 1983.

5. L.P. Schmidt and T. Itoh, "Spectral Domain Analysis of Dominant and Higher Order Modes in Fin-Lines," *IEEE Trans. Microwave Theory Tech.*, Vol. MTT-28, pp. 981–985, Sept. 1980.

6. T. Kitazawa and R. Mittra, "Analysis of Fin-Line with Finite Metallization Thickness," *IEEE Trans. Microwave Theory Tech.*, Vol. MTT-32, pp. 1484–1487, Nov. 1984.

7. P.K. Saha and G.G. Mazumder, "Cut-Off and Bandwidth Characteristics of Inhomogeneous Rectangular Waveguide with Two Double Ridges," *JIETE*, Sept. 1986.

8. R. Vahldieck and W.J.R. Hoefer, "The Influence of Metallization Thickness and Mounting Grooves on the Characteristics of Fin-Lines," *IEEE MTT-S Int. Microwave Symp. Digest*, 1985, pp. 143–144.

9. S. Tedjini and E. Pic, "Investigation of Nonreciprocal Fin-Line Devices," *IEE Proc.*, Vol. 131, Pt. H, No. 1, pp. 61–63, Feb. 1984.

10. S. Tedjini, E. Pic, and P. Saguet, "On the Research in Nonreciprocal Fin-Line Devices," *13th Eur. Microwave Conf. Digest*, 1983, pp. 814–820.

11. J. Bornemann, "Rigorous Field Theory Analysis of Quasi-Planar Waveguides," *IEE Proc.*, Vol. 132, Pt. H, No. 1, pp. 1–6, Feb. 1985.

12. D. Mirshekar-Syahkal and J.B. Davies, "An Accurate, Unified Solution to Various Fin-Line Structures, of Phase Constant, Characteristic Impedance and Attenuation," *IEEE Trans. Microwave Theory Tech.*, Vol. MTT-30, pp. 1854–1861, Nov. 1982.

13. H. Callsen, L.P. Schmidt, and K. Solbach, "Breitbandige Finlei-tungs-Richtkoppler," *Wiss. Ber. AEG Telefunken,* Vol. 54, pp. 241–250, 1981.
14. A.K. Sharma and W.J.R. Hoefer, "Propagation in Coupled Unilat-eral and Bilateral Fin-Lines," *IEEE Trans. Microwave Theory Tech.,* Vol. MTT-31, pp. 498–502, June 1983.

Chapter 6
Fin-Line Transitions

6.1 INTRODUCTION

Transition from fin line to commensurate rectangular waveguide is important because of the need for an interface of fin-line circuits with standard waveguide components, mostly for testing their performance. Transitions between different types of fin lines and from fin lines to other planar structures such as microstrip, suspended microstrip, and coplanar lines are also commonly encountered in several mixed integrated millimeter-wave circuit components. In all such components, the circuit pattern is generally printed on a common dielectric substrate and the entire substrate, including the transition, is mounted in the E-plane of a split-block metal waveguide housing. One such commonly used integrated circuit component is the balanced mixer, in which fin line is combined with coplanar line to realize a broadband 180° hybrid junction, and either a microstrip or a suspended stripline is used for filtering out the IF component.

In this chapter, after presenting some basic structural features of the fin line (Sec. 6.2), transitions from fin line to rectangular waveguide are described (Sec. 6.3). Although the discussion pertains to the unilateral fin line, the design formulas are also applicable to other fin-line configurations. Transitions between fin lines and different types of planar transmission lines are included in Sec. 6.4.

6.2 FIN-LINE CONSTRUCTION

Fin-line construction basically involves mounting a planar circuit in the E-plane of a rectangular waveguide housing. The planar circuit consists of a printed pattern defined on a thin dielectric substrate by using the conventional thin-film photolithographic technique. The most commonly used substrate is copper-clad RT-duroid™ 5880 ($\epsilon_r = 2.22$) with standard thicknesses of 0.254 mm (for Ka band) and 0.127 mm (for Ka band and above). Being a soft material, it can be securely clamped between the two halves of the metal housing. Semiconductor devices with soft gold beam leads can be soldered onto the circuit pattern. Alternatively, small chips of quartz with semiconductor devices mounted on them can be directly integrated into the circuit as an upside-down overlay. Among hard substrates, fused quartz ($\epsilon_r = 3.78$) with a thickness of 0.125 mm can be used. When such hard substrates are used, the tolerance requirements on the housing become rather stringent where the two halves mate with the substrate.

Two types of housing are adopted in practice; one that is suitable for all passive circuitry (Fig. 6.1(a)) and another that has provision for dc biasing of active semiconductor devices. (Note that Fig. 6.1(b) is due to Meier [1]). In Fig. 6.1(a), the substrate is cut to size to fit the narrow channel on one of the two housing blocks. When assembled, the second block clamps the substrate in place. The mating surfaces of the two blocks should be precision milled to ensure proper contact. The serrated pattern on the dielectric substrate serves to prevent any wave propagation outside the waveguide enclosure through the substrate. In the second structure (Fig. 6.1(b)), the substrate is aligned by means of dielectric dowels and the two halves of the housing are bolted together in the flange region. The main differences as compared with the structure shown in Fig. 6.1(a) are that the substrate protrudes out through the broad walls of the guide and the fins are easily accessible for dc biasing of any semiconductor device mounted in the circuit.

There is provision for inserting thin insulators to prevent contact between the printed pattern and the housing. The thickness of the broad walls of the guide is chosen equal to one quarter-wavelength in the dielectric to present an effective RF short at the inner walls of the guide in the dielectrically loaded region. This quarter-wave choke prevents any TEM-mode propagation out through the broad walls.

It may be pointed out that dc connection is also possible in the structure shown in Fig. 6.1(a), but at the expense of structural complication. A portion of the waveguide block near the clamping region will need to be removed to allow the circuit board to penetrate out.

Variations in the two basic structures given above are incorporated in practice whenever different types of fin lines and other planar circuits are to be integrated. For example, in the case of double-dielectric fin lines, additional spacers are inserted to position the two dielectric circuit boards symmetrically in the E-plane (see Fig. 2.5). In applications where the weight of the housing needs to be reduced, the housing may be molded from a platable plastic material, e.g., acrylonitrile butadiene styrene (ABS).

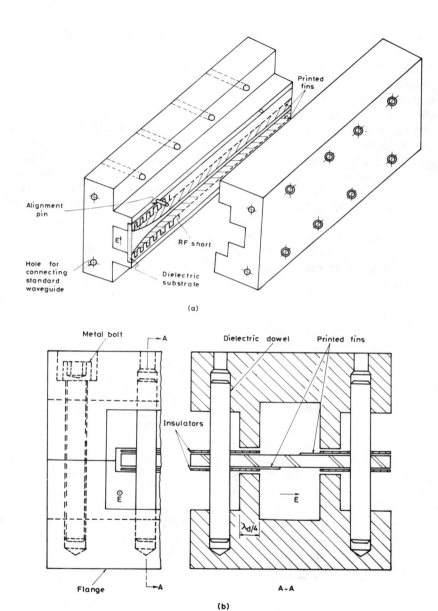

Fig. 6.1 Fin-line construction.

(Fig. 6.1(b) from Meier [1], Copyright © 1978 IEEE, reprinted with permission.)

6.3   TRANSITION BETWEEN FIN LINE AND WAVEGUIDE

Broadband transitions between rectangular waveguides and fin lines generally employ *tapered fin-line* sections in which the slot width of the fin line is gradually increased to the full waveguide height. The discontinuity effect, which is due to the finite thickness of the dielectric substrate at the tapered end facing the empty waveguide, is minimized by introducing one or two *quarter-wave transformer* sections. Such quarter-wave transformers take the form of stepped protrusions or notches cut in the substrate, or quarter-wave printed steps in continuation of the fin-line taper. Figure 6.2 shows the schematic of a typical transition consisting of a fin-line taper followed by a stepped protrusion. In the following, we present the design aspects of transitions in two parts: fin-line tapers (Sec. 6.3.1) and quarter-wave transformers (Sec. 6.3.2) in the form of stepped protrusions, notches, and also printed steps. Fin-line tapers, discussed below, can also be used in the design of several fin-line circuits, such as filters, matching networks, and circulators.

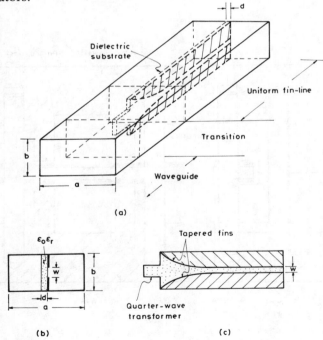

Fig. 6.2   (a) Schematic of waveguide to fin-line transition.
(b) Cross section of a uniform fin line.
(c) Transition details on the substrate.

6.3.1 Fin-Line Tapers

The design of a fin-line taper involves choosing a smooth impedance variation along the taper so that the reflection loss is below a tolerable limit over a prescribed bandwidth, while keeping the physical length of the taper as small as possible. Furthermore, when the impedance variation is translated into the slot width variation, it should result in a smooth taper contour, which can be easily implemented in practice. These are contradictory requirements and a compromise is usually necessary to enable ease of fabrication.

Analytical Methods for Fin-Line Taper Design

The analysis of tapers in TEM structures is well known [2–3]. The *impedance technique* of analysis results in the following expression for the input reflection coefficient of a gradual TEM taper (Fig. 6.3(a)):

$$\tau = -\int_0^l \rho(z) \exp(-2j\beta z) \; dz \tag{6.1a}$$

where

$$\rho(z) = -\frac{1}{2}\frac{d}{dz}[\ln Z(z)] \tag{6.1b}$$

$Z(z)$ is the impedance at any distance z along the tapered line and β is the propagation constant. In the case of fin lines (non-TEM line), β is also a function of the distance z. The expression for the overall reflection coefficient in a fin-line taper (Fig. 6.3(b)) can be written as

$$\tau = -\int_0^l \rho(z) \exp\left(-2j\int_0^z \beta(\zeta)d\zeta\right) \; dz \tag{6.2}$$

where $\rho(z)$ is given by (6.1b).

Another approach for deriving the reflection coefficient of a taper is to start from the expression for the input impedance of a transmission line section [4–5]. Let us refer to Fig. 6.3. If Z_{in} is the input impedance of the taper at a distance z and $Z_{in} + dZ_{in}$ is the input impedance at $(z + dz)$, then

$$Z_{in} + dZ_{in} = Z(z)\cdot\frac{Z_{in} + jZ(z)\tan\{d[\beta(z)z]\}}{Z(z) + jZ_{in}\tan\{d[\beta(z)z]\}} \tag{6.3}$$

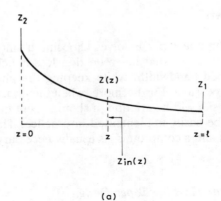

(a)

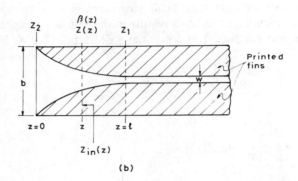

(b)

Fig. 6.3 (a) Schematic representation of a tapered transmission line.
(b) Schematic of a typical fin-line taper.

In writing (6.3), it is assumed that the characteristic impedance $Z(z)$ and the propagation constant $\beta(z)$ are constant over the incremental length dz. For small $d(\beta(z) \cdot z)$, $\tan\{d[\beta(z) \cdot z]\} \approx \beta(z)dz$. With this approximation, (6.3) reduces to the following Riccati equation:

$$\frac{dZ_{in}}{dz} = j\beta(z)Z(z) - j\frac{\beta(z)}{Z(z)}Z_{in}^2 \qquad (6.4)$$

The local reflection coefficient $\tau(z)$ at a given point z and the input impedance Z_{in} are related by

$$Z_{in} = \left[\frac{1 + \tau(z)}{1 - \tau(z)}\right]Z(z) \qquad (6.5)$$

From (6.4) and (6.5), we obtain

$$\frac{d\tau(z)}{dz} = \frac{1}{2Z(z)}\left\{[\tau^2(z) - 1]\frac{dZ(z)}{dz} - j\,4\tau(z)Z(z)\beta(z)\right\} \qquad (6.6)$$

Evaluation of the overall reflection coefficient of the taper by using either (6.2) or (6.6) requires knowledge of the impedance function $Z(z)$ as well as $\beta(z)$. Let us refer to Fig. 6.3, where the impedance functions for the exponential, parabolic, cosine, and cosine-squared tapers can be written in the following form:

Exponential taper:

$$Z(z) = Z_2 \exp\left[\frac{z}{l}\ln\left(\frac{Z_1}{Z_2}\right)\right] \qquad (6.7)$$

Parabolic taper:

$$Z(z) = \left[\pm\sqrt{Z_2} + \frac{z}{l}\,(\pm\sqrt{Z_1} \mp \sqrt{Z_2})\right]^2 \qquad (6.8)$$

Cosine taper:

$$Z(z) = Z_2 \cos\left[\frac{z}{l}\cos^{-1}\left(\frac{Z_1}{Z_2}\right)\right] \qquad (6.9)$$

Cosine-squared taper:

$$Z(z) = Z_2 \cos^2\left[\frac{z}{l}\cos^{-1}\left(\frac{Z_1}{Z_2}\right)^{1/2}\right] \qquad (6.10)$$

The value of β for various slot widths along the taper can be obtained from the fin-line dispersion relations. Closed-form expressions for the evaluation of β in unilateral and bilateral fin lines are available in Schieblich *et al.* [6] (also see Ch. 2). Figure 6.4 shows typical frequency responses of exponential, parabolic, and cosine-squared tapers in a unilateral fin line [5].

Another formula that is also in the form of Riccati's differential equation governing $\tau(z)$, $Z(z)$, and $\beta(z)$ has been reported by Beyer and Wolff [7]. This formula has been derived by using the generalized telegraphy equation for waveguides of varying cross section. In all the methods considered above, optimization of the taper involves choosing a proper contour function, which offers the minimum reflection coefficient for a given taper length or *vice versa*. A knowledge of the fin-line impedance characteristics is necessary in all of the formulas.

Taper designs that are based on knowledge of the propagation constant and cut-off frequency of the fin lines, rather than on the wave impedances, have been reported by several investigators [6, 8, 9]. In particular, Schieblich *et al.* [6] have presented a procedure for synthesizing the slot width profile by choosing suitable coupling distribution functions (for optimal tapers). This method is reported to be applicable to unilateral as well as bilateral fin lines having either centered or off-centered slots. A general technique based on the coupled modes together with the spectral domain technique has been reported by Mirshekar-Syahkal and Davies [10]. The method requires the evaluation of coupling coefficient from the field components and does not make use of the impedances. This method is applicable to a broad class of planar transmission line tapers as well as fin-line tapers.

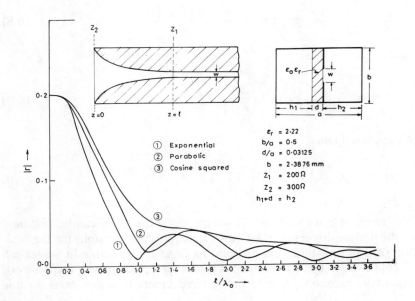

Fig. 6.4 Typical frequency response of tapered fin lines.
(From Pramanick and Bhartia [5], Copyright © 1984 IEEE, reprinted with permission.)

While accurate analytical methods and synthesis techniques such as those cited above are available, they require considerable computation to obtain the taper dimensions. Optimized taper designs generally yield arbitrary contour functions, which are difficult to produce accurately in practice using conventional mask cutters. Furthermore, it has been found experimentally that fin-line tapers are not very critical in their dimensions. Therefore, it is more practical to adopt empirical designs to facilitate easy fabrication. Thus, in the following, we will present some useful empirical designs.

Circular Arc Tapers [11]

From the viewpoint of quick design and easy adaptation to conventional mask cutters, Beyer and Wolff [11] have provided empirical design formulas for circular arc tapers.

Typical geometrical features of a circular arc taper are presented in Fig. 6.5. For a fin line constructed in a waveguide of dimensions a and b, employing a dielectric substrate of thickness d and relative dielectric constant ϵ_r, the procedure for drawing the circular arc taper is as follows:

- Specify the slot width w_1 of the uniform fin line to be matched to the waveguide height $b = w_2$ (or any intermediate slot width w_2).
- From the impedance characteristics of the fin line (Ch. 4 and 5), determine the impedance Z_1 corresponding to the slot width w_1 (at $z = l$) and the impedance Z_2 corresponding to the slot width w_2 (at $z = 0$), where l is the length of the taper. Let P_1 and P_2 represent the two points at $z = l$ and $z = 0$, respectively, between which the taper is to be drawn.
- Take the average value $Z_m = (Z_1 + Z_2)/2$ as the impedance at half of the taper length ($z = l/2$). Corresponding to Z_m, find the slot width $w_m = (w_1 + \Delta w_1)$ and locate the point P_m at a vertical height $w_m/2$ at $z = l/2$.
- For most practical structures, the condition $\Delta w_1 < \delta$ applies. Determine the radius r_f by using

$$r_f = \frac{l^2 + (\Delta w_1)^2}{4\Delta w_1} \tag{6.11}$$

The center P_0 of the arc lies on the vertical line at $z = l$ at a height $r_f + (w_1/2)$. With P_0 as the center and r_f as the radius, draw a circular arc passing through P_1 and P_m.

●   Calculate the radius r_h of the second circular arc from

$$r_h = \left[\frac{l^2 + \left(\dfrac{b - w_1}{2} \right)^2}{(b - w_1)} - r_f \right] \tag{6.12}$$

Locate the center P_0' of the second arc at a vertical distance r_h below the point P_2. With P_0' as the center and $r_h = P_0'P_2$ as the radius, draw a circular arc starting from P_2 to join the first arc at some point P_3. The curve $P_2P_3P_1$ then forms the taper contour.

It may be noted that for slot widths satisfying the condition $w_1 + (\delta/2) < w_m < w_1 + \delta$, the radius r_h is nearly equal to zero.

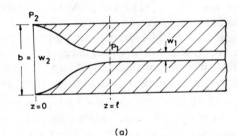

(a)

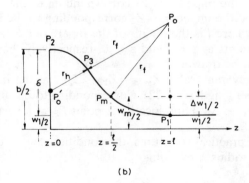

(b)

Fig. 6.5   (a) Circular arc taper.

           (b) Geometrical parameters for drawing circular arcs.
(After Beyer and Wolff [11])

Typical Taper Contours

In order to compare some of the typical taper contours employed in practice, consider the example of a unilateral fin line at Ka band using a 0.254 mm thick RT-duroid® substrate. The impedance as a function of the normalized slot width of the fin line calculated from the spectral domain formulas is plotted in Fig. 6.6. Figure 6.7(a) shows four different impedance profiles specified by (6.7) to (6.10) for the exponential, parabolic, cosine, and cosine-squared tapers, respectively. In all cases, the impedances Z_1 and Z_2 at the two ends of the taper are chosen equal to 200 Ω (for slot width $w_1 = 0.4$ mm) and 350 Ω (for slot width $w_2 \approx 1.35$ mm), respectively. By using Fig. 6.6, we obtain the slot width profiles corresponding to the above four impedance profiles. These are shown in Fig. 6.7(b).

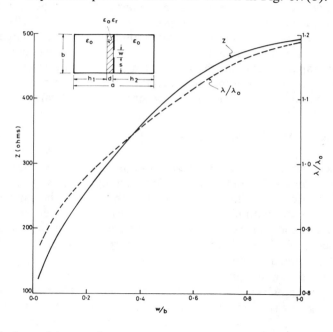

Fig. 6.6 Impedance and normalized guide wavelength as a function of w/b for a unilateral fin line:

$a = 7.112$ mm $b = 3.556$ mm
$d = 0.254$ mm $\epsilon_r = 2.22$
$h_1 = 3.302$ mm $h_2 = 3.556$ mm
$s = (b - w)/2$ frequency = 34 GHz

An empirical slot width profile that is reported to work reasonably well is [10]:

$$w(z) = b - (b - w_1) \sin^2\left(\frac{\pi z}{2l}\right), \quad 0 \leqslant z \leqslant l \tag{6.13}$$

The taper contour corresponding to (6.13) for matching the two slot widths $w_1 = 0.4$ mm and $w_2 = b = 3.556$ mm is plotted in Fig. 6.8. The x- and y-axes are drawn to the same scale in order to illustrate the actual profile. The length of the taper is chosen equal to 5 mm, which corresponds to about $0.57\lambda_0$ at the design frequency of 34 GHz.

For the same set of parameters $w_1 = 0.4$ mm, $w_2 = 3.556$ mm, and $l = 5$ mm, the circular arc taper computed by using (6.11), (6.12), and Fig. 6.6 is also drawn in Fig. 6.8. For comparison, the exponential taper and the cosine-squared taper corresponding to (6.7) and (6.10), respectively, are superposed. The curve corresponding to (6.13) matches reasonably well with the circular arc taper as well as the cosine-squared taper. For longer taper lengths on the order of a wavelength, as are normally used in practice, the difference between the various taper profiles reduces considerably, and a return loss on the order of 20–25 dB can be achieved.

6.3.2 Quarter-Wave Transformers

Even with an optimal taper profile, the fin-line taper section by itself cannot offer an ideal match to the hollow rectangular waveguide because of the dielectric discontinuity at the end of the taper. The magnitude of the impedance discontinuity that it presents to the commensurate hollow waveguide depends on the substrate thickness d and its dielectric constant ϵ_r. In practical fin lines, this impedance step is small because of the light dielectric loading. In order to minimize this discontinuity effect, practical designers have adopted quarter-wave transformers in the form of a stepped protrusion or a notch cut in the substrate itself [1, 12]. Theoretical formulas for the design of such transformers (Figs. 6.9 and 6.10) and for *printed step transformers* (Fig. 6.11) have been derived by Hoefer and Verver [13–14]. The formulas are based on the perturbation theory and homogeneous waveguide models.

Single-section quarter-wave transformers are reported to offer in practice an improvement in the return loss on the order of 5 dB over the entire waveguide band [13]. Two-section transformers can offer even wider bandwidth. Printed step transformers have the advantage that they can be realized as integral parts of the fin-line pattern by using the photolithographic process. They also eliminate the need to cut the substrate, and

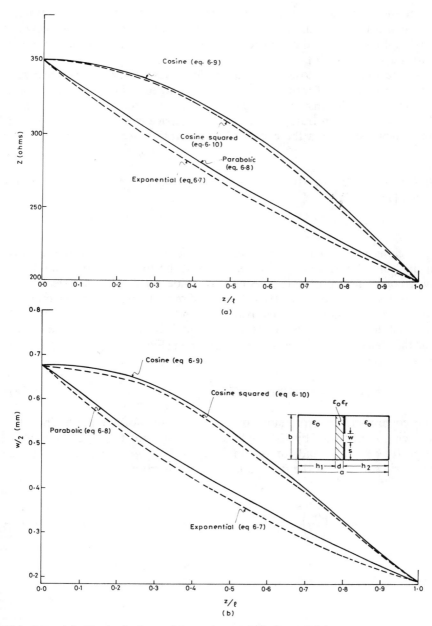

Fig. 6.7 (a) Typical plots of impedance functions $Z(z)$.
(b) Corresponding slot width profiles $w(z)$.

hence these transformers are adaptable to fin lines that use hard substrates. The bandwidth of printed step transformers is reported to be somewhat smaller than that of the transformers using notches and protrusions cut into the substrate [14].

In the following, closed-form design formulas [13–14] are summarized for all three types of transformers. In all the formulas below, a and b are the waveguide dimensions, ϵ_r and d are the relative dielectric constant and thickness of the substrate, and λ_0 is the free-space wavelength. The design frequency is chosen at the center of the operating band.

Single-Section Quarter-Wave Transformer Using a Stepped Protrusion or Notch [13]

Regions 1, 2, and 3 as marked in Fig. 6.9(a, b) refer to the three regions in the guide housing the substrate. Each of the three regions is modeled by a commensurate homogeneous waveguide filled with a dielectric of equivalent permittivity k_{ei} (i = 1–3) as shown in Fig. 6.9(c). It may be noted that for region 3, the equivalent permittivity k_{e3} corresponds to that of a slab-loaded guide with slab height equal to the waveguide height b. For the transformer with a stepped protrusion (Fig. 6.9(a)), the expression for k_{ei} is given by

$$k_{ei} = [1 - (\epsilon_r - 1) \, h_i d/(ab)]^{-2} \tag{6.14}$$

The corresponding expression for the notch transformer is obtained by replacing h_i in (6.14) by $(b - g_i)$. In both cases, for region 2, $h_2 = b - g_2 = 0$ ($k_{e2} = 1$), and for region 3, $h_3 = b - g_3 = b$. The effective dielectric constant of the ith region is obtained from

$$\epsilon_{\text{eff}_i} = k_{ei} - \left(\frac{\lambda_0}{2a}\right)^2 \tag{6.15}$$

The wave impedance Z_{0i} of the ith region is inversely proportional to the square root of its effective dielectric constant. Thus, for the quarter-wave transformer, $Z_{01} = (Z_{02}Z_{03})^{1/2}$ or $\epsilon_{eff1} = (\epsilon_{eff2} \epsilon_{eff3})^{1/2}$. This relation, along with (6.14) and (6.15), leads to the following formulas for the calculation of dimensions of the quarter-wave transformer:

$$l_1 = \frac{\lambda_0}{4} (k_{e1} - p^2)^{-1/2} \tag{6.16}$$

$$h_1 = (b - g_1) = \frac{(\sqrt{k_{e1}} - 1) \, ab}{\sqrt{k_{e1}} \, (\epsilon_r - 1)d} \tag{6.17}$$

where

$$p = \frac{\lambda_0}{2a} \tag{6.18a}$$

$$k_{e1} = \{p^2 + [(1 - p^2)(k_{e3} - p^2)]^{1/2}\} \tag{6.18b}$$

$$k_{e3} = \left[1 - (\epsilon_r - 1)\frac{d}{a}\right]^{-2} \tag{6.18c}$$

Two-Section Quarter-Wave Transformer Using Stepped Protrusions or Notches [14]

The equivalent permittivity and the effective dielectric constant for the four regions ($i = 1-4$) marked in Fig. 6.10 can be obtained from (6.14) and (6.15), respectively, by substituting appropriate values for h_i and g_i. Formulas for calculating the impedances of quarter-wave sections in multisection transformers of the binomial type as well as the Chebyshev type are available in Collin [2]. It is well known that for a given number of sections and for a specified reflection coefficient, the Chebyshev transformer offers the maximum bandwidth. However, as reported by Hoefer and Verver [14], for a two-section transformer, both types yield nearly the same performance over the full waveguide band. Let us refer to Fig. 6.10, where the impedances of the four regions according to binomial transformer design are related by the following:

$$Z_{01} = Z_{03}^{1/4} Z_{04}^{3/4} \tag{6.19a}$$

$$Z_{02} = Z_{03}^{3/4} Z_{04}^{1/4} \tag{6.19b}$$

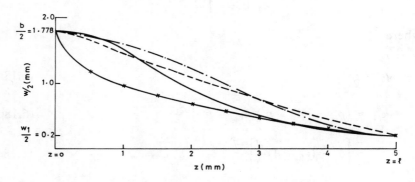

Fig. 6.8 Comparison between some practical taper contours:
$a = 7.112$ mm $\qquad\qquad$ $b = 3.556$ mm
$d = 0.254$ mm $\qquad\qquad$ $\epsilon_r = 2.22$
$h_1 = 3.302$ mm $\qquad\qquad$ $h_2 = 3.556$ mm
$l = 5$ mm ($0.57\ \lambda_0$ at 34 GHz) frequency = 34 GHz

In (6.19), Z_{03} is the impedance of the hollow rectangular waveguide and Z_{04} is the impedance of the fin line with $w = b$. The effective dielectric constants of the four regions satisfy the same relations as given in (6.19). These relations coupled with (6.14) and (6.15) yield the following formulas for determining the dimensions of the two-section quarter-wave transformer:

$$l_1 = \frac{\lambda_0}{4} (k_{e1} - p^2)^{-1/2} \tag{6.20}$$

$$l_2 = \frac{\lambda_0}{4} (k_{e2} - p^2)^{-1/2} \tag{6.21}$$

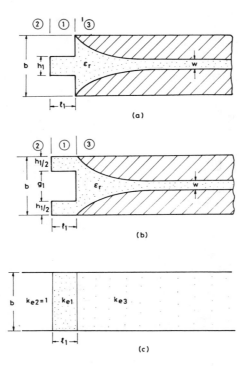

Fig. 6.9 (a) Single-section quarter-wave transformer using protrusions.
(b) Single-section quarter-wave transformer using notches.
(c) Equivalent homogeneous waveguide model.
(After Verver and Hoefer [13])

$$h_1 = b - g_1 = \frac{ab(\sqrt{k_{e1}} - 1)}{\sqrt{k_{e1}}(\epsilon_r - 1) \cdot d} \tag{6.22}$$

$$h_2 = b - g_2 = \frac{ab(\sqrt{k_{e2}} - 1)}{\sqrt{k_{e2}}(\epsilon_r - 1) \cdot d} \tag{6.23}$$

where

$$k_{e1} = p^2 + [(1 - p^2)(k_{e4} - p^2)^3]^{1/4} \tag{6.24a}$$

$$k_{e2} = p^2 + [(1 - p^2)^3(k_{e4} - p^2)]^{1/4} \tag{6.24b}$$

$$k_{e4} = [1 - (\epsilon_r - 1)d/a]^{-2} \tag{6.24c}$$

and p is given by (6.18a).

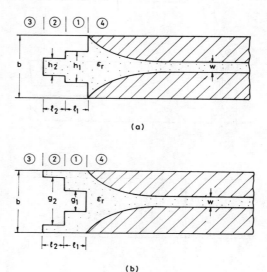

(a)

(b)

Fig. 6.10 Two-section quarter-wave transformers:
           (a) using stepped protrusions.
           (b) using stepped notches.
(From Hoefer and Verver [14], first presented at the 14th European
Microwave Conference, reprinted with permission.)

Single-Section Printed Step Transformer [14]

Let Z_{03} be the impedance of a fin line with slot width equal to w_3. Z_{01}
and Z_{02} are the wave impedances of regions 1 and 2, respectively. The
quarter-wave transformer is the slab-loaded section marked 1 in Fig.
6.11(a). The length l_1 of this section is obtained from

$$l_1 = \frac{\lambda_0}{4} (k_{e1} - p^2)^{-1/2} \tag{6.25}$$

where p is given by (6.18a), and

$$k_{e1} = [1 - (\epsilon_r - 1)d/a]^{-2} \tag{6.26}$$

The wave impedances Z_{01} and Z_{02} are related by

$$\frac{Z_{01}}{Z_{02}} = \left[\frac{(1 - p^2)}{(k_{e1} - p^2)}\right]^{1/2} \tag{6.27}$$

Furthermore,

$$Z_{01} = [Z_{02} \, Z_{03}]^{1/2} \tag{6.28}$$

Because the wave impedance Z_{02} of the hollow guide is known, Z_{01} can be calculated from (6.27). Substituting for Z_{01} and Z_{02} in (6.28) gives the value of Z_{03}. From the spectral domain formula or the closed-form formulas for fin-line design (Ch. 2 and 3), the slot width w_3 corresponding to Z_{03} is then determined.

Two-Section Printed Step Transformer

The first section of the transformer (region 1) is a fin-line section of length l_1 and slot width w_1 and the second section (region 2) is a slab-loaded waveguide of length l_2. (See Fig. 6.11(b).) Let Z_{01} and Z_{04} represent the impedances of a fin line of slot widths w_1 and w_4, respectively. Z_{03} and Z_{02} are the wave impedances of the hollow guide and the slab-loaded guide, respectively. We use the binomial transformer design for which (6.19) applies. We have

$$\frac{Z_{02}}{Z_{03}} = \left[\frac{(1 - p^2)}{(k_{e2} - p^2)}\right]^{1/2} \tag{6.29}$$

where p is given by (6.18a), and

$$k_{e2} = [1 - (\epsilon_r - 1)d/a]^{-2} \tag{6.30}$$

From (6.19) and (6.29), we can write

$$\frac{Z_{01}}{Z_{02}} = \left(\frac{Z_{02}}{Z_{03}}\right)^2 = \left(\frac{1 - p^2}{k_{e2} - p^2}\right) \tag{6.31}$$

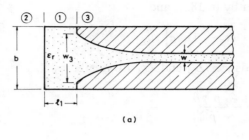

(a)

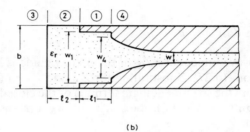

(b)

Fig. 6.11 (a) Single-section printed step transformers.
              (b) Two-section printed step transformers.

(From Hoefer and Verver [14], first presented at the 14th European
Microwave Conference, reprinted with permission.)

By eliminating Z_{03} from (6.19a) and (6.19b), we get

$$Z_{04} = Z_{01}^{3/2} \cdot Z_{02}^{-1/2} \tag{6.32}$$

Because the waveguide impedance Z_{03} is known, Z_{01} and Z_{02} can be
calculated by using (6.30) and (6.31). By substituting for Z_{01} and Z_{02} in
(6.32), Z_{04} can be determined. Thus, the slot widths w_1 and w_4 correspond
to the fin-line impedances Z_{01} and Z_{04}, respectively, which can be obtained
from the fin-line impedance characteristics. The length l_2 is obtained from

$$l_2 = \frac{\lambda_0}{4} [k_{e2} - p^2]^{-1/2} \tag{6.33}$$

The length l_1 is equal to a quarter-wavelength in the fin line of slot width
w_1. Spectral domain formulas or closed-form expressions given in Ch. 2
and 3 can be used for this purpose. It may be noted that all calculations
refer to the center frequency of the operating bandwidth.

6.4 TRANSITIONS BETWEEN FIN LINES AND PLANAR TRANSMISSION LINES

6.4.1 Fin Line to Microstrip

Transitions from rectangular waveguides to microstrip lines are commonly realized via an intermediate section of *antipodal fin line* [15–17]. Taper designs for transforming the impedance of a hollow waveguide to a fin line were discussed in Sec. 6.3. Figures 6.12 and 6.13 demonstrate two different ways of converting the E-field lines from an antipodal fin line to a microstrip. In Fig. 6.12, over the transition length l, the two fins on opposite sides of the substrate are tapered to form a somewhat circular arc. Beyond the arc, one of the fins forms the ground plane of the microstrip. The half of the waveguide under the microstrip ground terminates

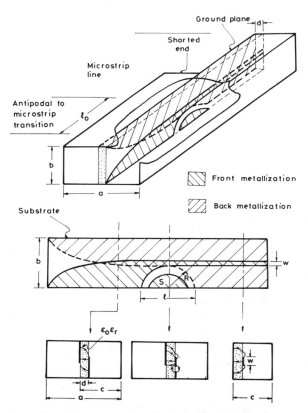

Fig. 6.12 Details of the transition from antipodal fin line to microstrip.

in a short, slightly beyond the transition. The performance of the transition depends on the radius R of the arc. For example, Dydyk and Moore [15] have reported a radius R equal to 0.0375 inch as the nearly optimal value for a V-band transition designed at 53 GHz. The additional metalization in the shaded area S serves to prevent the metal free space below the taper from resonating in the operating frequency band [16].

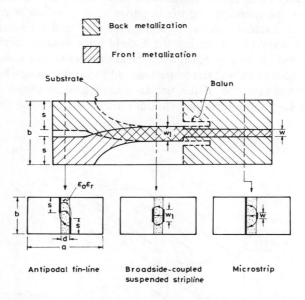

Fig. 6.13 Details of the transition from antipodal fin line to microstrip.

The transition shown in Fig. 6.13 is part of the waveguide to microstrip transition described by Van Heuven [17]. In this transition, the two fins of the antipodal fin line are gradually tapered to a symmetrical parallel line. Along the taper, the E-field lines of the antipodal fin line are gradually rotated and become concentrated between the two strip conductors. The cross section of the guide at the end of the tapered section is that of a broadside-coupled suspended stripline in odd-mode excitation. The symmetrical line is then matched to the asymmetrical microstrip line by means of a *balun*. In the balun section, the upper strip conductor is narrowed down to the microstrip width and slots are cut on the ground plane side so as to match the impedances of the two lines. The ground plane of the microstrip isolates the lower portion of the guide. No propagation takes place in the region below the ground plane because its cut-off frequency lies far above the waveguide band. As shown in Fig. 6.12, this portion of the guide can be terminated in a short, slightly beyond the balun section.

6.4.2   Fin Line to Suspended Microstrip

Figure 6.14(a) shows a transition from an *edge-coupled fin line* to a suspended microstrip. The printed pattern on the substrate is shown in Fig. 6.14(b), including the feeding arrangement using two unilateral fin lines for achieving oppositely directed E-field lines in the two slots of the edge-coupled fin line. The edge-coupled fin line can also be considered as a coplanar line in even-mode excitation.

In the transition region from coplanar line to suspended microstrip, the two fins on either side of the central strip are gradually tapered until the fins terminate in zero width at the broadside walls of the guide. Over the transition length, the left side wall of the guide (Fig. 6.14(a)) is also tapered until the spacing h_1 reduces to the required height h between the substrate and the lower ground plane of the suspended microstrip.

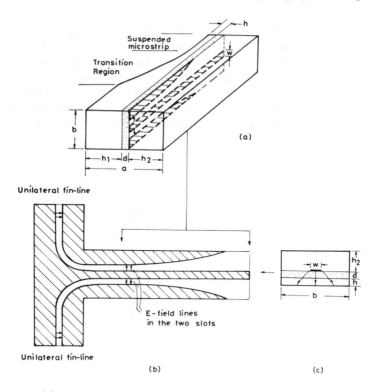

Fig. 6.14   (a) Transition from edge-coupled fin line to suspended microstrip.

(b) Printed pattern on the substrate.

(c) Suspended microstrip.

As the ground plane is brought nearer to the substrate, the E-field lines emerging from the strip conductor begin to terminate increasingly on the ground plane and less on the adjacent fins, thus transforming the fin-line mode into the suspended microstrip mode.

The fields in a *double-dielectric antipodal fin line* with fins facing the side walls can be easily transformed to a suspended microstrip (Fig. 6.15). This is achieved by simply tapering the printed fins. One of the fins is widened to form the ground plane and the other is narrowed to form the strip conductor. The dielectric substrate supporting the ground plane can be considered as an overlay in the suspended microstrip. In the case where no dielectric overlay is required, a special double-dielectric antipodal fin line can be used to construct the transition (Fig. 6.16).

6.4.3 Fin Line to Inverted Microstrip

A transition to inverted microstrip can be realized by adopting a double-dielectric antipodal fin line with fins printed on the inner surfaces of the two substrates (Fig. 6.17). A gradual tapering of the two fins, as shown in the figure, enables transformation of field lines from the antipodal fin line into the inverted microstrip. One of the fins widens to form the ground plane of the inverted microstrip. The portion of the guide under the ground plane can be terminated by a short, slightly beyond the transition.

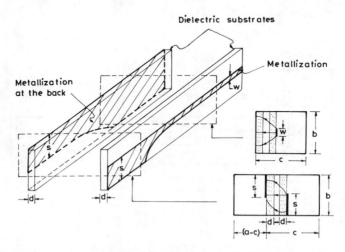

Fig. 6.15 Details of the transition from double-dielectric antipodal fin line to suspended microstrip with dielectric overlay on the ground plane.

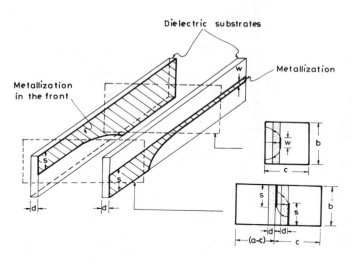

Fig. 6.16 Details of the transition from double-dielectric fin line to suspended microstrip.

A transition from unilateral fin line to inverted microstrip can also be realized by using the configuration shown in Fig. 6.14. Instead of tapering the left side wall, the right side wall is tapered to reduce the spacing h_2 to the required air gap with respect to the strip conductor. Thus, the structure reduces to an inverted microstrip with the right side wall serving as the ground plane.

6.4.4 Fin Line to Coplanar Lines

Figure 6.18 shows the schematic of a junction between a unilateral fin line and a coplanar line. For this case, the E-field lines in the two slots of the coplanar line are oriented in the same direction (odd-mode excitation). Junctions of this type are useful in the design of fin-line balanced mixers and *magic tee*.

A transition from a unilateral single-slot fin line to a coupled-slot fin line (coplanar line) can also be achieved via a tapered center conductor as shown in Fig. 6.19. In this scheme, only the odd-mode becomes excited in the coplanar line. This type of transition is extremely useful in fabricating fin-line isolators using coupled lines [18].

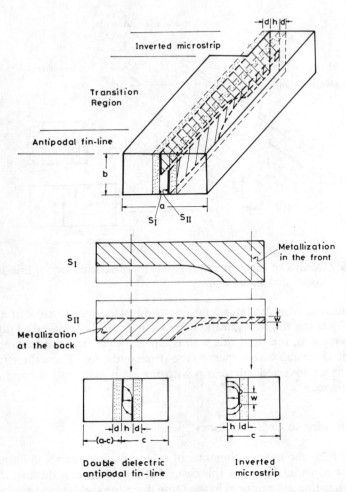

Fig. 6.17 Details of the transition from double-dielectric antipodal fin line to inverted microstrip.

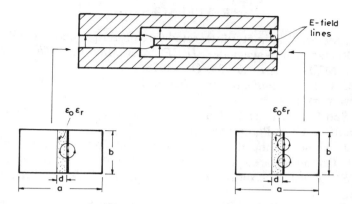

Fig. 6.18   Unilateral fin line to coplanar line junction.

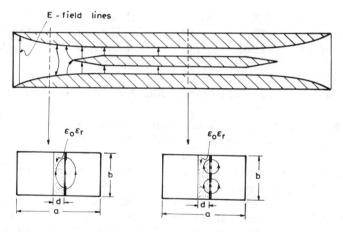

Fig. 6.19   Unilateral single-slot fin line to coupled-slot fin-line transition.

REFERENCES

1. P.J. Meier, "Millimeter Integrated Circuits Suspended in the E-plane of Rectangular Waveguide," *IEEE Trans. Microwave Theory Tech.*, Vol. MTT-26, pp. 726–733, Oct. 1978.
2. R.E. Collin, *Foundations for Microwave Engineering*, McGraw-Hill, New York 1966.
3. F. Sporleder and H.G. Unger, *Waveguide Tapers, Transitions and Couplers*, Peter Peregrinus, Stevenage, 1979.
4. M.J. Ahmed, "Impedance Transformation Equations for Exponential, Cosine-Squared and Parabolic Tapered Transmission Lines," *IEEE Trans. Microwave Theory Tech.*, Vol. MTT-29, pp. 67–68, Jan. 1981.
5. P. Pramanick and P. Bhartia, "Analysis and Synthesis of Tapered Fin Lines," *IEEE MTT-S Int. Microwave Symp. Digest*, May 1984, pp. 336–338.
6. C. Schieblich, J.K. Piotrowski, and J.H. Hinken, "Synthesis of Optimum Fin Line Tapers using Dispersion Formulas for Arbitrary Slot Widths and Locations," *IEEE Trans. Microwave Theory Tech.*, Vol. MTT-32, pp. 1638–1645, Dec. 1984.
7. A. Beyer and I. Wolff, "Calculation of the Transmission Properties of Inhomogeneous Fin Lines," *10th Eur. Microwave Conf. Proc.*, 1980, pp. 322–326.
8. A.M.K. Saad and K. Schunemann, "Design of Fin Line Tapers, Transitions, and Couplers," *11th Eur. Microwave Conf. Proc.*, 1981, pp. 305–308.
9. J.H. Hinken, "Simplified Analysis and Synthesis of Fin Line Tapers," *Arch. Elek. Ubertragung.*, Vol. 37, pp. 375–380, Nov.–Dec. 1983.
10. D. Mirshekar-Syahkal and J.B. Davies, "Accurate Analysis of Tapered Planar Transmission Lines for Microwave Integrated Circuits," *IEEE Trans. Microwave Theory Tech.*, Vol. MTT-29, pp. 123–128, Feb. 1981.
11. A. Beyer and I. Wolff, "Fin Line Taper Design Made Easy," *IEEE MTT-S Int. Microwave Symp. Digest*, 1985, pp. 493–496.
12. L.D. Cohen, "Advances in Printed Millimeter Wave Oscillator Circuits," *IEEE MTT-S Int. Microwave Symp. Digest*, 1980, pp. 264–266.
13. C.J. Verver and W.J.R. Hoefer, "Quarter-Wave Matching of Waveguide to Fin Line Transitions," *IEEE Trans. Microwave Theory Tech.*, Vol. MTT-32, pp. 1645–1648, Dec. 1984.
14. W.J.R. Hoefer and C.J. Verver, "Optimal Waveguide to E-plane Circuit Transitions with Binomial and Chebyshev Transformers,"

14th Eur. Microwave Conf. Digest, Sept. 1984, pp. 305–310.

15. M. Dydyk and B.D. Moore, "Shielded Microstrip Aids V-band Receiver Designs," *Microwaves,* Vol. 21, pp. 77–82, March 1982.

16. G. Begemann, "An X-band Balanced Fin Line Mixer," *IEEE Trans. Microwave Theory Tech.,* Vol. MTT-26, pp. 1007–1011, Dec. 1978.

17. J.H.C. Van Heuven, "An Integrated Waveguide-Microstrip Transition," *IEEE Trans. Microwave Theory Tech.,* Vol. MTT-24, pp. 144–147, March 1976.

18. D.B. Sillars and L.E. Davis, "Coupled-Slot Fin-Line Isolators," *Electron. Lett.,* Vol. 21, No. 3, pp. 97–98, Jan. 1985.

Chapter 7
Fin-Line Resonators

7.1 INTRODUCTION

A *slot resonator* in fin line is a basic circuit element that is used extensively as a building block in the design of fin-line filters. It is also useful in other millimeter-wave circuits, such as oscillators and mixers. The most commonly used resonator pattern is a rectangular slot of uniform width. Lowest order resonance occurs when the electrical length of the resonator becomes equal to half the guide wavelength in fin line. The physical length is slightly shorter than the electrical length because of the end effects.

The analysis technique followed here for the slot resonator problem is an extension of the spectral domain analysis presented in Ch. 3 for uniform fin lines. Only the additional steps that pertain specifically to the resonator are provided in this chapter. The analysis is then extended to parallel-coupled and end-coupled resonators in unilateral fin line, and broadside-coupled and broadside-end coupled resonators in bilateral and double-dielectric fin-line configurations. Representative graphs are presented to illustrate qualitatively the resonance behavior of resonators in some of the configurations. All results reported in Sec. 7.3 and 7.4 refer to fin lines in a standard WR-28 waveguide (for Ka band) with a cross section of 7.112 mm × 3.556 mm. The dielectric substrate is RT-duroid™ having a relative dielectric constant $\epsilon_r = 2.22$ and a thickness of either 0.127 mm or 0.254 mm.

Slot resonators etched from a metallic sheet and inserted in the E-plane of a waveguide are useful in the design of high-Q ($\sim$2500) circuits. This type of resonator, including the ridge-guide resonator, is discussed in Sec. 7.7.

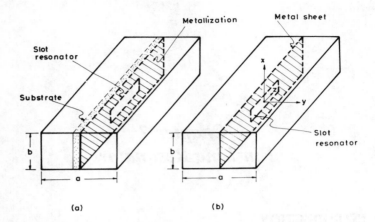

Fig. 7.1 (a) Fin-line slot resonator.
            (b) Metal insert E-plane slot resonator.

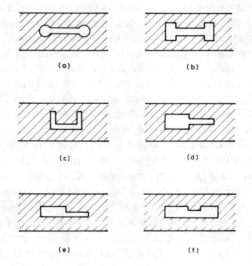

Fig. 7.2 Variants of rectangular slot resonator:
            (a) dumbbell slot
            (b) H-slot
            (c) U-slot
            (d) resonator with a symmetric step
            (e) resonator with an asymmetric step
            (f) resonator with a notch

7.2 BASIC PROPERTIES OF SLOT RESONATORS

Figure 7.1 shows the schematic of a *rectangular slot resonator* in a fin line as well as in a pure metal insert E-plane configuration. In addition to the popularly used rectangular slot pattern, several variants of the rectangular slot are used in practice to achieve specific circuit functions (Fig. 7.2). For example, the dumbbell-shaped pattern (Fig. 7.2(a)) and the H-shaped pattern (Fig. 7.2(b)) help to shorten the physical length of the resonator as compared with a rectangular slot for a specified resonant frequency. These shapes as well as the U-shaped pattern (Fig. 7.2(c)) are used in circuits having space constraints. The symmetrical and asymmetrical step resonators (Fig. 7.2(d) and (e)) can be used as impedance transforming elements at the ends of multiresonator-element filter circuits. A notch in a rectangular resonator (Fig. 7.2(f)) serves as a trimming facility for adjusting the resonant frequency. All of these variants basically offer additional flexibility in circuit design.

In order to understand the operating principle of these resonators, we shall consider the example of a rectangular resonator, as shown in Fig. 7.1(b). For TE mode excitation, Fig. 7.3(a) shows the evanescent magnetic field in the bifurcated waveguide. The reactive energy associated with it is essentially inductive. The electric and magnetic field distributions in the vicinity of the resonator are shown in Fig. 7.3(b). The electric field variation is nearly sinusoidal along the length of the slot (Fig. 7.3(c)). Current flows

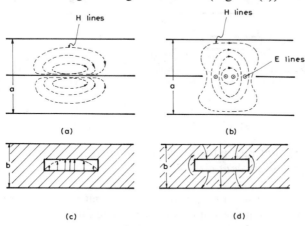

Fig. 7.3 Field and current distribution in the vicinity of slot resonator:
(a) evanescent magnetic field in a bifurcated guide
(b) field distribution in the resonator
(c) electric field variation in the slot
(d) current distribution around the slot

around the shorted ends of the resonator (Fig. 7.3(d)), and, as a result, appreciable magnetic energy is stored behind the termination. The effect of this is equivalent to presenting an inductive reactance jX_l at the end of the resonator as shown in the equivalent circuit in Fig. 7.4. Because an inductive reactance can be replaced by a short-circuited section of transmission line, the electrical short of the resonator can be considered to lie a short distance Δl beyond its physical short, such that

$$jX_l = jZ \tan(\beta \Delta l) \tag{7.1}$$

where Z is the characteristic impedance and β is the propagation constant of a uniform fin line of slot width w.

Figure 7.5(a) demonstrates coupling between a resonator and the input and output propagating waveguides. The magnetic field of the main input guide is coupled to the resonator region through an inductive stub of width s. The narrower the inductive stub, the stronger the coupling. As shown in the equivalent circuit (Fig. 7.5(c)), the stub is represented by a T-network of inductive elements. The circuit behaves like a bandpass filter with the passband centered at the half-wave resonance frequency of the resonator.

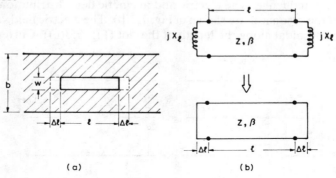

(a)   (b)

Fig. 7.4   (a) Slot resonator showing end correction (Δl).
(b) Equivalent circuit.

Figure 7.6(a) shows a rectangular slot resonator that is parallel coupled to the main propagating slot of an asymmetric fin line. It is apparent from the equivalent circuit (Fig. 7.6(b)) that this circuit possesses the property of a bandstop filter. The smaller is the spacing between the resonator and the main line, the tighter will be the coupling and the larger will be the bandwidth.

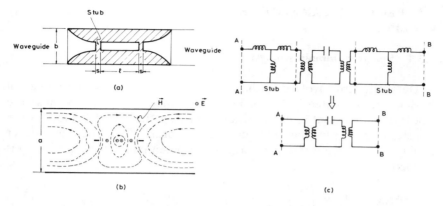

Fig. 7.5 (a) Pattern of resonator coupled to input and output guides.
(b) Magnetic field coupling.
(c) Equivalent circuit.

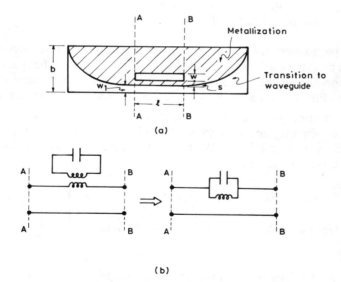

Fig. 7.6 (a) Rectangular resonator coupled to the main slot of
asymmetric fin line.
(b) Equivalent circuit.

7.3   RECTANGULAR SLOT RESONATOR IN UNILATERAL FIN LINE

7.3.1   Spectral Domain Analysis

Detailed steps involved in the spectral domain analysis of a unilateral fin line are presented in Ch. 3. For the resonator problem, because the slot is of finite extent in the direction of propagation, we will consider the Fourier transform of the field quantities in terms of x as well as z (refer to Fig. 7.7). The Fourier transform of the potential function $\phi(x, y, z)$ is defined as

$$\dot{\phi}(\alpha_n, y, \beta) = \int_{-\infty}^{\infty} \int_{-b/2}^{b/2} \phi(x, y, z)\, e^{j\alpha_n x}\, e^{j\beta z}\, dx\, dz \qquad (7.2)$$

where

$$\alpha_n = \begin{cases} 2n\pi/b, & \phi^h \text{ even in } x \\ (2n - 1)\pi/b, & \phi^h \text{ odd in } x \end{cases} \qquad (7.3)$$

The parameter α_n is the discrete Fourier variable with respect to x, and β is the continuous Fourier variable with respect to z. All field expressions corresponding to the three regions in the cross-sectional plane of the resonator (Fig. 7.7(a)) as well as other symbols used here remain as in Ch. 3. The Fourier transform of the current densities $\hat{J}_x(\alpha_n, \beta)$ and $\hat{J}_z(\alpha_n, \beta)$ on the conducting fins are related to the Fourier transform of the electric fields $\hat{E}_x(\alpha_n, \beta)$ and $\hat{E}_z(\alpha_n, \beta)$ in the slot region (complementary to the conductors) via the equation:

$$\begin{bmatrix} \hat{G}_{11}(\alpha_n, \beta, k_0) & \hat{G}_{12}(\alpha_n, \beta, k_0) \\ \hat{G}_{21}(\alpha_n, \beta, k_0) & \hat{G}_{22}(\alpha_n, \beta, k_0) \end{bmatrix} \begin{bmatrix} \hat{E}_z(\alpha_n, \beta) \\ \hat{E}_x(\alpha_n, \beta) \end{bmatrix} = \begin{bmatrix} \hat{J}_x(\alpha_n, \beta) \\ \hat{J}_z(\alpha_n, \beta) \end{bmatrix}$$
$$(7.4)$$

The expressions for the Fourier transforms of the dyadic Green's functions $\hat{G}_{ij}(\alpha_n, \beta, k_0)$ are the same as $\hat{G}_{ij}(\alpha_n, \beta)$ given in (3.38) and (3.39) of Ch. 3. It is worthwhile mentioning that the meaning of β is different for the two cases. We now eliminate $\hat{J}_x(\alpha_n, \beta)$ and $\hat{J}_z(\alpha_n, \beta)$ using Galerkin's procedure and Parseval's relation [1–2] and solve for $\hat{E}_x(\alpha_n, \beta)$ and $\hat{E}_z(\alpha_n, \beta)$. To this end, we first define an inner product of two functions as

$$\langle \hat{\psi}_1(\alpha_n, \beta) \quad \hat{\psi}_2^*(\alpha_n, \beta) \rangle = \sum_{n=-\infty}^{\infty} \int_{-\infty}^{\infty} \hat{\psi}_1(\alpha_n, \beta)\hat{\psi}_2^*(\alpha_n, \beta) \, d\beta \qquad (7.5)$$

We now expand the electric field distributions $\hat{E}_x(\alpha_n, \beta)$ and $\hat{E}_z(\alpha_n, \beta)$ in terms of the known basis functions $\hat{e}_{xm}(\alpha_n, \beta)$ and $\hat{e}_{zm}(\alpha_n, \beta)$, respectively, as

$$\hat{E}_x(\alpha_n, \beta) = \sum_{m=1}^{M} \xi_m \, \hat{e}_{xm}(\alpha_n, \beta) \qquad (7.6a)$$

$$\hat{E}_z(\alpha_n, \beta) = \sum_{m=1}^{N} \zeta_m \, \hat{e}_{zm}(\alpha_n, \beta) \qquad (7.6b)$$

where ξ_m and ζ_m are unknown constants. If we substitute (7.6) in (7.4) and take the inner products with regard to $\hat{e}_{xi}^*(\alpha_n, \beta)$ and $\hat{e}_{zi}^*(\alpha_n, \beta)$, respectively, we obtain the following algebraic equations:

$$\sum_{m=1}^{N} P_{im} \, \zeta_m + \sum_{m=1}^{M} Q_{im} \, \xi_m = 0, \quad i = 1, 2, \ldots, M \qquad (7.7a)$$

$$\sum_{m=1}^{N} R_{im} \, \zeta_m + \sum_{m=1}^{M} S_{im} \, \xi_m = 0, \quad i = 1, 2, \ldots, N \qquad (7.7b)$$

$$P_{im} = \sum_{n=-\infty}^{\infty} \int_{-\infty}^{\infty} \hat{e}_{xi}^*(\alpha_n, \beta) \, \hat{G}_{11}(\alpha_n, \beta, k_0)\hat{e}_{zm}(\alpha_n, \beta) \, d\beta,$$
$$i = 1, 2, \ldots, M \qquad (7.8a)$$

$$Q_{im} = \sum_{n=-\infty}^{\infty} \int_{-\infty}^{\infty} \hat{e}_{xi}^*(\alpha_n, \beta) \, \hat{G}_{12}(\alpha_n, \beta, k_0)\hat{e}_{xm}(\alpha_n, \beta) \, d\beta,$$
$$i = 1, 2, \ldots, M \qquad (7.8b)$$

$$R_{im} = \sum_{n=-\infty}^{\infty} \int_{-\infty}^{\infty} \hat{e}_{zi}^*(\alpha_n, \beta) \, \hat{G}_{21}(\alpha_n, \beta, k_0)\hat{e}_{zm}(\alpha_n, \beta) \, d\beta,$$
$$i = 1, 2, \ldots, N \qquad (7.8c)$$

$$S_{im} = \sum_{n=-\infty}^{\infty} \int_{-\infty}^{\infty} \hat{e}_{zi}^*(\alpha_n, \beta) \, \hat{G}_{22}(\alpha_n, \beta, k_0) \hat{e}_{xm}(\alpha_n, \beta) \, d\beta,$$

$$i = 1, 2, \ldots, N \tag{7.8d}$$

The inner products on the right-hand side of (7.4) vanish by application of Parseval's theorem because the fields E_x and E_z and the currents J_x and J_z exist only in the complementary regions at the interface $y = 0$. The characteristic equation for determining the resonant frequencies is obtained by setting the determinant of the coefficient matrix in (7.7) equal to zero.

The basic matrix equation given in (7.7) is exact. A numerical solution is obtained by introducing a known set of basis functions. The accuracy of the solution depends on the accuracy with which the basis functions represent the true electric field distribution in the resonating slot. In the case of slotline, the longitudinal component of the electric field (directed along the length of the slot) is known to be negligible as compared with the transverse component across the width of the slot, i.e., $e_z(x, z) = 0$ [3]. With this assumption, the characteristic equation for determining the resonant frequency reduces to a single equation as given below:

$$\sum_{m=1}^{M} \sum_{n=-\infty}^{\infty} \int_{-\infty}^{\infty} \xi_m \, \hat{G}_{12} \, (\alpha_n, \beta, k_0) \, |\hat{e}_{xm}(\alpha_n, \beta)|^2 \, d\beta = 0 \tag{7.9}$$

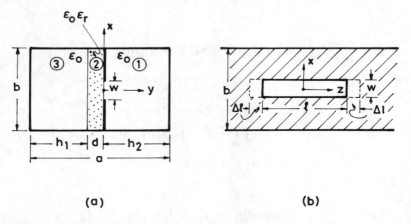

(a)   (b)

Fig. 7.7   Rectangular slot resonator in unilateral fin line:
        (a) cross-sectional view
        (b) resonator pattern showing end correction Δl

Furthermore, considering a one-term approximation ($M = 1$), we get

$$\sum_{n=-\infty}^{\infty} \int_{-\infty}^{\infty} \hat{G}_{12}\,(\alpha_n,\,\beta,\,k_0)\,|\hat{e}_x\,(\alpha_n,\,\beta)|^2 \; d\beta = 0 \qquad (7.10)$$

where $\hat{e}_{x1}\,(\alpha_n,\,\beta)$ is set equal to $\hat{e}_x(\alpha_n,\,\beta)$. The resonant frequency evaluated from (7.10) can be considered as the first-order solution ($M = 1, N = 0$). A second-order solution would be with $M = N = 1$ in (7.7) when considering both the transverse and the longitudinal components of the electric field. Computations of the resonant frequencies show that the first- and second-order solutions match reasonably well. With a suitable choice of the basis function corresponding to a one-term approximation in (7.10), reasonably accurate results can be obtained for the resonant frequency.

The slot resonator problem can also be formulated by enclosing the slot in a fin-line cavity [4]. The cavity is formed by placing conducting walls symmetrically at some distance from the resonator (Fig. 7.8). The Fourier transform of the potential function $\phi(x, y, z)$ is then defined as

$$\hat{\phi}(\alpha_n, y, \beta_k) = \int_{-l/2}^{l/2} \int_{-b/2}^{b/2} \phi(x, y, z) e^{j\alpha_n x} e^{j\beta_k z} \; dx \; dz \qquad (7.11)$$

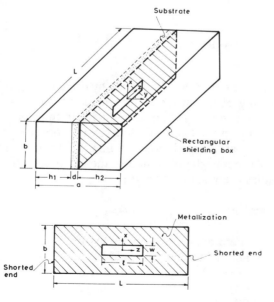

Fig. 7.8 Slot resonator in a fin-line cavity.

where

$$
\alpha_n = \begin{cases} \dfrac{2n\pi}{b}, & \phi^h \text{ even in } x \\[3mm] (2n-1)\dfrac{\pi}{b}, & \phi^h \text{ odd in } x \end{cases}
\tag{7.12a}
$$

$$
\beta_k = \begin{cases} \dfrac{2k\pi}{l}, & \phi^h \text{ odd in } z \\[3mm] (2k-1)\dfrac{\pi}{l}, & \phi^h \text{ even in } z \end{cases}
\tag{7.12b}
$$

The inner product of two functions is defined as

$$
<\hat{\psi}_1(\alpha_n, \beta_k)\hat{\psi}_2^*(\alpha_n, \beta_k)> = \sum_{n=-\infty}^{\infty} \sum_{k=-\infty}^{\infty} \hat{\psi}_1(\alpha_n, \beta_k)\hat{\psi}_2^*(\alpha_n, \beta_k)
\tag{7.13}
$$

With this, the integral in the characteristic equation (7.10) is replaced by summation to give

$$
\sum_{n=-\infty}^{\infty} \sum_{k=-\infty}^{\infty} \hat{G}_{12}(\alpha_n, \beta_k, k_0) \, |\hat{e}_x(\alpha_n, \beta_k)|^2 = 0
\tag{7.14}
$$

When computing the resonant frequency by using (7.14), it is important to keep the shorting planes at the end of the cavity (at $z = \pm L/2$) sufficiently far apart so as not to influence the fields in the slot. The resonant frequency of the slot resonator in a fin-line cavity is observed to be slightly smaller than that in an infinitely long fin line [5]. In order to reduce the effect of end walls to a negligible amount, the cavity length is required to be at least 15 times the resonator length.

7.3.2 Basis Functions

As discussed in the previous section, we assume $e_z(x, z) = 0$ within the slot. The x-component of the electric field in the slot region is expressed in the form:

$$
e_x(x, z) = e_x(x) \, e_x(z)
\tag{7.15}
$$

The Fourier transform of (7.15) is given by

$$\hat{e}_x(\alpha_n, \beta) = \hat{e}_x(\alpha_n) \cdot \hat{e}_x(\beta) \tag{7.16}$$

where

$$\hat{e}_x(\alpha_n) = \int_{-w/2}^{w/2} e_x(x) \, e^{j\alpha_n x} \, dx \tag{7.17a}$$

$$\hat{e}_x(\beta) = \int_{-l/2}^{l/2} e_x(z) \, e^{j\beta z} \, dz \tag{7.17b}$$

Basis Functions for $e_x(x)$ in Region $|x| \leq \dfrac{w}{2}, |z| \leq \dfrac{l}{2}$

The following are some of the simple basis functions for $e_x(x)$ and their Fourier transforms:

(1)

$$e_x(x) = 1 \tag{7.18a}$$

$$\hat{e}_x(\alpha_n) = \frac{w \cdot \sin\left(\dfrac{\alpha_n w}{2}\right)}{\left(\dfrac{\alpha_n w}{2}\right)} \tag{7.18b}$$

(2)

$$e_x(x) = \frac{1}{\sqrt{\left(\dfrac{w}{2}\right)^2 - x^2}} \tag{7.19a}$$

$$\hat{e}_x(\alpha_n) = \pi \, J_0\!\left(|\alpha_n|\frac{w}{2}\right) \tag{7.19b}$$

(3)

$$e_x(x) = \left(1 + \left|\frac{2x}{w}\right|^3\right) \tag{7.20a}$$

$$
\hat{e}_x(\alpha_n) = \frac{2w \cdot \sin\left(\dfrac{\alpha_n w}{2}\right)}{\left(\dfrac{\alpha_n w}{2}\right)} + \frac{3w}{\left(\dfrac{\alpha_n w}{2}\right)^2}
$$

$$
\cdot \left\{ \cos\left(\frac{\alpha_n w}{2}\right) - \frac{2\sin\left(\dfrac{\alpha_n w}{2}\right)}{\left(\dfrac{\alpha_n w}{2}\right)} + \frac{\sin^2\left(\dfrac{\alpha_n w}{4}\right)}{\left(\dfrac{\alpha_n w}{4}\right)^2} \right\} \qquad (7.20b)
$$

The relative accuracy of the above three functions in predicting the guide wavelength for infinitely long fin lines has been reported in Ch. 4 (Table 4.1). It has been shown that among the three functions, the cubic distribution specified by (7.20) gives the best results, nearly matching those obtained by using the series expansion function of Schmidt *et al.* [3].

Basis Functions for $e_x(z)$ in Region $|x| \leq \dfrac{w}{2}, |z| \leq \dfrac{l}{2}$

The basis function $e_x(z)$ must satisfy the condition that its amplitude at the terminating ends of the slot ($z = \pm l/2$) must become zero. A simple distribution satisfying this condition is

$$
e_x(z) = \cos\left(\frac{\pi z}{l}\right) \qquad (7.21a)
$$

The Fourier transform of this function is given by

$$
\hat{e}_x(\beta) = \left[\frac{2\pi l \cdot \cos\left(\dfrac{\beta l}{2}\right)}{\pi^2 - (\beta l)^2} \right] \qquad (7.21b)
$$

An end-corrected basis function, which takes into account the presence of the evanescent modes, has been reported by Knorr [4]. It is given by

$$
e_x(z) = \left[\cos\left(\frac{2\pi}{\lambda} z\right) - \frac{\cos\left(\dfrac{\pi l}{\lambda}\right)}{\cosh\left(\dfrac{Kl}{2}\right)} \cdot \cosh\left(\frac{Kl}{2} \cdot \frac{2z}{l}\right) \right] \qquad (7.22a)
$$

where λ is the guide wavelength in fin line and K is a constant. The first term in (7.22a) represents the correct amplitude variation due to the dominant mode. The second term accounts for the evanescent modes, which give rise to reactive energy at the terminating ends of the slot. The rate of decay of the evanescent field is adjusted by the parameter $Kl/2$. The Fourier transform of (7.22a) is

$$
\hat{e}_x(\beta) = 2 \cos\left(\frac{\pi l}{\lambda}\right) \cdot \cos\left(\frac{\beta l}{2}\right)
$$
$$
\cdot \left\{ \frac{\left[\left(\frac{2\pi}{\lambda}\right) \tan\left(\frac{\pi l}{\lambda}\right) - \beta \tan\left(\frac{\beta l}{2}\right)\right]}{\left(\frac{2\pi}{\lambda}\right)^2 - \beta^2} \right.
$$
$$
\left. - \frac{\left[K \tanh\left(\frac{Kl}{2}\right) + \beta \tan\left(\frac{\beta l}{2}\right)\right]}{(K^2 + \beta^2)} \right\} \tag{7.22b}
$$

By using the basis function $e_x(x, z)$ as given by (7.22a), $(e_x(x) = 1)$, and with a value of $Kl/2$ equal to 10, Knorr [4] has shown good agreement between the theoretical and experimental results on end reactances of rectangular slot resonators in unilateral fin line at X band.

7.3.3 Determination of End Effects

The lowest resonant frequency of the structure corresponds to half-wave resonance. The end correction Δl at each end of the resonator (Fig. 7.7b) is calculated as follows:

For a specified value of the resonator length l and normalized width w/b, the resonant frequency f_0 is computed by seeking the root of (7.10). The guide wavelength λ corresponding to f_0 in an infinitely long fin line of normalized slot width w/b is determined from the modified characteristic equation, given by

$$
\sum_{n=-\infty}^{\infty} \hat{G}_{12}(\alpha_n, \lambda) \, |\hat{e}_x(\alpha_n, \lambda)|^2 = 0 \tag{7.23}
$$

In order to determine λ from (7.23) the same computer program used for evaluating (7.10) can be slightly modified by omitting the integration and replacing β by $2\pi/\lambda$. The apparent extension Δl is then obtained from

$$\Delta l = \frac{1}{2}\left(\frac{\lambda}{2} - l\right) \tag{7.24}$$

7.3.4 Resonance Characteristics

The resonance characteristics of rectangular slot resonators in unilateral fin lines are computed by using the following set of formulas. For a given resonator length l, the resonance frequency is computed by using

$$\sum_{n=-\infty}^{\infty} \int_{-\infty}^{\infty} \hat{G}_{12}(\alpha_n, \beta, k_0) |\hat{e}_x(\alpha_n)\,\hat{e}_x(\beta)|^2 \, d\beta = 0 \tag{7.25}$$

where

$$\hat{G}_{12}(\alpha_n, \beta, k_0) = \frac{-j}{P_0}\,(P_4 \sinh \gamma_2 d \cosh \gamma_2 d$$
$$+ P_5 \sinh^2\gamma_2 d + P_6) \tag{7.26a}$$

$$P_4 = \gamma_2[k_0^2\gamma_0^2(k_2^2 - \beta^2)\,(\coth^2\gamma_0 h_1 + \epsilon_r)$$
$$+ (k_0^2 - \beta^2)(k_2^2\gamma_0^2 + k_0^2\gamma_2^2)\,\coth\gamma_0 h_1 \coth \gamma_0 h_2] \tag{7.26b}$$

$$P_5 = \gamma_0[k_0^2\gamma_2^2(k_0^2 - \beta^2)\,(\coth^2\gamma_0 h_1 + \epsilon_r)\,\coth\gamma_0 h_2$$
$$+ (k_2^2 - \beta^2)(k_2^2\gamma_0^2 + k_0^2\gamma_2^2)\coth\gamma_0 h_1] \tag{7.26c}$$

$$P_6 = k_2^2\gamma_0\gamma_2^2\,(k_0^2 - \beta^2)\,(\coth\gamma_0 h_1 + \coth\gamma_0 h_2) \tag{7.26d}$$

$$P_0 = \omega\mu_0\gamma_0\gamma_2\,[(k_2^2\gamma_0^2 + k_0^2\gamma_2^2)\,\coth\gamma_0 h_1 \sinh\gamma_2 d \cosh\gamma_2 d$$
$$+ k_0^2\gamma_0\gamma_2(\coth^2\gamma_0 h_1 + \epsilon_r)\sinh^2\gamma_2 d + k_2^2\gamma_0\gamma_2] \tag{7.26e}$$

$$\gamma_0^2 = \alpha_n^2 + \beta^2 - k_0^2 \tag{7.26f}$$

$$\gamma_2^2 = \alpha_n^2 + \beta^2 - k_2^2; \quad k_2^2 = k_0^2\,\epsilon_r \tag{7.26g}$$

The basis function is chosen as the product of (7.20) and (7.21). Thus,

$$\hat{e}_x(\alpha_n, \beta) = \hat{e}_x(\alpha_n)\hat{e}_x(\beta) = \left\{ \frac{2 w \sin\left(\frac{\alpha_n w}{2}\right)}{\left(\frac{\alpha_n w}{2}\right)} + \frac{3 w}{\left(\frac{\alpha_n w}{2}\right)^2} \right.$$

$$\left. \cdot \left[\cos\left(\frac{\alpha_n w}{2}\right) - \frac{2\sin\left(\frac{\alpha_n w}{2}\right)}{\left(\frac{\alpha_n w}{2}\right)} + \frac{\sin^2\left(\frac{\alpha_n w}{4}\right)}{\left(\frac{\alpha_n w}{4}\right)^2} \right] \right\}$$

$$\cdot \left[\frac{2\pi l \cos\left(\frac{\beta l}{2}\right)}{\pi^2 - (\beta l)^2} \right] \tag{7.27}$$

The end correction is then computed by using (7.23) and (7.24).

Figures 7.9 to 7.11 show some typical resonance characteristics of a

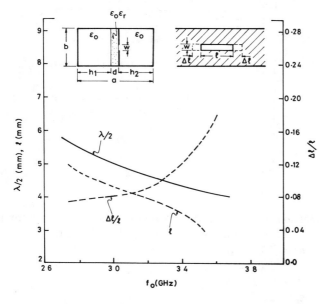

Fig. 7.9 Variation in l, $\Delta l/l$ and λ versus resonant frequency f_0 of
rectangular slot resonator in unilateral fin line (λ is the guide
wavelength in fin line):

   $a = 7.112$ mm $b = 3.556$ mm
   $d = 0.127$ mm $\epsilon_r = 2.22$
   $h_1 = 2.8$ mm $h_2 = 4.185$ mm
   $w/b = 0.1$

rectangular resonator in unilateral fin line operating at Ka band. We consider both centered and off-centered fin locations (with respect to the side walls). Figure 7.9 depicts the variation in the length l, the normalized end correction $\Delta l/l$ in the resonator, and the guide wavelength λ in the fin line, as a function of the resonant frequency f_0. The normalized slot width (w/b) is chosen equal to 0.1. An interesting observation is the rapid increase in $\Delta l/l$ with increasing frequency at higher frequencies in the Ka band. For a slot resonator of fixed length ($l = 3.6$ mm), the variations of f_0 and Δl as a function of w/b are shown in Figs. 7.10 and 7.11, respectively. The resonant frequency curves of the resonator for off-centered fin locations ($h_2 \neq h_1 + d$) lie below the curve for the centered fin case (Fig. 7.10).

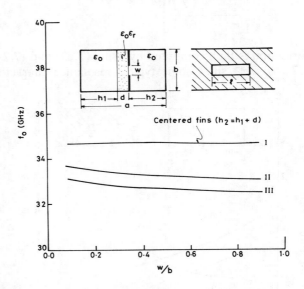

Fig. 7.10   Resonant characteristics of rectangular slot resonator in unilateral fin line for centered and off-centered fins:

$a = 7.112$ mm
$b = 3.556$ mm
$d = 0.127$ mm
$\epsilon_r = 2.22$
$l = 3.6$ mm
(I) $h_1 = 3.429$ mm $h_2 = 3.556$ mm
(II) $h_1 = 2.8$ mm $h_2 = 4.185$ mm
(III) $h_1 = 4.185$ mm $h_2 = 2.8$ mm

(From Agrawal and Bhat [6], Copyright © 1984 IEEE, reprinted with permission.)

Correspondingly, the end correction required for resonators in off-centered fin locations is higher than that in centered fin location (Fig. 7.11). The end effect also increases with an increase in the slot width and reaches an appreciable fraction of the length l for off-centered fin locations.

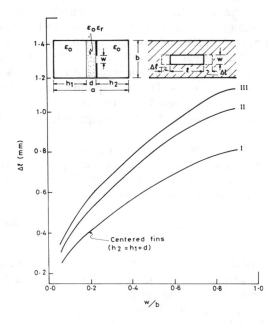

Fig. 7.11 End correction Δl in a rectangular slot resonator in unilateral fin line for centered and off-centered fins:

  $a = 7.112$ mm
  $b = 3.556$ mm
  $d = 0.127$ mm
  $\epsilon_r = 2.22$
  $l = 3.6$ mm
  (I) $h_1 = 3.429$ mm $h_2 = 3.556$ mm
  (II) $h_1 = 2.8$ mm $h_2 = 4.185$ mm
  (III) $h_1 = 4.185$ mm $h_2 = 2.8$ mm

(From Agrawal and Bhat [6], Copyright © 1984 IEEE, reprinted with permission.)

Resonant frequency measurements carried out on a single slot resonator etched on RT-duroid™ substrates ($d = 0.127$ mm) are reported in Agarwal and Bhat [6]. The resonator was excited from a Ka-band waveguide through a tapered fin-line transition (see Fig. 7.5(a) for the schematic).

An important practical aspect in the experiment is the optimization of inductive coupling (stub width s in Fig. 7.5(a)) between the fin line and the slot resonator such that the influence of the inductive stub on the resonant frequency is negligible. A stub width (s) of about 0.4 mm was used in the experiments. For larger stub widths, the power at the output port reduces and resonance peak broadens, thus making it difficult to locate the resonance frequency accurately. For slot widths in the range of 0.25 mm and 2.2 mm, the theoretical and measured resonant frequencies reported by Agarwal and Bhat [6] match within 1.5%, thus demonstrating the accuracy of the basis function adopted in theory, at least for determining the resonant frequencies. The corresponding error in end correction Δl, however, is likely to be larger. For better accuracy, a more appropriate basis function, which accounts for the evanescent fields at the shorted ends, needs to be used.

One such function is given in (7.22a) (due to Knorr [4]). However, because the value of the parameter $Kl/2$ appearing in (7.22a) is not known for the various resonator configurations considered in this chapter, this basis function is not used in the calculations.

7.3.5 Stepped Rectangular Slot Resonators

The characteristic equation given in (7.10) is general and can be applied to slot resonators of arbitrary shape. Table 7.1 lists simple basis functions that can be assumed for rectangular resonators with an asymmetric step, a symmetric step, and a notch. The resonant frequencies of the resonators can be determined by substituting the Fourier transforms of the basis functions in (7.10) and seeking the root of the equation. It may be noted that the x-dependent electric field $e_x(x)$ is well represented by the cubic distribution, whereas the z-dependent component $e_x(z)$ is only approximately specified by the cosine function. For a more accurate representation of $e_x(z)$, suitable correction terms that account for the presence of evanescent modes at the resonator ends as well as at the step junctions will have to be introduced. As pointed out in Sec. 7.3.4, such correction terms are important for accurate characterization of end effects, but not so critical for the evaluation of resonant frequency.

7.4 COUPLED RECTANGULAR SLOT RESONATORS IN UNILATERAL FIN LINE

7.4.1 Electric Field Distribution in Coupled Slots

Coupled rectangular slot resonators in unilateral fin line can be arranged to provide three useful types of coupling: (1) *parallel coupling* (Fig. 7.12b); (2) *parallel-offset coupling* (Fig. 7.12c); and (3) *end coupling* (Fig. 7.13). The assumed electric field distributions across the coupled slots for the even-mode and odd-mode excitations are also plotted in the respective figures. The plane of symmetry AA' marked in all three configurations represents a magnetic wall for the even-mode and an electric wall for the odd-mode.

Let $\hat{e}_{xp}(\alpha_n, \beta)$, $\hat{e}_{xf}(\alpha_n, \beta)$, and $\hat{e}_{xd}(\alpha_n, \beta)$ denote the transformed electric field distributions in the parallel-coupled, parallel-offset coupled, and end-coupled resonators, respectively. These fields can be expressed in terms of the electric field distribution $\hat{e}_x(\alpha_n, \beta)$ of the single centered slot resonator by the application of the shifting theorem. They are given by

$$\hat{e}_{xp}(\alpha_n, \beta) = K_p\, \hat{e}_x(\alpha_n, \beta) \tag{7.28a}$$

$$\hat{e}_{xf}(\alpha_n, \beta) = K_f\, \hat{e}_x(\alpha_n, \beta) \tag{7.28b}$$

$$\hat{e}_{xd}(\alpha_n, \beta) = K_d\, \hat{e}_x(\alpha_n, \beta) \tag{7.28c}$$

where

$$K_p = [e^{j\alpha_n\left(\frac{s+w}{2}\right)} + \delta e^{-j\alpha_n\left(\frac{s+w}{2}\right)}] \tag{7.29a}$$

$$K_f = [e^{j\alpha_n\left(\frac{s+w}{2}\right)} \cdot e^{-j\frac{\beta l}{4}} + \delta e^{-j\alpha_n\left(\frac{s+w}{2}\right)} \cdot e^{j\frac{\beta l}{4}}],\ \beta l = 2\pi \tag{7.29b}$$

$$K_d = [e^{j\beta\left(\frac{l+g}{2}\right)} - \delta e^{-j\beta\left(\frac{l+g}{2}\right)}] \tag{7.29c}$$

and

$$\delta = \begin{cases} -1, & \text{even-mode} \\ 1, & \text{odd-mode} \end{cases} \tag{7.29d}$$

The subscripts p, f, and d refer to parallel-coupled, parallel-offset coupled, and end-coupled resonators, respectively.

Table 7.1

SLOT RESONATOR PATTERNS AND CORRESPONDING BASIS FUNCTIONS

Basis function $e_x(x, z) = e_x(x) \cdot e_z(z)$, p = constant	Slot resonator pattern
$e_x(x) = \begin{cases} \dfrac{1}{w}\left(1 + \left\|\dfrac{2x}{w}\right\|^3\right), & -\dfrac{w}{2} \le x \le w_1,\ 0 \le z \le \dfrac{l}{2} \\[4pt] & \|x\| \le \dfrac{w}{2},\ -\dfrac{l}{2} \le z \le 0 \\[4pt] 0, & \text{elsewhere} \end{cases}$ $e_z(z) = \begin{cases} \dfrac{2}{l}\cos\left(\dfrac{\pi z}{l}\right), & -\dfrac{w}{2} \le x \le w_1,\ -\dfrac{l}{2} \le z \le 0 \\[4pt] \dfrac{p}{l}\sin\left(\dfrac{2\pi z}{l}\right), & w_1 \le x \le \dfrac{w}{2},\ -\dfrac{l}{2} \le z \le 0 \\[4pt] 0, & \text{elsewhere} \end{cases}$	• Rectangular resonator with a asymmetric step change in width
$e_x(x) = \begin{cases} \dfrac{1}{w}\left(1 + \left\|\dfrac{2x}{w}\right\|^3\right), & \|x\| \le \dfrac{w_1}{2},\ 0 \le z \le \dfrac{l}{2} \\[4pt] & \|x\| \le \dfrac{w}{2},\ -\dfrac{l}{2} \le z \le 0 \\[4pt] 0, & \text{elsewhere} \end{cases}$ $e_x(x) = \begin{cases} \dfrac{2}{l}\cos\left(\dfrac{\pi z}{l}\right), & \|x\| \le \dfrac{w_1}{2},\ \|z\| \le \dfrac{l}{2} \end{cases}$	• Rectangular resonator with a symmetric step change in width

- Rectangular resonator with a symmetric step change in width

- Rectangular resonator with a notch

$$e_x(z) = \begin{cases} \dfrac{p}{l}\sin\left(\dfrac{2\pi z}{l}\right), & \dfrac{w_1}{2} \le x \le \dfrac{w}{2},\; -\dfrac{l}{2} \le z \le 0 \\[2mm] & -\dfrac{w}{2} \le x \le -\dfrac{w_1}{2},\; -\dfrac{l}{2} \le z \le 0 \\[2mm] 0, & \text{elsewhere} \end{cases}$$

$$e_x(x) = \begin{cases} \dfrac{1}{w}\left(1 + \left|\dfrac{2x}{w}\right|^3\right), & -\dfrac{w}{2} \le x \le w_1,\; |z| \le \dfrac{s}{2}, \\[2mm] & |x| \le \dfrac{w}{2},\; \dfrac{s}{2} \le z \le \dfrac{l}{2},\; -\dfrac{l}{2} \le z \le -\dfrac{s}{2} \\[2mm] 0, & \text{elsewhere} \end{cases}$$

$$e_x(z) = \begin{cases} \dfrac{p}{l}\sin\left[\pi(z - s/2)/\left(\dfrac{l - s}{2}\right)\right], & w_1 \le x \le \dfrac{w}{2},\; \dfrac{s}{2} \le z \le \dfrac{l}{2} \\[2mm] \dfrac{p}{l}\sin\left[\pi(z + s/2)/\left(\dfrac{-l + s}{2}\right)\right], & w_1 \le x \le \dfrac{w}{2},\; -\dfrac{l}{2} \le z \le -\dfrac{s}{2} \\[2mm] 0, & \text{elsewhere} \end{cases}$$

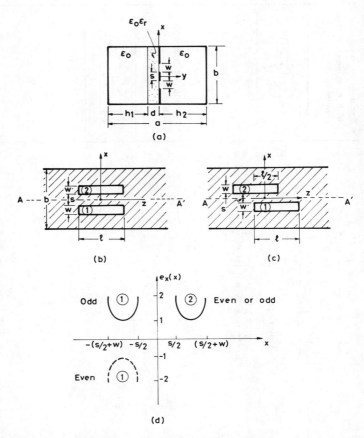

Fig. 7.12 Parallel coupled resonators in unilateral fin line:
(a) cross-sectional view
(b) parallel coupled resonators
(c) parallel-offset coupled resonators
(d) even-mode and odd-mode electric field distribution in
(b) and (c)

7.4.2 Characteristic Equations

The characteristic equation for determining the even-mode and odd-mode resonant frequencies can be written as

$$\sum_{n=-\infty}^{\infty} \int_{-\infty}^{\infty} \hat{G}_{12}(\alpha_n,\ \beta,\ k_0)|K_{p\,f\,d}\ \hat{e}_x(\alpha_n,\ \beta)|^2\ d\beta = 0 \qquad (7.30)$$

The expression for $\hat{G}_{12}(\alpha_n, \beta, k_0)$ is the same as that given by (7.26) for the unilateral fin line. The basis function $\hat{e}_x(\alpha_n, \beta)$ is that of a single slot resonator centered in the E-plane. The results reported in the following sections are computed by using (7.27) as the basis function.

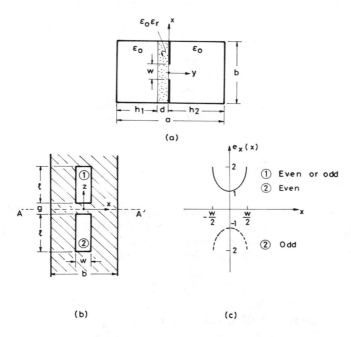

Fig. 7.13   End-coupled resonators in unilateral fin line:
   (a) cross-sectional view (at the slot)
   (b) resonator pattern
   (c) even-mode and odd-mode electric field distribution

7.4.3   Even-Mode and Odd-Mode Resonance Characteristics [7]

(1) *Parallel-Coupled Resonators*

The resonant frequency characteristics of parallel-coupled resonators in unilateral fin line are plotted as a function of the resonator length l in Fig. 7.14, the normalized width w/b in Fig. 7.15 and normalized spacing s/b in Fig. 7.16. Only the odd-mode characteristics are shown because this is the mode normally excited in practice. The resonant frequency curve of a single rectangular slot resonator of the same width w and length l and

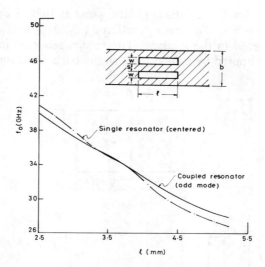

Fig. 7.14   Comparison of resonant frequency characteristic of a parallel
coupled resonator (odd-mode) with that of a single resonator
(centered) in unilateral fin line:

$a = 7.112$ mm $b = 3.556$ mm
$d = 0.127$ mm $\epsilon_r = 2.22$
$h_2 = h_1 + d$ $w/b = 0.1$
$s/b = 0.1$

(From Agrawal and Bhat [7], reprinted with permission of Taylor and
Francis Ltd.)

centered at $x = 0$, $z = 0$ is also superposed for comparison. As expected,
in the limit $s/b = 0$, the odd-mode resonant frequency of coupled resonators reduces to that of a single resonator of length l and width $2w$ (see
Fig. 7.16). Furthermore, when the center to center spacing between the
two resonators is equal to $b/2$, the odd-mode resonant frequency is the
same as that of a single resonator in a fin line with side wall spacing equal
to $b/2$. In Fig. 7.16, this frequency corresponds to $s/b = 0.4$ (for
$w/b = 0.1$). Because the axis of symmetry represents an electric wall, the
resonant frequency curve is symmetrical with respect to $s/b = 0.4$.

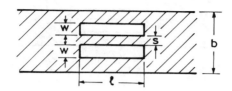

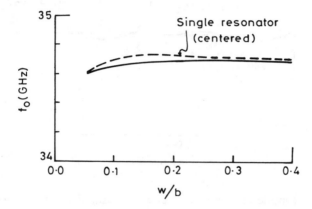

Fig. 7.15 Odd-mode resonant frequency of parallel coupled resonators in unilateral fin line:

$a = 7.112$ mm $b = 3.556$ mm
$d = 0.127$ mm $\epsilon_r = 2.22$
$h_2 = h_1 + d$ $l = 3.6$ mm
$s/b = 0.1$

(From Agrawal and Bhat [7], reprinted with permission of Taylor and Francis Ltd.)

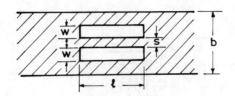

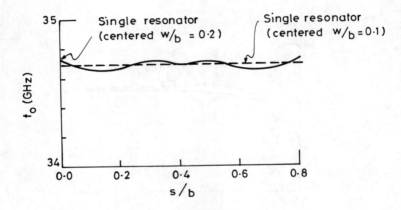

Fig. 7.16 Odd-mode resonant frequency of parallel coupled resonators
in unilateral fin line:
$a = 7.112$ mm $b = 3.556$ mm
$d = 0.127$ mm $\epsilon_r = 2.22$
$h_2 = h_1 + d$ $l = 3.6$ mm
$w/b = 0.1$

(From Agrawal and Bhat [7], reprinted with permission of Taylor and
Francis Ltd.)

(2) Parallel-Offset Coupled Resonators

Figure 7.17 shows typical resonant frequency characteristic of parallel-
offset coupled resonators. It is interesting to note that the resonant frequency curve of a single centered slot resonator of the same length l and
width w lies between the even- and odd-mode resonant frequency curves
of the coupled resonators.

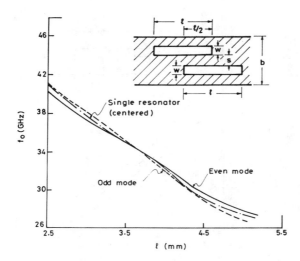

Fig. 7.17 Even-mode and odd-mode resonant frequencies of parallel
offset coupled resonators in unilateral fin line:

$a = 7.112$ mm $b = 3.556$ mm
$d = 0.127$ mm $\epsilon_r = 2.22$
$h_2 = h_1 + d$ $w/b = s/b = 0.1$

(From Agrawal and Bhat [7], reprinted with permission of Taylor and
Francis Ltd.)

(3) End-Coupled Resonators

Typical resonance characteristics of end-coupled resonators depicted in
Figs. 7.18 and 7.19 show that the resonant frequency of the odd-mode is
higher than that of the even-mode. The resonant frequency curve of an
isolated slot resonator of the same length and width lies between the even-
and odd-mode curves. This is to be expected because in the even-mode
the fringing electric fields in the dielectric at the adjacent ends of the two
resonators are in the same direction, whereas in the odd-mode they are
oppositely directed and hence tend to cancel. Consequently, the end effect
(or end correction Δl) is larger for the even-mode, resulting in lower
resonant frequency than that with the odd-mode.

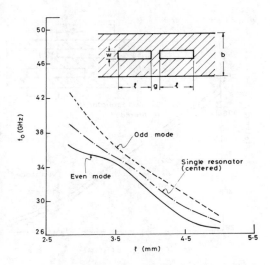

Fig. 7.18   Even-mode and odd-mode resonant frequencies *versus l* of
end-coupled resonators in unilateral fin line:
$$a = 7.112 \text{ mm} \quad b = 3.556 \text{ mm}$$
$$d = 0.127 \text{ mm} \quad \epsilon_r = 2.22$$
$$h_2 = h_1 + \text{d} \quad w/b = g/b = 0.1$$
(From Agrawal and Bhat [7], reprinted with permission of Taylor and
Francis Ltd.)

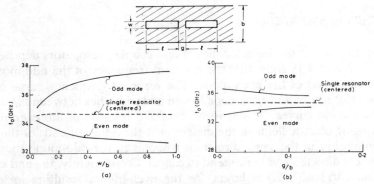

Fig. 7.19   Even-mode and odd-mode resonant frequencies of end-
coupled resonators in unilateral fin line:
$$a = 7.112 \text{ mm} \quad b = 3.556 \text{ mm}$$
$$d = 0.127 \text{ mm} \quad \epsilon_r = 2.22$$
$$h_2 = h_1 + d \quad l = 3.6 \text{ mm}$$
(a) $g/b = 0.1$ \quad (b) $w/b = 0.1$
(From Agrawal and Bhat [7], reprinted with permission of Taylor and
Francis Ltd.)

7.5 BROADSIDE-COUPLED SLOT RESONATORS IN FIN LINE

7.5.1 Broadside-Coupled Resonators in Double-Dielectric Fin Line [8]

Broadside-coupled resonators in double-dielectric fin line can be arranged in two ways: (1) with fins facing the side walls (Fig. 7.20(a)) and (2) with fins facing each other (Fig. 7.20(b)). The two resonator patterns form mirror images of each other with respect to the symmetry plane AA'. In the even-mode excitation, the plane AA' represents a magnetic wall, and in the odd-mode excitation, it represents an electric wall.

By denoting $\hat{G}_{12e}(\alpha_n, \beta, k_0)$ and $\hat{G}_{12o}(\alpha_n, \beta, k_0)$ as the Green's functions for the even-mode and odd-mode, respectively, we can write the characteristic equation as

$$\sum_{n=-\infty}^{\infty} \int_{-\infty}^{\infty} \hat{G}_{12e,o}\ (\alpha_n, \beta, k_0)|\hat{e}_x(\alpha_n, \beta)|^2\ d\beta = 0 \tag{7.31}$$

The expressions for $\hat{G}_{12e}$ and $\hat{G}_{12o}$ for the two structures are obtained from (7.26) by introducing the following change in the parameters.

(1) *Structure with Fins Facing the Side Walls* (Fig. 7.20(a))

For the even-mode Green's function, replace $\coth(\gamma_0 h_2)$ by $\coth(\gamma_0 h_1)$, and $\coth(\gamma_0 h_1)$ by $\tanh(\gamma_0 h_2)$, and for the odd-mode Green's function, interchange h_1 and h_2 in (7.26). Thus,

$$\hat{G}_{12e,o}(\alpha_n, \beta, k_0) = \frac{-j}{P_{0e,o}}\ (P_{4e,o} \sinh \gamma_2 d \cdot \cosh \gamma_2 d$$
$$+ P_{5e,o} \sinh^2 \gamma_2 d + P_{6e,o}) \tag{7.32}$$

where

$$P_{0e} = \omega\mu_0\ \gamma_0\gamma_2\ [(k_2^2\gamma_0^2 + k_0^2\gamma_2^2)\ \tanh \gamma_0 h_2 \sinh \gamma_2 d \cosh \gamma_2 d$$
$$+ k_0^2\gamma_0\gamma_2\ (\tanh^2 \gamma_0 h_2 + \epsilon_r)\ \sinh^2 \gamma_2 d + k_2^2\gamma_0\gamma_2] \tag{7.33a}$$

$$P_{4e} = \gamma_2\ [k_0^2\gamma_0^2\ (k_2^2 - \beta^2)\ (\tanh^2 \gamma_0 h_2 + \epsilon_r) + (k_0^2 - \beta^2)$$
$$\cdot (k_2^2\gamma_0^2 + k_0^2\gamma_2^2)\ \tanh \gamma_0 h_2 \coth \gamma_0 h_1] \tag{7.33b}$$

$$P_{5e} = \gamma_0\ [k_0^2\gamma_2^2\ (k_0^2 - \beta^2)\ (\tanh^2 \gamma_0 h_2 + \epsilon_r)\ \coth \gamma_0 h_1$$
$$+ (k_2^2 - \beta^2)\ (k_2^2\gamma_0^2 + k_0^2\gamma_2^2)\ \tanh \gamma_0 h_2] \tag{7.33c}$$

$$P_{6e} = k_2^2 \gamma_0 \gamma_2^2 \, (k_0^2 - \beta^2) \, (\tanh \gamma_0 h_2 + \coth \gamma_0 h_1) \tag{7.33d}$$

$$P_{0o} = \omega \mu_0 \, \gamma_0 \gamma_2 \, [(k_2^2 \gamma_0^2 + k_0^2 \gamma_2^2) \coth \gamma_0 h_2 \sinh \gamma_2 d \cosh \gamma_2 d \\ + k_0^2 \gamma_0 \gamma_2 \, (\coth^2 \gamma_0 h_2 + \epsilon_r) \sinh^2 \gamma_2 d + k_2^2 \gamma_0 \gamma_2] \tag{7.33e}$$

$$P_{4o} = \gamma_2 \, [k_0^2 \gamma_0^2 (k_2^2 - \beta^2) \, (\coth^2 \gamma_0 h_2 + \epsilon_r) \\ + (k_0^2 - \beta^2) \, (k_2^2 \gamma_0^2 + k_0^2 \gamma_2^2) \coth \gamma_0 h_2 \coth \gamma_0 h_1] \tag{7.33f}$$

$$P_{5o} = \gamma_0 \, [k_0^2 \gamma_2^2 \, (k_0^2 - \beta^2) \, (\coth^2 \gamma_0 h_2 + \epsilon_r) \coth \gamma_0 h_1 \\ + (k_2^2 - \beta^2) \, (k_2^2 \gamma_0^2 + k_0^2 \gamma_2^2) \coth \gamma_0 h_2] \tag{7.33g}$$

$$P_{6o} = k_2^2 \gamma_0 \gamma_2^2 \, (k_0^2 - \beta^2) \, (\coth \gamma_0 h_2 + \coth \gamma_0 h_1) \tag{7.33h}$$

(2) *Structure with Fins Facing Each Other* (Fig. 7.20(b))

The Green's function for the even-mode is obtained from (7.26) by replacing coth $\gamma_0 h_2$ by tanh $\gamma_0 h_2$. For the odd-mode, the expression is the same as (7.26). The Green's function expression can be written as in (7.32), where the various parameters are given by

$$P_{0e} = P_{0o} \\ = \omega \mu_0 \, \gamma_0 \gamma_2 \, [(k_2^2 \gamma_0^2 + k_0^2 \gamma_2^2) \coth \gamma_0 h_1 \sinh \gamma_2 d \cosh \gamma_2 d \\ + k_0^2 \gamma_0 \gamma_2 \, (\coth^2 \gamma_0 h_1 + \epsilon_r) \sinh^2 \gamma_2 d + k_2^2 \gamma_0 \gamma_2] \tag{7.34a}$$

$$P_{4e} = \gamma_2 \, [k_0^2 \gamma_0^2 \, (k_2^2 - \beta^2) \, (\coth^2 \gamma_0 h_1 + \epsilon_r) \\ + (k_0^2 - \beta^2) \, (k_2^2 \gamma_0^2 + k_0^2 \gamma_2^2) \coth \gamma_0 h_1 \tanh \gamma_0 h_2] \tag{7.34b}$$

$$P_{5e} = \gamma_0 \, [k_0^2 \gamma_2^2 \, (k_0^2 - \beta^2) \, (\coth^2 \gamma_0 h_1 + \epsilon_r) \tanh \gamma_0 h_2 \\ + (k_2^2 - \beta^2) \, (k_2^2 \gamma_0^2 + k_0^2 \gamma_2^2) \coth \gamma_0 h_1] \tag{7.34c}$$

$$P_{6e} = k_2^2 \gamma_0 \gamma_2^2 \, (k_0^2 - \beta^2) \, (\coth \gamma_0 h_1 + \tanh \gamma_0 h_2) \tag{7.34d}$$

$$P_{4o} = \gamma_2 \, [k_0^2 \gamma_0^2 \, (k_2^2 - \beta^2) \, (\coth^2 \gamma_0 h_1 + \epsilon_r) \\ + (k_0^2 - \beta^2) \, (k_2^2 \gamma_0^2 + k_0^2 \gamma_2^2) \coth \gamma_0 h_1 \coth \gamma_0 h_2] \tag{7.34e}$$

$$P_{5o} = \gamma_0 \, [k_0^2 \gamma_2^2 \, (k_0^2 - \beta^2) \, (\coth^2 \gamma_0 h_1 + \epsilon_r) \coth \gamma_0 h_2 \\ + (k_2^2 - \beta^2) \, (k_2^2 \gamma_0^2 + k_0^2 \gamma_2^2) \coth \gamma_0 h_1] \tag{7.34f}$$

$$P_{6o} = k_2^2 \gamma_o \gamma_2^2 \, (k_0^2 - \beta^2) \, (\coth \gamma_0 h_1 + \coth \gamma_0 h_2) \tag{7.34g}$$

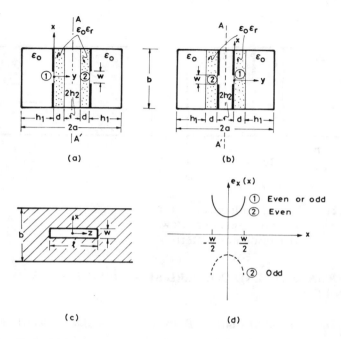

Fig. 7.20 Broadside-coupled resonators in double-dielectric fin line:
- (a) cross-sectional view (fins facing side walls)
- (b) cross-sectional view (fins facing each other)
- (c) slot resonator pattern
- (d) electric field distribution in slots

7.5.2 Bilateral Fin-Line Resonators

The bilateral fin-line resonator (Fig. 7.21) is considered as a special case of the broadside-coupled resonator with fins facing the sides (Fig. 7.20(a)), when the air gap is reduced to zero. By setting $2h_2 = 0$ and $h_1 = h$ in (7.33) and substituting in (7.32), the Green's functions for the even-mode and odd-mode reduce to

$$\hat{G}_{12e}(\alpha_n, \beta, k_0) = -\frac{j}{\omega\mu_0\gamma_0\gamma_2}[\gamma_0(k_2^2 - \beta^2) \tanh \gamma_2 d$$
$$+ \gamma_2(k_0^2 - \beta^2) \coth \gamma_0 h] \qquad (7.35a)$$

$$\hat{G}_{12o}(\alpha_n, \beta, k_0) = -\frac{j}{\omega\mu_0\gamma_0\gamma_2}[\gamma_0(k_2^2 - \beta^2) \coth \gamma_2 d$$
$$+ \gamma_2 (k_0^2 - \beta^2) \coth \gamma_0 h] \qquad (7.35b)$$

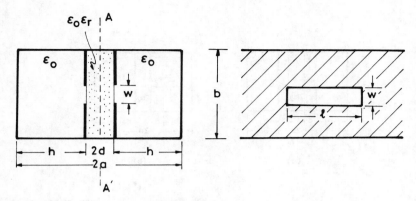

Fig. 7.21 Bilateral fin line resonator:
  (a) cross-sectional view
  (b) resonator pattern

7.6 BROADSIDE-END COUPLED SLOT RESONATORS IN FIN LINE

7.6.1 Broadside-End Coupled Resonators in Double-Dielectric Fin Line

The configurations of the broadside-end coupled resonators in the two double-dielectric configurations are shown in Fig. 7.22. The end-coupled resonator patterns on the two substrates form mirror images of each other. The structure has two planes of symmetry marked as AA′ and BB′. Two different excitations are pertinent to these structures: (1) even-even (*ee*) mode excitation, in which both AA′ and BB′ represent magnetic walls, and (2) even-odd (*eo*) mode excitation, in which AA′ is a magnetic wall and BB′ is an electric wall. The characteristic equation for determining the resonant frequencies of broadside-end coupled resonators in even-even and even-odd mode excitations is given by

$$\sum_{n=-\infty}^{\infty} \int_{-\infty}^{\infty} \hat{G}_{12e}(\alpha_n, \beta, k_0) |K_d \, \hat{e}_x(\alpha_n, \beta)|^2 \, d\beta = 0 \qquad (7.36)$$

where

$$K_d = [e^{\,j\beta\left(\frac{l+g}{2}\right)} - \delta e^{-j\beta\left(\frac{l+g}{2}\right)}] \qquad (7.37a)$$

$$\delta = \begin{cases} -1, & \text{even-even mode} \\ 1, & \text{even-odd mode} \end{cases} \qquad (7.37b)$$

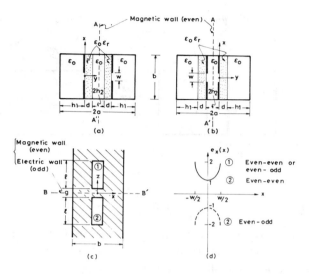

Fig. 7.22 Broadside-end-coupled resonators in double-dielectric fin line:

    (a) cross-sectional view (fins facing side walls)

    (b) cross-sectional view (fins facing each other)

    (c) end-coupled resonator pattern

    (d) electric field distribution across end-coupled slots for even-even (ee) and even-odd (eo) excitations

For the structure shown in Fig. 7.22(a) (fins facing side walls), $\hat{G}_{12e}(\alpha_n, \beta, k_0)$ is given by (7.32) and (7.33a–d), and for the structure shown in Fig. 7.22(b) (fins facing each other), $\hat{G}_{12e}(\alpha_n, \beta, k_0)$ is obtained from (7.32) and (7.34a–d). The basis function $\hat{e}_x(\alpha_n, \beta)$ corresponds to that of a single resonator centered at $z = 0$.

7.6.2 End-Coupled Resonators in Bilateral Fin Line

The geometry of the end-coupled resonators in bilateral fin line (Fig. 7.23) is a special case of the structure shown in Fig. 7.22(a) with $2h_2 = 0$ and $h_1 = h$. In the characteristic equation (7.36), the expressions for $\hat{G}_{12e}$ and K_d are substituted from (7.35a) and (7.37), respectively. The expression for $\hat{e}_x(\alpha_n, \beta)$ is the same as in (7.27).

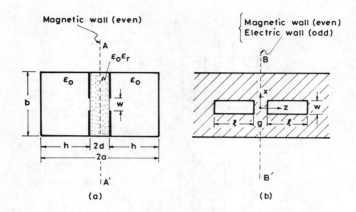

Fig. 7.23 Broadside-end-coupled slot resonators in bilateral fin line:
(a) cross-sectional view
(b) end-coupled resonator pattern

7.7 METAL INSERT RECTANGULAR SLOT RESONATORS

For a pure-metal-insert rectangular slot resonator (see Fig. 7.24(a)), Konishi *et al.* [9] have reported the following expression for the admittance Y as viewed from the slot:

$$Y = j \sum_{n,m}^{\infty} \frac{\pi^2 \, P_n \, Q_m}{\eta \epsilon_n \epsilon_m bc \, \tanh\left(\dfrac{\tau_{nm}a}{2}\right) \left[\left(\dfrac{n\pi}{c}\right)^2 + \left(\dfrac{m\pi}{b}\right)^2\right]}$$
$$\cdot \left(\frac{m^2 k_0}{\tau_{nm}b^2} - \frac{n^2 \tau_{nm}}{k_0 c^2}\right) \tag{7.38}$$

where

$$P_n = \left[\frac{2c^2 l}{\pi(n^2 l^2 - c^2)} \cos\left(\frac{n\pi l}{2c}\right)\right]^2 \tag{7.39a}$$

$$Q_m = \left(\frac{2b}{m\pi} \sin\frac{m\pi w}{2b}\right)^2 \tag{7.39b}$$

$$\tau_{nm}^2 = \left(\frac{n\pi}{c}\right)^2 + \left(\frac{m\pi}{b}\right)^2 - k_0^2 \qquad (7.39c)$$

$$\epsilon_n, \epsilon_m = \begin{cases} 1; & n, m = 0 \\ 0.5; & n, m \neq 0 \end{cases} \qquad (7.39d)$$

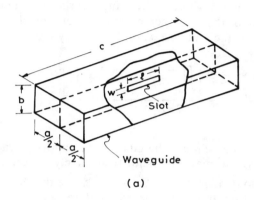

(a)

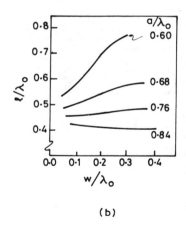

(b)

Fig. 7.24 Metal insert slot resonator and its characteristic.
(From Konishi *et al.* [9], Copyright © 1974 IEEE, reprinted with permission.)

The root of the equation $Y = 0$ gives the resonant frequency of the slot resonator. A typical graph of the resonator characteristics reported in [9] is reproduced in Fig. 7.24(b).

If the slot resonator of Fig. 7.24 is displaced down the E-plane so as to touch the lower broadside wall, the resulting configuration is a ridge-guide resonator. Konishi and Matsumura [10] have analyzed the end effect at the shorted end of a ridge-guide by using a variational method. Referring to the geometry of the ridge-guide with shorted end shown in Fig. 7.25, the expression for the end correction is given by [10]:

$$\Delta l = \frac{\lambda_1^{(1)} \sum_{n=1}^{\infty} Z_n^{(2)} \left[\iint_S \overrightarrow{e}_{nt}^{(2)} \times \overrightarrow{h}_{1t} \cdot \hat{z} \, dS \right]^2}{j2\pi Z_1^{(1)}} \tag{7.40}$$

where $\lambda_1^{(1)}$, $Z_1^{(1)}$, and $\overrightarrow{h}_{1t}$ are the guide wavelength, characteristic impedance, and transverse magnetic field, respectively, of the dominant mode in an infinitely long ridge-guide; $Z_n^{(2)}$ and $\overrightarrow{e}_{nt}^{(2)}$ are the characteristic impedance and normalized transverse electric field, respectively, of the nth mode

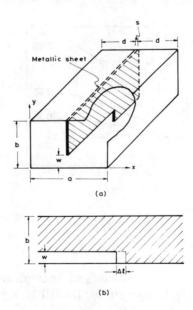

(a)

(b)

Fig. 7.25 (a) Geometry of the ridge guide with shorted end.
(b) Ridge pattern showing end correction (Δl).

in the cut-off waveguide (bifurcated guide region), and S is the cross section of the cut-off waveguide. The expressions for the various parameters appearing in (7.40) are

$$h_{1y} = A \sum_{n=1}^{\infty} P_n \cosh(\gamma_n x) \sin\left(\frac{n\pi y}{b}\right) \tag{7.41a}$$

$$h_{1x} = A\left[Q \sin(k_c x) + \sum_{n=1}^{\infty} R_n \sin(\gamma_n x) \cos\left(\frac{n\pi y}{b}\right)\right] \tag{7.41b}$$

$$P_n = \frac{2 \sin\left(\dfrac{n\pi w}{b}\right)}{b\gamma_n \sinh(\gamma_n d)} \cos\left(\frac{k_c s}{2}\right) \tag{7.41c}$$

$$Q = \frac{w}{b \sin(k_c d)} \cos\left(\frac{k_c s}{2}\right) \tag{7.41d}$$

$$R_n = \frac{2 \sin\left(\dfrac{n\pi w}{b}\right)}{n\pi \sinh(\gamma_n d)} \tag{7.41e}$$

$$2A^2 \int_0^d \int_0^b (h_{1x}^2 + h_{1y}^2) \, dx \, dy = 1 \tag{7.41f}$$

$$\gamma_n^2 = \left(\frac{n\pi}{b}\right)^2 - k_c^2, \quad k_c = \frac{2\pi}{\lambda_c} \tag{7.41g}$$

$$e_{ny}^{(2)} = -A_n \frac{\pi}{d} \sin\left(\frac{\pi x}{d}\right) \cos\left(\frac{n\pi y}{b}\right) \tag{7.41h}$$

$$e_{nx}^{(2)} = A_n \frac{n\pi}{b} \cos\left(\frac{\pi x}{d}\right) \sin\left(\frac{n\pi y}{b}\right) \tag{7.41i}$$

$$A_n = \frac{2}{\sqrt{2db} \cdot \left[\left(\dfrac{\pi}{d}\right)^2 \epsilon_n + \left(\dfrac{n\pi}{b}\right)^2\right]^{1/2}}; \quad \epsilon_n = \begin{cases} 2, & n = 0 \\ 1, & n \geq 1 \end{cases} \tag{7.41j}$$

$$Z_n^{(2)} = \frac{j\omega\mu_0}{\gamma_n^{(2)}} \text{ (TE mode)} \tag{7.41k}$$

$$Z_n^{(2)} = \frac{\gamma_n^{(2)}}{j\omega\epsilon_0} \text{ (TM mode)} \tag{7.41l}$$

In (7.41), $\gamma_n^{(2)}$ represents the propagation constant in the bifurcated guide and takes positive real values.

The inset to Fig. 7.26 shows the geometry of a ridge-guide resonator. In order to calculate the resonator length corresponding to half-wave resonance at a given frequency f_0, the end correction Δl is first determined by using (7.40). The resonator length l is then obtained from

$$l = \left(\frac{\lambda_1^{(1)}}{2} - 2\Delta l \right) \tag{7.42}$$

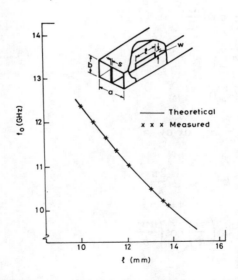

Fig. 7.26 Theoretical and measured values of resonant frequency of
ridge guide resonator:
    $a = 19$ mm
    $b = 9.5$ mm
    $s = 0.3$ mm
    $w = 1.7$ mm
(From Konishi and Matsumura [10], Copyright © 1979 IEEE, reprinted with permission.)

A typical characteristic of the ridge resonator as reported in [10] is reproduced in Fig. 7.26.

REFERENCES

1. I. Stakgold, *Boundary Value Problems of Mathematical Physics,* Vol. 2, McGraw-Hill, New York, 1968.
2. J.W. Dettmann, *Mathematical Methods in Physics and Engineering,* McGraw-Hill, New York, 1962.
3. L.P. Schmidt, T. Itoh, and H. Hofmann, "Characteristics of Unilateral Fin-Line Structures with Arbitrarily Located Slots," *IEEE Trans. Microwave Theory Tech.,* Vol. MTT-29, pp. 352–355, April 1981.
4. J.B. Knorr, "Equivalent Reactance of a Shorting Septum in a Fin Line: Theory and Experiment," *IEEE Trans. Microwave Theory Tech.,* Vol. MTT-29, pp. 1196–1202, Nov. 1981.
5. A.K. Sharma and W.J.R. Hoefer, "Evaluation of Resonant Frequency of a Rectangular Slot in Fin Line," *Proc. Joint Symp.* (IEEE/ APS, URSI, and EMP), Univ. of New Mexico, Albuquerque, NM, May 1982.
6. A.K. Agrawal and B. Bhat, "Resonant Characteristics and End Effects of a Slot Resonator in Unilateral Fin-Line," *Proc. IEEE,* Vol. 72, pp. 1416–1418, Oct. 1984.
7. A.K. Agrawal and B. Bhat, "Characteristics of Coupled Rectangular Slot Resonators in Fin-Line Configurations," *Int. J. Electronics,* Vol. 58, No. 5, pp. 781–792, 1985.
8. A.K. Agrawal and B. Bhat, "Characteristics of Double Dielectric Fin-Line Resonators," *Int. J. Electronics,* Vol. 58, No. 5, pp. 793–806, 1985.
9. Y. Konishi, K. Uenakada, and N. Hoshino, "The Design of Planar Circuit Mounted in Waveguide and Application to Low Noise 12 GHz Converter," *IEEE MTT-S Int. Microwave Symp. Digest,* pp. 168–170, 1974.
10. Y. Konishi and H. Matsumura, "Short End Effect of Ridge Guide with Planar Circuit Mounted in a Waveguide," *IEEE Trans. Microwave Theory Tech.,* Vol. MTT-27, pp. 168–170, Feb. 1979.

Chapter 8
Discontinuities and their Characterization

8.1 TYPES OF DISCONTINUITIES AND THEIR NETWORK EQUIVALENTS

Fin-line circuits, both passive and active, invariably incorporate one type of discontinuity or another. Some of the commonly encountered discontinuities in symmetric and asymmetric fin-line configurations and their equivalent network representations are shown in Fig. 8.1.

A step change in width can be represented by a *shunt susceptance* (capacitive) and an *impedance transformer* as shown in Fig. 8.1(a). Small *capacitive strips* (Fig. 8.1(b)), *inductive notches* (Fig. 8.1(c)), and *inductive strips* (Fig. 8.1(d)) can be represented as either a *π-network* or a *T-network*.

In the T-network for the capacitive strip and the π-network for the notch, the series element is inductive and the shunt element is capacitive when the element length ($2l$) is less than half the wavelength. For a narrow inductive strip, all of the network elements are inductive, L_p representing the coupling inductance, and L_{s1} and L_{s2} representing stray inductances (Fig. 8.1(d)). Step discontinuities, capacitive strips, and notches are used for performing impedance transformation. *Low-pass filters* are often realized by cascading capacitive strips and inductive notches. A capacitive strip in an asymmetric fin line is useful for mounting *beam-lead* semiconductor devices. A narrow inductive strip bridging a slot (Fig. 8.1(d)) serves as a coupling element to the transmission and reflection types of resonators.

Figure 8.1(e) shows a narrow slit in metalization, which can be used as a dc separation in a complex circuit. A single step degenerated to a short circuit (zero slot width) is shown in Fig. 8.1(f), and one reduced to an open circuit (slot width equals the waveguide height) in Fig. 8.1(g).

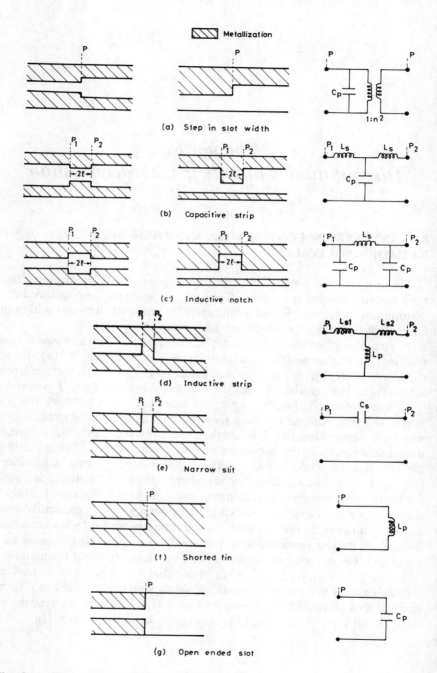

Fig. 8.1　Types of fin-line discontinuities.

Figure 8.2(a) shows an abrupt transition from a bilateral to a unilateral fin line and its equivalent circuit. Two such cascaded transitions may be represented by a T-network in which the elements can be either inductive or capacitive, depending on the dimensional parameters (Fig. 8.2 (b,c)). These two complementary combinations of unilateral and bilateral fin lines are useful in semiconductor biasing networks. For example, in Fig. 8.2(b), the RF circuit can be printed on one side of the substrate in the unilateral fin-line configuration, and the metallic strip on the back side can be used for applying the bias voltage to a semiconductor diode.

The various discontinuities shown in Fig. 8.1(a–g) can be incorporated in unilateral, bilateral, insulated, and also double-dielectric fin-line configurations. Several variations of the above-mentioned slot discontinuities are possible by adopting incongruent shapes for the upper and lower metal fins. Furthermore, the distance between the slot and the broad walls of the fin-line housing can be varied, depending on the circuit requirements.

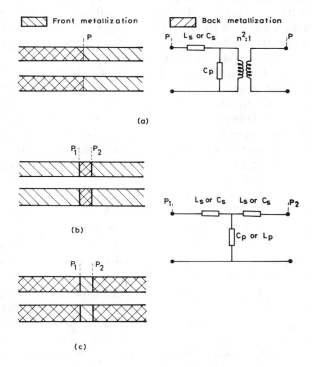

Fig. 8.2 (a) Step transition between bilateral and unilateral fin line.
(b) Cascade of bilateral fin-line section with unilateral fin line.
(c) Cascade of unilateral fin-line section with bilateral fin line.

For accurate design of fin-line circuits, it is important to characterize the discontinuities that are required to be incorporated in them. In the following, we first present the analytical techniques for solving the discontinuity problems, and then discuss the equivalent circuit parameters.

8.2 DISCONTINUITY ANALYSIS TECHNIQUES

Of the various discontinuities, the *inductive strip* and the *impedance step* have received the most widespread attention, and have been analyzed using different approaches. Earlier investigations were due to Meier [1], who used an empirical approach to characterize a narrow inductive strip as an element in a printed E-plane circuit, and to Konishi and Uenakada [2, 3], who treated the same structure with no dielectric backing by using the Raleigh-Ritz variational technique. The main difference between a discontinuity in a pure-metal-insert E-plane circuit and a fin-line circuit is that the higher order mode effect is relatively small in the former. Conversely, in a fin-line circuit, due to the presence of the dielectric, the field becomes concentrated in the slot region, thus causing a stronger excitation of the higher order modes at the discontinuity.

An analysis of inductive strip discontinuity in unilateral and bilateral fin lines that takes into account the higher order modes has been presented by Saad and Schunemann [4, 5]. This method makes use of fin-line modeling by a set of rectangular waveguides with homogeneous dielectric. An experimental approach for characterizing fin-line discontinuities has been reported by Pic and Hoefer [6]. They have obtained equivalent circuit parameters of inductive strips and impedance steps in unilateral fin lines from the measured resonant frequencies of a rectangular cavity containing the discontinuity elements. By using a rigorous hybrid-mode spectral domain approach [7], Koster and Jansen [8] have analyzed the equivalent circuit parameters of symmetric and asymmetric inductive strip discontinuities in unilateral fin lines. The effect of finite metalization thickness and the influence of mount slits on the calculation of step discontinuities have been treated by Beyer [9].

The *short-circuit end effect* in a pure-metal-insert E-plane circuit has been investigated by Konishi and Matsumura [10], using a rigorous field-expansion approach. The short-circuit end effect can also be determined by considering a rectangular slot resonator and solving for the resonant frequency by using spectral domain analysis. This approach is described in Ch. 7.

A general *modal analysis* technique described by Wexler [11] for solving waveguide discontinuities has been applied to fin-line discontinuities by

Hennawy and Schunemann [12–14]. In this method, the fields on either side of the junction are calculated in terms of a suitable set of fin-line modes and then matched at the junctions. The method is applicable to a broad class of fin-line discontinuities, and hence will be discussed in detail in this section. Another equally important analytical tool is the *transverse resonance technique* developed by Sorrentino and Itoh [15]. This technique is reported to offer considerable saving in computer time as compared with the direct modal analysis method [12–14]. A technique that combines the spectral domain approach with the direct modal analysis for calculating the scattering matrix elements of a fin-line discontinuity has been reported by Helard *et al.* [16].

8.2.1 Modal Analysis [11–13]

In order to derive the basic formulas governing the modal analysis technique, let us consider the example of a cascade of two impedance steps in a fin line, as shown in Fig. 8.3. The coordinate system is chosen such that $z = 0$ is the plane of junction 1, and x and y are the transverse coordinates. We assume that the dominant mode is incident from a matched source in guide A. When the wave encounters junction 1, part of the incident energy is reflected back into guide A, and a number of higher order modes are generated at the discontinuity. Any of the transmitted propagating or evanescent modes which reach the second discontinuity (junction 2) will partially reflect and generate a new set of backscattered modes. Some of these will reach junction 1. At junction 1, the total field consists of the positively directed waves and waves reflected from junction 2. The modal analysis takes into account the interaction effects of dominant and higher order modes between the discontinuities. The amplitudes of the normal modes are chosen such that the boundary conditions are satisfied at the discontinuity. The two boundary conditions are that (1) the transverse fields at the aperture are continuous, and (2) the tangential electric field at the conducting surface of the discontinuity is zero. The scattering coefficients and, hence, the equivalent circuit parameters are derived by computing the power apportioned among the various modes.

Let us refer to Fig. 8.3, where the electric and magnetic fields of each mode in the guiding structure can be expressed as

$$\bar{e}_i\,(x,\,y,\,z) = a_i\,\overrightarrow{e}_i\,(x,\,y)\,e^{-\gamma_i z} \tag{8.1a}$$

$$\tilde{h}_i\,(x,\,y,\,z)\,=\,a_i\,\overrightarrow{h}_i\,(x,\,y)\,e^{-\gamma_i z} \tag{8.1b}$$

The propagation is assumed to be in the positive z-direction, and the subscript i refers to the ith mode; $\overrightarrow{e}_i$ and $\overrightarrow{h}_i$ are the transverse vector functions of the electric and magnetic field, respectively; γ_i is the propagation constant; and a_i is the mode coefficient. Consider a single propagating mode with mode coefficient a_1 emanating from a matched source in guide A. At junction 1 ($z = 0$), let ρ be the reflection coefficient of this mode, and let a_i with $i = 2, 3, \ldots$ be the mode coefficients of the scattered modes. The total transverse fields that are just to the left of junction 1 (in waveguide A) can be expressed in terms of these modes to yield

$$\overrightarrow{E}_A\,=\,(1\,+\,\rho)a_1\,\overrightarrow{e}_{a1}\,+\,\sum_{i=2}^{\infty}\,a_i\,\overrightarrow{e}_{ai} \tag{8.2a}$$

$$\overrightarrow{H}_A\,=\,(1\,-\,\rho)a_1\,\overrightarrow{h}_{a1}\,-\,\sum_{i=2}^{\infty}\,a_i\,\overrightarrow{h}_{ai} \tag{8.2b}$$

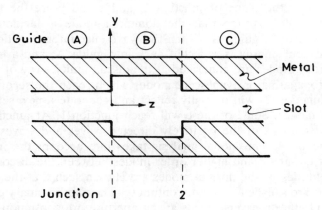

Fig. 8.3 Fin-line guiding system with two discontinuity junctions.

Just to the right of junction 1, the aperture fields can be expressed in terms of the modes in waveguide B. If waveguide B were to be match-terminated, then the transverse electric field of mode j can be expressed as $b_j\,\overrightarrow{e}_{bj}$. Thus,

$$\overrightarrow{E}_B\,=\,\sum_{j=1}^{\infty}\,b_j\,\overrightarrow{e}_{bj} \tag{8.3a}$$

$$\overrightarrow{H_B} = \sum_{j=1}^{\infty} b_j \overrightarrow{h_{bj}} \tag{8.3b}$$

If waveguide B encounters a discontinuity, as considered in Fig. 8.3, each of these forward propagating modes $j = 1, 2, \ldots$, *etc.*, generates an infinite set of back-scattered modes with mode coefficients b_k ($k = 1, 2, \ldots, \infty$) at that junction. Let s_{jk} denote the scattering coefficient of mode k, which is equal to the mode coefficient b_k transformed in amplitude and phase to junction 1 from junction 2. By summing all the forward and back-scattered modes, the total transverse electric and magnetic field that is just to the right of junction 1 can be expressed as

$$\overrightarrow{E_B} = \sum_{j=1}^{\infty} b_j (\overrightarrow{e_{bj}} + \sum_{k=1}^{\infty} s_{jk} \overrightarrow{e_{bk}}) \tag{8.4a}$$

$$\overrightarrow{H_B} = \sum_{j=1}^{\infty} b_j (\overrightarrow{h_{bj}} - \sum_{k=1}^{\infty} s_{jk} \overrightarrow{h_{bk}}) \tag{8.4b}$$

Equations (8.2) to (8.4) are general, and can be applied irrespective of the relative cross-sectional sizes of the guides on either side of the junction. The problem is to evaluate the unknown parameters ρ, a_i and b_j by matching the boundary conditions. We presume that s_{jk} due to the second discontinuity is known; otherwise, it must be evaluated by solving the second discontinuity first.

Expressions for s_{jk}

In the case of a single step discontinuity, and with waveguide B terminated in a matched load (see Fig. 8.4(a)), we have

$$s_{jk} = 0 \tag{8.5}$$

Discontinuities shown in Fig. 8.1(a, f–g) belong to this category. When two identical step discontinuities are connected back-to-back as in Figs. 8.1(b, c) and 8.2(b), there exists a *plane of symmetry* midway between the two junctions. An example of a strip with a plane of symmetry at $z = l$ is shown in Fig. 8.4(b). The equivalent circuit of such symmetric step discontinuities can be found from a symmetrical (even) and an antisymmetrical (odd) excitation of the two ports, which result in an open circuit and a short circuit, respectively, at the plane of symmetry. The problem reduces to solving for the first junction with guide B terminated in an open circuit at $z = l$ for the even mode and a short circuit for the odd mode. These terminations exhibit the property of causing an independent reflection of each mode incident upon it, irrespective of the amplitude and phase of any other mode. Hence,

$$s_{jk} = 0, \quad j \neq k \tag{8.6a}$$

and

$$s_{jj} = \frac{1 - y_{bj}}{1 + y_{bj}} = \pm e^{-j2\beta_{bj}l} \tag{8.6b}$$

In (8.6b), y_{bj} is the normalized input admittance of the jth mode in guide B measured at $z = 0$, and β_{bj} is the propagation constant of the mode.

We now consider the mathematical formulation of the boundary conditions at the discontinuity junction using the field expansion given in (8.2) and (8.4). For this purpose, we classify the discontinuities in two categories: (1) *step-down junction* in which the cross-sectional aperture of guide A is larger than that of guide B, and (2) *step-up junction* (complement of the "step-down") in which the aperture of guide B is larger than that of guide A.

Step-Down Junction

An impedance step in a uniform fin line from a larger slot width (w_a) to a smaller slot width (w_b) constitutes a step-down junction. This is shown in Fig. 8.4(a). The fin-line section on the left, which has a wider slot, is referred to as guide A, and the fin-line section on the right of the junction is referred to as guide B. A wave of amplitude a_1 is assumed to be incident from guide A. A symmetric strip (Fig. 8.4(b)) can be analyzed as a step-down junction by considering the left half of the structure, with the symmetry plane representing an open circuit for even excitation and a short circuit for odd excitation (Fig. 8.4(c)). In order to satisfy the boundary conditions at the junction, we proceed as follows:

Cross-multiply (8.2a) with $\vec{h}_{am}$, integrate over the cross section of guide A, and substitute for the unknown aperture E-field from (8.4a). The resulting equation is

$$(1 + \rho)a_1 \int_A \overrightarrow{e}_{a1} \times \overrightarrow{h}_{am} \cdot \hat{z} \, dx \, dy + \sum_{i=2}^{\infty} a_i \int_A \overrightarrow{e}_{ai} \times \overrightarrow{h}_{am} \cdot \hat{z} \, dx \, dy$$

$$= \sum_{j=1}^{\infty} \left[b_j \left(\int_B \overrightarrow{e}_{bj} \times \overrightarrow{h}_{am} \cdot \hat{z} \, dx \, dy + \sum_{k=1}^{\infty} s_{jk} \int_B \overrightarrow{e}_{bk} \right. \right.$$

$$\left. \left. \times \overrightarrow{h}_{am} \cdot \hat{z} \, dx \, dy \right) \right] \qquad (8.7a)$$

Because $\overrightarrow{E}_A$ exists on the common aperture only, the integral on the right-hand side of (8.7a) must be taken over the cross section of guide B. Next, take the cross product of $\overrightarrow{e}_{bn}$ with (8.4b), integrate over the cross section of guide B, and substitute for the aperture H-field from (8.2b). We then obtain

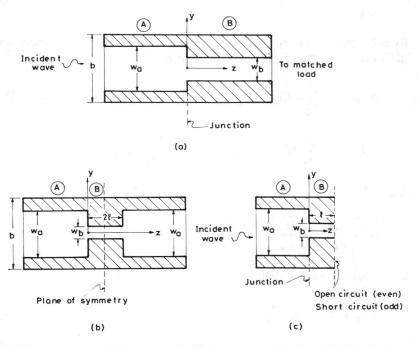

Fig. 8.4 (a) Schematic of a step-down junction.
         (b) Symmetric step.
         (c) Left half of (b) as a step-down junction

$$(1 - \rho)a_1 \int_B \overrightarrow{e}_{bn} \times \overrightarrow{h}_{a1} \cdot \hat{z} \, dx \, dy - \sum_{i=2}^{\infty} a_i \int_B \overrightarrow{e}_{bn} \times \overrightarrow{h}_{ai} \cdot \hat{z} \, dx \, dy$$

$$= \sum_{j=1}^{\infty} \left[b_j \left(\int_B \overrightarrow{e}_{bn} \times \overrightarrow{h}_{bj} \cdot \hat{z} \, dx \, dy - \sum_{k=1}^{\infty} s_{jk} \int_B \overrightarrow{e}_{bn} \right. \right.$$

$$\left. \left. \times \overrightarrow{h}_{bk} \cdot \hat{z} \, dx \, dy \right) \right] \tag{8.7b}$$

Here, guides A and B are uniform fin lines, inhomogeneously filled with isotropic dielectric. In a uniform lossless guide (homogeneous or inhomogeneous), the following orthogonality relation holds for nondegenerate modes:

$$\int_A \overrightarrow{e}_{ai} \times \overrightarrow{h}_{am} \cdot \hat{z} \, dx \, dy = 0 \text{ if } i \neq m \tag{8.8}$$

By using the known incident wave amplitude a_1 as the normalization factor, (8.7) can be written in compact form as follows:

$$\rho \, I_{a1am} + \sum_{i=2}^{\infty} \bar{a}_i I_{aiam} - \sum_{j=1}^{\infty} \bar{b}_j \left(I_{bjam} + \sum_{k=1}^{\infty} s_{jk} I_{bkam} \right) = -I_{a1am} \tag{8.9a}$$

$$\rho \, I_{bna1} + \sum_{i=2}^{\infty} \bar{a}_i I_{bnai} + \sum_{j=1}^{\infty} \bar{b}_j \left(I_{bnbj} - \sum_{k=1}^{\infty} s_{jk} I_{bnbk} \right) = I_{bna1} \tag{8.9b}$$

where

$$\bar{a}_i = \frac{a_i}{a_1}, \quad \bar{b}_j = \frac{b_j}{a_1} \tag{8.10}$$

and the notation I_{aibj} denotes

$$I_{aibj} = \int \overrightarrow{e}_{ai} \times \overrightarrow{h}_{bj} \cdot \hat{z} \, dx \, dy \tag{8.11}$$

with integration to be carried out over the aperture plane. If guide B is terminated in a matched load, then $s_{jk} = 0$ in (8.9). When the termination is a short circuit or an open circuit, as in Fig. 8.4(c), (8.9) reduces to

$$\rho \, I_{a1am} + \sum_{i=2}^{\infty} \bar{a}_i \, I_{aiam} - \sum_{j=1}^{\infty} \bar{b}_j (1 + s_{jj}) \, I_{bjam} = -I_{a1am} \tag{8.12a}$$

$$\rho \, I_{bna1} + \sum_{i=2}^{\infty} \bar{a}_i \, I_{bnai} + \sum_{j=1}^{\infty} \bar{b}_j (1 - s_{jj}) \, I_{bnbj} = I_{bna1} \qquad (8.12b)$$

where s_{jj} is given by (8.6b).

Step-Up Junction

If guides A and B in Fig. 8.4(a) are interchanged, with wave incident from guide A (now having a smaller slot width w_a), then the problem corresponds to that of a step-up junction. This situation is illustrated in Fig. 8.5(a). Figure 8.5(b) shows a symmetric notch, which can be analyzed as a step-up junction by considering the symmetric left half of the structure (Fig. 8.5(c)).

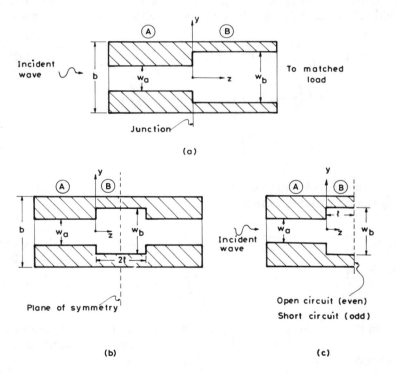

(a)

(b)   (c)

Fig. 8.5 (a) Schematic of a step-up junction.
(b) Symmetric notch.
(c) Left half of (b) as a step-up junction.

Cross-multiply (8.4b) by $\overrightarrow{e}_{am}$, integrate over the cross section of guide A, and substitute for the unknown H-field at the aperture from (8.2b). We then obtain

$$(1 - \rho)\, a_1 \int_A \overrightarrow{e}_{am} \times \overrightarrow{h}_{a1} \cdot \hat{z}\, dx\, dy - \sum_{i=2}^{\infty} a_i \int_A \overrightarrow{e}_{am} \times \overrightarrow{h}_{ai} \cdot \hat{z}\, dx\, dy$$

$$= \sum_{j=1}^{\infty} \left[b_j \left(\int_A \overrightarrow{e}_{am} \times \overrightarrow{h}_{bj} \cdot \hat{z}\, dx\, dy - \sum_{k=1}^{\infty} s_{jk} \int_A \overrightarrow{e}_{am} \right.\right.$$

$$\left.\left. \times\, \overrightarrow{h}_{bk} \cdot \hat{z}\, dx\, dy \right) \right] \qquad (8.13a)$$

Next, cross-multiply (8.4a) by $\overrightarrow{h}_{bn}$, integrate over the cross section of guide B, and substitute (8.2a) for the unknown aperture E-field. This gives

$$(1 + \rho)\, a_1 \int_A \overrightarrow{e}_{a1} \times \overrightarrow{h}_{bn} \cdot \hat{z}\, dx\, dy + \sum_{i=2}^{\infty} a_i \int_A \overrightarrow{e}_{ai} \times \overrightarrow{h}_{bn} \cdot \hat{z}\, dx\, dy$$

$$= \sum_{j=1}^{\infty} \left[b_j \left(\int_B \overrightarrow{e}_{bj} \times \overrightarrow{h}_{bn} \cdot \hat{z}\, dx\, dy + \sum_{k=1}^{\infty} s_{jk} \int_B \overrightarrow{e}_{bk} \right.\right.$$

$$\left.\left. \times\, \overrightarrow{h}_{bn} \cdot \hat{z}\, dx\, dy \right) \right] \qquad (8.13b)$$

By normalizing with respect to a_1 and using the abbreviation in (8.11), (8.13) can be written in the form:

$$\rho\, I_{ama1} + \sum_{i=2}^{\infty} \bar{a}_i\, I_{amai} + \sum_{j=1}^{\infty} \bar{b}_j (I_{ambj} - \sum_{k=1}^{\infty} s_{jk}\, I_{ambk}) = I_{ama1} \qquad (8.14a)$$

$$\rho\, I_{a1bn} + \sum_{i=2}^{\infty} \bar{a}_i\, I_{aibn} - \sum_{j=1}^{\infty} \bar{b}_j (I_{bjbn} + \sum_{k=1}^{\infty} s_{jk}\, I_{bkbn}) = -I_{a1bn} \qquad (8.14b)$$

As in the step-down junction problem, if guide B is match-terminated, then $s_{jk} = 0$ in (8.14). When the guide is terminated in a short circuit or an open circuit, as in Fig. 8.5(c), (8.14) reduces to

$$\rho\, I_{ama1} + \sum_{i=2}^{\infty} \bar{a}_i\, I_{amai} + \sum_{j=1}^{\infty} \bar{b}_j (1 - s_{jj})\, I_{ambj} = I_{ama1} \qquad (8.15a)$$

$$\rho\, I_{a1bn} + \sum_{i=2}^{\infty} \bar{a}_i\, I_{aibn} - \sum_{j=1}^{\infty} \bar{b}_j (1 + s_{jj})\, I_{bjbn} = -I_{a1bn} \qquad (8.15b)$$

where s_{jj} is given by (8.6b).

In practical problems, only a finite number of modes must be taken in guides A and B. Thus, the infinite series in (8.9) and (8.14) may be truncated at $i = M$ and $j = N$. The unknowns ρ, $\bar{a}_i$, and $\bar{b}_j$ then reduce to $(M + N)$ in number. These can be evaluated by solving the $(M + N)$ linear equations generated from (8.9) or (8.14)

Fin-Line Eigenmodes

The transverse functions $\vec{e}_i$ and $\vec{h}_i$ appearing in the integrand of the various integrals in (8.9) and (8.14) can be obtained from the eigenmode analysis of the fin lines. The procedure was described in Ch. 3.

In the case of an inductive strip discontinuity (Fig. 8.6), the part of the structure containing the inductive strip corresponds to a bifurcated waveguide (Fig. 8.6(c)). The fields in region 1 of the bifurcated waveguide (guide B) are of the form:

$$E_{bx}^{(1)} = \sum_{m=0}^{\infty} \sum_{n=1}^{\infty} A_{bn1} \cos(\gamma_{b1}x) \cdot \sin(\alpha_n y) \qquad (8.16a)$$

$$H_{bx}^{(1)} = \sum_{m=1}^{\infty} \sum_{n=0}^{\infty} B_{bn1} \sin(\gamma_{b1}x) \cdot \cos(\alpha_n y) \qquad (8.16b)$$

where

$$\gamma_{b1} = \frac{m\pi}{h_2}, \quad \alpha_n = \frac{n\pi}{b}, \quad n \text{ even} \qquad (8.17a)$$

and

$$\alpha_n^2 + \gamma_{b1}^2 - \beta_{bz1}^2 = k_0^2 \qquad (8.17b)$$

The parameter β_{bz1} is the propagation constant in region 1, and k_0 is the free-space propagation constant. The x components of the fields in regions 2 and 3 are given by

$$E_{bx}^{(2)} = \sum_{n=1}^{\infty} A_{bn2} \cos(\gamma_{b2}x) \cdot \sin(\alpha_n y) \qquad (8.18a)$$

$$H_{bx}^{(2)} = \sum_{n=0}^{\infty} B_{bn2} \sin (\gamma_{b2}x) \cdot \cos (\alpha_n y) \tag{8.18b}$$

$$E_{bx}^{(3)} = - \sum_{n=1}^{\infty} A_{bn2} \frac{\gamma_{b2}}{\gamma_{b3}} \frac{\sin (\gamma_{b2}d)}{\sin (\gamma_{b3}h_1)} \cos[\gamma_{b3}(x + d + h_1)] \cdot \sin (\alpha_n y) \tag{8.19a}$$

$$H_{bx}^{(3)} = - \sum_{n=1}^{\infty} B_{bn2} \frac{\sin (\gamma_{b2}d)}{\sin (\gamma_{b3}h_1)} \sin[\gamma_{b3}(x + d + h_1)] \cdot \cos (\alpha_n y) \tag{8.19b}$$

where

$$\alpha_n^2 + \gamma_{b2}^2 - \beta_{bz2}^2 = k_0^2 \epsilon_r \tag{8.20a}$$

$$\alpha_n^2 + \gamma_{b3}^2 - \beta_{bz3}^2 = k_0^2 \tag{8.20b}$$

The y and z components of the E- and H-fields in the three regions can be derived from the x component of the fields given above. The propagation constants in regions 2 and 3 can be computed from the following eigenvalue equations:

$$- \frac{\gamma_{b2}}{\epsilon_r} \tan (\gamma_{b2}d) = \gamma_{b3} \cdot \tan (\gamma_{b3}h_1), \quad \text{for LSM}(x) \text{ mode} \tag{8.21a}$$

$$- \frac{\tan (\gamma_{b2}d)}{\gamma_{b2}} = \frac{\tan (\gamma_{b3}h_1)}{\gamma_{b3}}, \quad \text{for LSE}(x) \text{ mode} \tag{8.21b}$$

Basis Functions

For accurate evaluation of the discontinuities, the propagation constants of the eigenmodes in the fin lines must first be known. For a slot centered in the E-plane, with the origin of the axes in the centre of the slot, the basis functions for the slot fields can be specified as [13]:

$$E_y(y) = \sum_{l=0}^{L} c_l y^{2l} \left[\left(\frac{w}{2}\right)^2 - y^2 \right]^{-1/2}, \quad |y| \leq \frac{w}{2} \tag{8.22a}$$

$$E_z(y) = \sum_{l=1}^{L} d_l y^{(2l-1)} \left[\left(\frac{w}{2}\right)^2 - y^2 \right]^{1/2}, \quad |y| \leq \frac{w}{2} \tag{8.22b}$$

If the slot is asymmetrically located in the E-plane, as shown in Fig. 8.6(b), the basis function should be modified as follows:

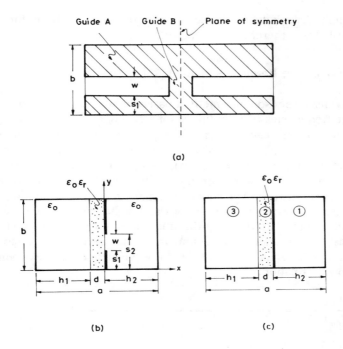

Fig. 8.6 (a) Inductive strip discontinuity.
(b) Cross section in the slot region.
(c) Cross section in the strip region.

$$E_y(y) = \sum_{l=0}^{L} c_l \, y^l \left[\left(\frac{w}{2} \right)^2 - y'^2 \right]^{-1/2}, \quad s_1 \leqslant y \leqslant s_2 \qquad (8.23a)$$

$$E_z(y) = \sum_{l=0}^{L} d_l \, y^l \left[\left(\frac{w}{2} \right)^2 - y'^2 \right]^{1/2}, \quad s_1 \leqslant y \leqslant s_2 \qquad (8.23b)$$

where

$$y' = y - \left(\frac{s_1 + s_2}{2} \right) \qquad (8.24)$$

A choice of $L = 4$ is reported to give accurate results up to the 30th mode [13].

It may be pointed out that the efficiency of the modal analysis technique in solving fin-line discontinuities depends on the accurate evaluation of the eigenmodes. Suitable choice of a set of basis functions for the slot aperture fields is therefore very important.

8.2.2 Transverse Resonance Method [15]

The transverse resonance method basically involves computation of the resonant frequencies of a fin-line resonator cavity containing the discontinuity. The cavity can be formed by placing electric or magnetic walls some distance away from the discontinuity. Figure 8.7(a) shows an impedance step in a unilateral fin-line cavity with shorted ends. The equivalent circuit of the cavity is shown in Fig. 8.7(b). The discontinuity is modeled as a two-port network. This model assumes that only the dominant mode propagates in the two fin-line sections and higher order modes generated at the discontinuity have negligible amplitudes at the shorting planes. For the transverse resonance condition, the admittance at the discontinuity junction must be equal to zero. From the equivalent circuit, we then obtain the following relation:

$$\frac{1}{(Z_a + Z_{11} - Z_{12})} + \frac{1}{(Z_b + Z_{22} - Z_{12})} + \frac{1}{Z_{12}} = 0 \qquad (8.25)$$

or

$$(Z_a + Z_{11})(Z_b + Z_{22}) - Z_{12}^2 = 0 \qquad (8.26)$$

where

$$Z_a = jZ_{oa} \tan(\beta_a l_a) \qquad (8.27a)$$

$$Z_b = jZ_{ob} \tan(\beta_b l_b) \qquad (8.27b)$$

The parameters Z_{oa} and β_a represent the characteristic impedance and propagation constant, respectively, of the fin line with slot width w_a, while Z_{ob} and β_b are the corresponding parameters of the fin line with slot width w_b. Z_{11}, Z_{22}, and Z_{12} are the impedance parameters of the discontinuity. These can be evaluated from (8.26) by substituting three different pairs of lengths l_a and l_b for any specified resonant frequency f_o.

In the absence of the discontinuity, $Z_{oa} = Z_{ob} = Z$, and $\beta_a = \beta_b = \beta$. The structure reduces to a uniform fin-line section of length l ($= l_a + l_b$) with perfectly shorted ends. Equation (8.26) then gives $\beta l = n\pi$ at the resonant frequency with $n = 1$ for the lowest order resonance. Thus, by computing the resonant length of the fin-line section corresponding to slot widths w_a and w_b separately, the propagation constants β_a and β_b can be determined. This method is an alternative to the spectral domain technique described in Ch. 3.

For determining the resonant frequencies of the cavity with the discontinuity present, the fields in the three regions (marked 1 to 3) of the cavity are expanded in terms of LSE and LSM modes of a rectangular waveguide with inner dimensions l and b. For example, in region 1 ($0 < x < h_2$), the transverse electric fields (with respect to x) are of the form:

$$\overrightarrow{E}_t = \sum_m \sum_n \left\{ \left(A_{mn} \hat{x} \times \nabla_t \Psi_{mn} - \frac{B_{mn} k_{mn}}{j\omega\epsilon_0} \nabla_t \Phi_{mn} \right) \right.$$

$$\left. \cdot \sin\left[k_{mn}(x - h_2) \right] \right\} \qquad (8.28)$$

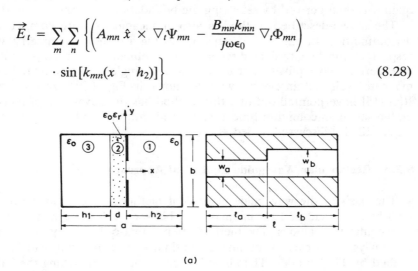

(a)

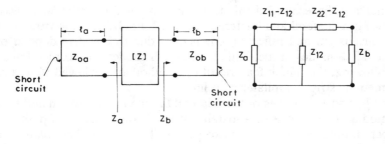

(b)

Fig. 8.7   (a) Cross-sectional views of a step discontinuity in a fin-line cavity with shorted ends.
(b) Equivalent circuit.

where

$$k_{mn}^2 = k_0^2 - \left(\frac{m\pi}{l}\right)^2 - \left(\frac{n\pi}{b}\right)^2 \tag{8.29}$$

Φ_{mn} and Ψ_{mn} are the TE and TM potentials of the rectangular waveguide with inner dimensions l and b, and A_{mn} and B_{mn} are constants. In the plane $x = 0$, the slot fields are expanded in terms of a set of orthogonal basis functions. The characteristic equation for determining the resonant frequency is then derived by satisfying the boundary conditions at $x = 0$.

The above-described method is also applicable to more complicated discontinuities. In the case of steps possessing a plane of symmetry with respect to the longitudinal direction, the problem can be simplified by considering two equivalent structures with a single step terminated in a magnetic wall and an electric wall, as shown in Fig. 8.8. Sorrentino and Itoh [15] have pointed out that this method has the advantage of considerable saving in computer time as compared with the modal analysis technique [12, 13] discussed in Sec. 8.2.1.

8.2.3 Rectangular Waveguide Equivalent Approach [4, 5]

The basis of the waveguide equivalent method is the equivalence established by Saad and Schunemann [4] between a fin line and a set of rectangular waveguides. The method offers a first-order design theory for the analysis of a class of fin-line discontinuity structures that can be described by TE_{m0} modes. The analysis then reduces to matching the TE_{m0} modes between two sets of equivalent rectangular waveguides. Saad and Schunemann have applied this technique to solve metallic strip discontinuities in unilateral and bilateral fin lines. It has been demonstrated that the transmission and reflection coefficients due to the strip depend only on the TE_{m0} modes of the fin line, and other modes are averaged out. In the following, the salient features of the method are reviewed for the case of a metallic strip in a bilateral fin line.

The hybrid HE modes of the bilateral fin line are approximated by the TE modes. In the case of a metallic strip discontinuity, it is possible to neglect all other fin-line modes except the TE_{m0} modes. The bilateral fin-line modes can then be replaced by the TE_{m0} modes of m equivalent rectangular waveguides of cross section $a_m \times b$ and homogeneously filled with a dielectric of effective dielectric constant k_{em} as shown in Fig. 8.9(a).

The effective dielectric constant is defined by [1]:

$$k_{em} = k_{cm0}^2 / k_{cm}^2 \qquad (8.30)$$

where k_{cm} and k_{cm0} are the cut-off wavenumbers of the mth mode in fin line, with and without the dielectric, respectively. The guide wavelength λ_m and the broadside dimension a_m of the rectangular waveguide are given by

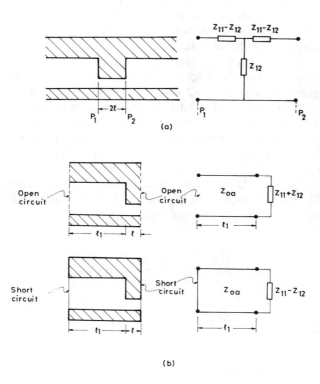

(b)

Fig. 8.8 (a) Capacitive strip discontinuity and T-equivalent network. (b) Equivalent circuit models for determining its Z-parameters.

$$\lambda_m = \frac{\lambda_0}{\left[k_{em} - \left(\frac{\lambda_0}{\lambda_{cm0}}\right)^2\right]^{1/2}} \tag{8.31}$$

$$a_m = \frac{m\pi}{k_{cm}} \tag{8.32}$$

where $\lambda_{cm0} = 2\pi/k_{cm0}$, and λ_0 is the free-space wavelength. The above relations hold true under the assumption that the substrate thickness is small ($2d/a \ll 1$) and ϵ_r is moderate. Practical fin lines using RT-duroid™ as the dielectric satisfy these criteria.

The rectangular waveguide equivalents of the fin-line sections A, B, and C are illustrated in Fig. 8.9(b). Only one-half of the fin-line structure with a magnetic wall at $x = a/2$ suffices for the purpose of analysis. In guide B, the metallic strip bifurcates the guide into two, and both operate below the cut-off frequency of the fundamental mode. The electric field having a peak in the slot region in guide A is shorted by the metallic fin of guide B at the junction $z = 0$. Guide B is modeled as a rectangular guide of cross section $h \times b$ and length s. The electric field in the region $h \le x \le a_m/2$ in guide B is set equal to zero. The total field in each of the guides A, B, and C is expanded in terms of TE_{m0} modes and matched at $z = 0$ and $z = s$. For instance, in guide A, the total field at $z = 0$ is given by [5]:

$$E_{yA} = \sum_{m=1,3,\ldots} (\epsilon_m + R_m) A_m \left(\frac{-j\omega\mu}{k_{xm}}\right) \sin(k_{xm} x) \tag{8.33a}$$

$$H_{xA} = \sum_{m=1,3,\ldots} (\epsilon_m - R_m) A_m \left(\frac{\beta_{zm}}{k_{xm}}\right) \sin(k_{xm} x) \tag{8.33b}$$

where R_m and A_m are constants, and

$$k_{xm} = k_{cm0} \tag{8.34a}$$

$$\beta_{zm} = (k_{cm0}^2 - k_{em}k_0^2)^{1/2}; \quad k_0 = \frac{2\pi}{\lambda_0} \tag{8.34b}$$

$$\epsilon_m = \begin{cases} 1, \text{ for } m = 1 \\ 0, \text{ otherwise} \end{cases} \tag{8.34c}$$

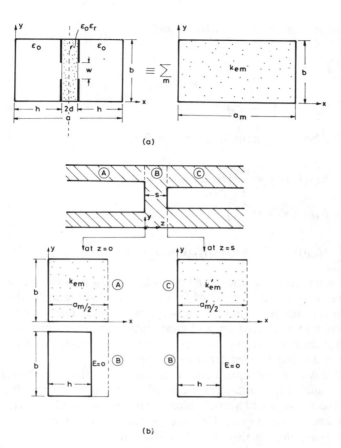

Fig. 8.9 (a) Bilateral fin line and its waveguide equivalent.
(b) Strip discontinuity and equivalent models for analysis.

The total field in guide B at $z = 0$ is given by

$$E_{yB} = \sum_{m=1,2,\ldots} (1 + R_p) A_p \left(\frac{-j\omega\mu}{k_{xp}} \right) \sin(k_{xp} x) \tag{8.35a}$$

$$H_{xB} = \sum_{m=1,2,\ldots} (1 - R_p) A_p \left(\frac{\beta_{zp}}{k_{xp}} \right) \sin(k_{xp} x) \tag{8.35b}$$

where R_p and A_p are constants, and

$$k_{xp} = \frac{p\pi}{l} \tag{8.36a}$$

$$\beta_{zp} = (k_{xp}^2 - k_0^2)^{1/2} \tag{8.36b}$$

The boundary conditions at $z = 0$ are

$$
\begin{aligned}
E_{yA}\left(0 \le x \le \frac{a_m}{2}\right) &= E_{yB}(0 \le x \le h); \\
E_{yB}\left(h \le x \le \frac{a_m}{2}\right) &= 0
\end{aligned}
\tag{8.37a}
$$

$$H_{xA}(0 \le x \le h) = H_{xB}(0 \le x \le h) \tag{8.37b}$$

Similar field equations and boundary conditions can be written for the junction at $z = s$. A total of four equations is obtained, which on solving yield the reflection and transmission coefficients due to the discontinuity. Calculated values of strip discontinuity parameters in unilateral and bilateral fin lines are reported to agree with the measured values at X band within a measurement accuracy of 3%.

The waveguide equivalent method is far simpler than the rigorous methods, which require determination of fin-line eigenmodes. It is well suited for the analysis of short-circuited slots, resonator elements, bandpass filters, and fin-line tapers. However, in the case of a notch or capacitive strip (involving step change in slot width), modes other than the TE_{m0} also influence the reflection and transmission coefficients. In such cases, the above-described method may not offer sufficiently accurate results.

8.2.4   Spectral Domain Approach

A general hybrid-mode spectral domain method has been described by Jansen [7] for computing the end effects in planar transmission lines that are abruptly terminated in an open or short circuit. The method employs Galerkin's approach in conjunction with a spectral-domain Green's function interpolation technique. The method is rigorous. Suitable expansion functions, however, will have to be assumed for describing the abrupt end. Based on this approach, the circuit parameters of symmetric and asymmetric strip discontinuities in unilateral fin line are described by Koster and Jansen [8].

A technique that combines the spectral domain approach with the direct modal analysis has been presented by Helard *et al.* [16]. An example of a symmetric step change in width in a unilateral fin line has also been considered by these same authors. The procedure involves determination of the first few eigenmodes of the fin line through the spectral domain method. Then, coupling coefficients between the various eigenmodes at the discontinuity plane, which must be introduced into the scattering matrix formulation in direct modal analysis, are computed in the spectral domain. This approach renders the computation easier to perform than in direct modal analysis.

8.2.5 Variational Method

The variational method has been applied by Konishi and Uenakada [2] to analyze pure metal strips mounted in the E-plane of a waveguide. A single metallic strip in a waveguide can be represented by an equivalent T-network (Fig. 8.10). Let Y_{sc} and Y_{oc} denote the input admittances of the network when an electric wall (short circuit) and a magnetic wall (open circuit), respectively, are placed at the symmetry plane P_0 through the center of the strip. The elements of the T-network can then be obtained from Y_{sc} and Y_{oc} by using the following relations:

$$Z_s = \frac{1}{Y_{sc}} \tag{8.38a}$$

$$Z_p = \frac{1}{2}\left(\frac{1}{Y_{oc}} - \frac{1}{Y_{sc}}\right) \tag{8.38b}$$

For determining the admittances Y_{oc} and Y_{sc}, it is adequate to consider the symmetric half of the structure with appropriate boundary conditions at the plane $z = s/2$ (Fig. 8.10(b)). The total transverse field in region $z < 0$ is expanded in terms of TE_{m0} (m odd) modes. Because the discontinuity is uniform along the y axis, these are the only higher order modes excited at the strip. In the bifurcated guide region, $0 \leq z \leq s/2$, all the modes can be assumed to be evanescent. By matching the boundary conditions at the junction $z = 0$ and solving, the following variational formula has been obtained in [2] for the normalized admittances $\overline{Y}_{oc}$ ($= Y_{oc}/Y_o$) and $\overline{Y}_{sc}$ ($= Y_{sc}/Y_o$):

$$\overline{Y}_{oc,sc} = \frac{\displaystyle\sum_{m=3...}^{\infty} Y_{om}\left(\sum_{n=1}^{N} A_{nm}\,\xi_n\right)^2 + a \sum_{n=1}^{N} \xi_n^2 Y_n Q_{n\ oc,sc}}{Y_{o1}\left(\displaystyle\sum_{n=1}^{N} \xi_n A_{n1}\right)^2} \tag{8.39}$$

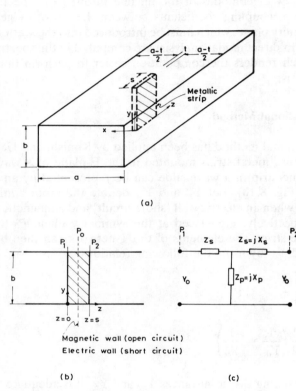

(a)

(b)

Magnetic wall (open circuit)
Electric wall (short circuit)

(c)

Fig. 8.10   (a) Geometry of an inductive strip in waveguide.
(b) View in the plane of the strip.
(c) Equivalent circuit of the inductive strip.

where

$$A_{nm} = (-1)^n \cdot \frac{8n\,a^{1/2}}{\pi(m^2 - 4n^2)} \tag{8.40a}$$

$$Y_{om} = \frac{1}{jk_0\eta_0}\left[\left(\frac{m\pi}{a}\right)^2 - k_0^2\right]^{1/2}, \quad m = 1, 3, \ldots, \infty \tag{8.40b}$$

$$Y_n = \frac{1}{jk_0\eta_0}\left[\left(\frac{2n\pi}{a-t}\right)^2 - k_0^2\right]^{1/2} \tag{8.40c}$$

$$Q_{n\ oc,sc} = \binom{\tanh}{\coth}\left\{\left[\left(\frac{2n\pi}{a-t}\right)^2 - k_0^2\right]^{1/2}\frac{s}{2}\right\} \tag{8.40d}$$

The parameter ξ_n is the coefficient in the series expansion (trial function) assumed for the electric field distribution $e(x)$ at $z = 0$. The trial function assumed in deriving (8.39) is

$$e(x) = \sum_{n=1,2,\ldots}^{N} \xi_n \sin\left(\frac{2n\pi x}{a-t}\right) \tag{8.40e}$$

By using the Raleigh-Ritz method [17], the amplitudes ξ_n are chosen so as to minimize the value of $|\overline{Y}_{oc,sc}|$ for every integer n. This yields a set of $(N - 1)$ equations given by

$$\frac{\partial \overline{Y}_{oc,sc}}{\partial \xi_j} = 0, \quad j = 2, 3, \ldots, N\ (\xi_1 = 1) \tag{8.40f}$$

8.3 EXPERIMENTAL TECHNIQUES

Fin-line discontinuities considered in this chapter are basically *two-port reciprocal networks*. We assume the network to be lossless so that the elements are purely reactive. Depending on the type of discontinuity, one or another of the three different forms of network representation shown in Table 8.1 would be useful for characterization.

8.3.1 Open-Circuit, Short-Circuit Method

The *open-circuit, short-circuit* method involves measuring the input impedance of the network at one port with the second port terminated in an open circuit and a short circuit. The measurements can be repeated with the two ports interchanged. Because an asymmetrical T- or π-network involves three unknown quantities, only three impedance measurements are adequate to characterize the discontinuity.

Let Z_{oc1} and Z_{sc1} denote the input impedances measured at port 1 (terminal P_1) with port 2 (terminal P_2) terminated in an open circuit and a short circuit, respectively. Similarly, let Z_{oc2} denote the input impedance measured at port 2 with port 1 open-circuited. The parameters of the T-network can then be obtained from the following relations:

$$Z_{11} = Z_{oc1} \qquad\qquad\qquad (8.41a)$$

$$Z_{22} = Z_{oc2} \qquad\qquad\qquad (8.41b)$$

$$Z_{12} = \pm[Z_{oc2}(Z_{oc1} - Z_{sc1})]^{1/2} \qquad\qquad (8.41c)$$

Table 8.1

EQUIVALENT REPRESENTATION OF A TWO-PORT RECIPRO-CAL NETWORK

Circuit parameters	Network
$Z_{11} = \dfrac{Y_{22}}{\Delta Y} = Z_A$ $Z_{22} = \dfrac{Y_{11}}{\Delta Y} = Z_B + \dfrac{Z_A}{n^4}$ $Z_{12} = \dfrac{Y_{12}}{\Delta Y} = \dfrac{Z_A}{n^2}$	(a) T – network
$Y_{11} = \dfrac{Z_{22}}{\Delta Z} = \dfrac{1}{Z_A} + \dfrac{1}{n^4 Z_B}$ $Y_{22} = \dfrac{Z_{11}}{\Delta Z} = \dfrac{1}{Z_B}$ $Y_{12} = \dfrac{Z_{12}}{\Delta Z} = \dfrac{1}{n^2 Z_B}$	(b) π – network
$Z_A = Z_{11} = \dfrac{Y_{22}}{\Delta Y}$ $Z_B = \dfrac{\Delta Z}{Z_{11}} = \dfrac{1}{Y_{22}}$ $n^2 = \dfrac{Z_{11}}{Z_{12}} = \dfrac{Y_{22}}{Y_{12}}$	(c) Transformer – network
$\Delta Z = (Z_{11}Z_{22} - Z_{12}^2); \quad \Delta Y = (Y_{11}Y_{22} - Y_{12}^2)$	

The choice of plus or minus sign depends on the nature of discontinuity. For example, in the case of an inductive strip, Z_{12} should be an inductive reactance.

For a π-network, it is more convenient to express the parameters in terms of the input admittances. By denoting

$$Y_{oc1} = \frac{1}{Z_{oc1}}, \; Y_{sc1} = \frac{1}{Z_{sc1}}, \; Y_{oc2} = \frac{1}{Z_{oc2}}$$

we can write

$$Y_{11} = Y_{sc1} \tag{8.42a}$$

$$Y_{22} = Y_{sc2} \tag{8.42b}$$

$$Y_{12} = \pm [Y_{sc2} (Y_{sc1} - Y_{oc1})]^{1/2} \tag{8.42c}$$

For strips and notches that have symmetry with respect to the longitudinal direction (e.g., Fig. 8.1(b, c)), the T- or π-network is symmetrical, and the number of unknowns reduces to two. The parameters can then be expressed in terms of the input impedances measured at just one port with the second port terminated in an open circuit and a short circuit. Let Z_{oc} and Z_{sc} denote these two input impedances. Then, for the T-network in Table 8.1, the parameters are given by

$$Z_{11} = Z_{22} = Z_{oc} \tag{8.43a}$$

$$Z_{12} = \pm [Z_{oc} (Z_{oc} - Z_{sc})]^{1/2} \tag{8.43b}$$

Similarly, the parameters of the symmetrical π-network can be expressed in terms of the two measured input admittances:

$$Y_{oc} = \frac{1}{Z_{oc}}, \; Y_{sc} = \frac{1}{Z_{sc}}$$

Thus,

$$Y_{11} = Y_{22} = Y_{sc} \tag{8.44a}$$

$$Y_{12} = \pm [Y_{sc}(Y_{sc} - Y_{oc})]^{1/2} \tag{8.44b}$$

Figure 8.11 shows the experimental arrangement for measuring the open-circuit and short-circuit impedance parameters of a fin-line discontinuity. The movable short circuit incorporates a choke type of plunger having a circular cross section. The plunger consists of alternating low and high impedance quarter-wave sections so that the front face of the plunger represents a nearly perfect short circuit. The sliding short is forked so as to straddle the substrate. The position of the short can be varied by adjusting the micrometer head connected to the plunger. The impedance parameters can be determined by using the conventional *nodal shift* method. The procedure is as follows:

- Adjust the short-circuit plunger to place a short circuit at the discontinuity plane P_1P_1'. Note the position of the voltage minimum on the slotted line (s_{min}).
- Move the short circuit to the discontinuity plane P_2P_2'. Note the shift in the position of the voltage minimum with respect to s_{min} on the slotted line (Δs_1).
- Place an open circuit at the plane passing through P_2P_2'. This is achieved by moving the short circuit away from P_2P_2' by a distance equal to one-quarter of the guide wavelength in a uniform fin line of slot width w. Note the shift in the position of the minimum with respect to s_{min} on the slotted line (Δs_2).
- Calculate $\Delta s_1/\lambda_g$ and $\Delta s_2/\lambda_g$, where λ_g is the guide wavelength in the slotted line. The short-circuit reactance ($Z_{sc} = jX_{sc}$) and the open-circuit reactance ($Z_{oc} = jX_{oc}$) are then read directly from a Smith chart by moving a distance corresponding to $\Delta s_1/\lambda_g$ and $\Delta s_2/\lambda_g$, respectively, from the short-circuit position on the VSWR = ∞ circle.

8.3.2 Cavity Resonance Method

The characterization of a fin-line discontinuity from the resonant frequencies of a closed rectangular cavity containing the discontinuity is described in Sec. 8.2.2. As discussed, computationally, the impedance parameters Z_{11}, Z_{12}, and Z_{22} of a discontinuity can be determined by noting three different pairs of lengths l_a and l_b (refer to Fig. 8.7), which give the same resonant frequency. Experimentally, the discontinuity parameters can be more easily determined by measuring the resonant frequencies of the cavity by placing the discontinuity at a voltage maximum and a voltage minimum. The procedure for determining the circuit parameters of inductive strips and impedance steps using this method has been reported

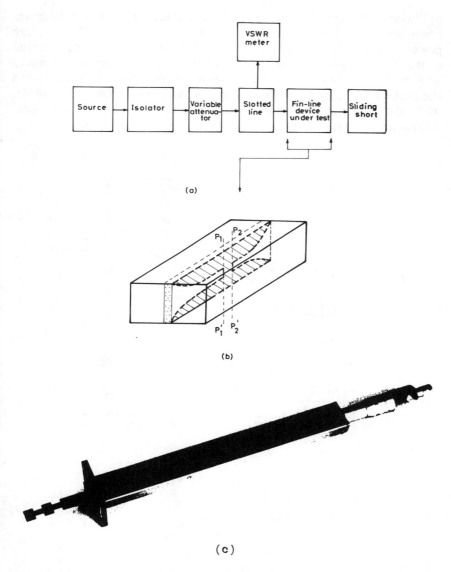

(a)

(b)

(c)

Fig. 8.11 (a) Experimental set up for measuring fin-line discontinuity parameters.
(b) Fin line containing a typical discontinuity.
(c) Photograph of sliding short.

by Pic and Hoefer [6]. Figure 8.12 shows the schematic of a rectangular cavity housing a discontinuity. The two loop probes shown are for coupling power into and out of the cavity. The resonant frequencies can be detected in the transmission mode and measured by means of a frequency meter or a frequency counter. It is important to optimize the coupling between the probe and the cavity so that the cavity loading is as small as possible, while the resonance response is sharp enough to enable accurate measurement of resonant frequencies.

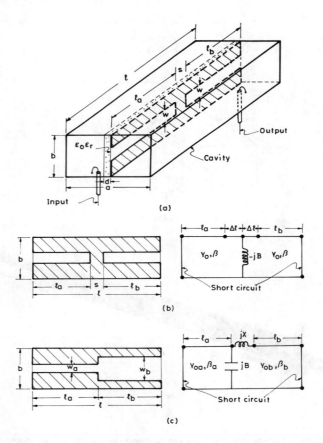

Fig. 8.12   (a) Rectangular cavity showing a typical discontinuity and coupling probes.
(b) Equivalent circuit of an inductive strip in a cavity.
(c) Equivalent circuit of an impedance step in a cavity.

The experiment involves measurement of resonant frequencies of quasi-TE_{10n} modes of the cavity. These measurements are taken with the discontinuity situated at the center and also at a distance of one-quarter of the cavity length ($l/4$) from one end. In the case of a symmetric inductive strip, the resonance condition when a voltage maximum appears at the discontinuity (see Fig. 8.12(b)) is given by

$$\cot [\beta(l_a + \Delta l)] + \cot[\beta(l_b + \Delta l)] = -\frac{B}{Y_0} \qquad (8.45a)$$

and the resonance condition when a voltage minimum appears at the discontinuity is

$$\tan [\beta(l_a + \Delta l)] + \tan [\beta(l_b + \Delta l)] = 0 \qquad (8.45b)$$

where $\beta = 2\pi/\lambda$ is the propagation constant in a uniform fin line of slot width w. The guide wavelengths (λ) at the measured resonant frequencies can be calculated by using the known formulas (Ch. 3). Because the distances l_a and l_b from the edges of the discontinuity to the adjacent end walls of the cavity are known, Δl and B/Y_o can be calculated from (8.45).

Similarly, when an impedance step (see Fig. 8.12(c)) is located at a voltage maximum and voltage minimum in the cavity, the resonance conditions are given by

$$\cot (\beta_a l_a) + \frac{Y_{ob}}{Y_{oa}} \cot (\beta_b l_b) = \frac{B}{Y_{oa}} \qquad (8.46a)$$

$$-\tan (\beta_a l_a) - \frac{Z_{ob}}{Z_{oa}} \tan (\beta_b l_b) = \frac{X}{Z_{oa}} \qquad (8.46b)$$

It is assumed that B/Y_{oa} and X/Z_{oa} vary linearly with frequency. Two independent resonance frequency measurements enable the determination of B/Y_{oa} and X/Z_{oa}. For a symmetric inductive strip discontinuity, Koster and Jansen [8] have compared the results of their rigorous hybrid-mode spectral domain analysis with the results of the empirical formulas (8.45) of [6]. It is reported [8] that the two results agree quite well for small values of s/b, but for larger strip widths (typically $s/b > 0.4$) and low frequencies, the shunt susceptance increases rather exponentially with s, and not in a linear fashion as predicted by the empirical formulas. However, because most practical circuits generally make use of small values of s/b, the empirical formulas of [6] should serve as a useful design aid.

8.4 DISCONTINUITY CHARACTERISTICS

In this section, we shall discuss the characteristics of some of the typical discontinuities in unilateral and bilateral fin-line configurations. The cross-sectional views of the two fin lines and the notations used in the fin-line discontinuity graphs (Figs. 8.14 to 8.19) refer to Fig. 8.13. The characteristics of discontinuities in E-plane circuits with no dielectric backing are discussed in Sec. 8.4.6 (Figs. 8.20 to 8.23), and the guide dimensions refer to the standard X-band waveguide.

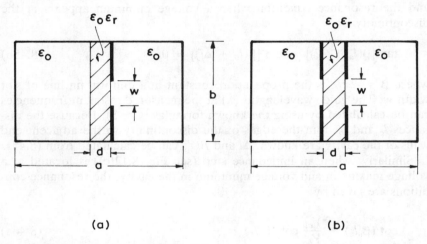

(a)   (b)

Fig. 8.13   Cross-sectional views of:
(a) unilateral fin line
(b) bilateral fin line

8.4.1 Impedance Step

A simple equivalent representation of a step change in slot width in a fin line makes use of a capacitive shunt susceptance and an impedance transformer. The characteristics of a single step in both unilateral and bilateral fin lines are reported in [13]. These are shown in Fig. 8.14. In the graph, the shunt susceptance B is normalized with respect to the wave admittance Y_{oa} of the uniform fin line of slot width w_a. It can be seen that the susceptance B increases with an increase in the slot width ratio w_b/w_a, and its values are higher for a bilateral fin line than for a unilateral fin line. The reverse trend can be observed for the *turns ratio* n^2. The nor-

malized series reactances have not been considered in this simplified equivalent circuit. Their values, however, are reported to be negligibly small,
except when near or very far above the cut-off frequency [13].

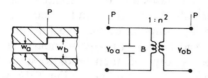

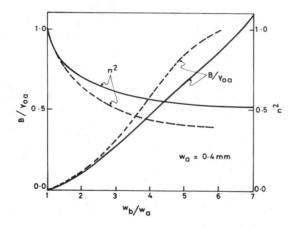

Fig. 8.14 Equivalent circuit parameters of a step discontinuity in (i)
unilateral fin line (————) and (ii) bilateral fin line (—————):
$a = 7.112$ mm $b = 3.556$ mm
$d = 0.254$ mm $\epsilon_r = 2.22$
$f = 30$ GHz

(From Hennawy and Schunemann [13], *IEE Proc.*, Pt. H, 1982, Vol. 129,
pp. 342–350, reprinted with permission of IEE.)

8.4.2 Inductive Strip

An inductive strip discontinuity can be characterized by a T-equivalent
network with series and shunt inductive elements. Koster and Jansen [8]
have obtained characteristics of inductive strips in unilateral fin lines by

using a rigorous hybrid-mode computer algorithm. They are reproduced in Figs. 8.15 and 8.16. In the case of a symmetric strip discontinuity (Fig. 8.15), as the strip width s is increased from a small value, the normalized series reactance X_s increases and the normalized shunt reactance X_p decreases. For larger values of s, the shunt reactance decreases almost exponentially, indicating coupling of the two fin lines through attenuation field components, and finally saturates to nearly zero value. The series reactance increases rapidly and then tends to saturate to the end-effect reactance of a shorted end in a fin line. In Fig. 8.16, we show the variation

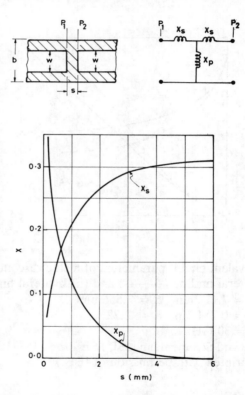

Fig. 8.15 Equivalent T-circuit parameters of a symmetrical inductive strip in unilateral fin line:

$a = 7.12$ mm $b = 3.56$ mm
$d = 0.254$ mm $\epsilon_r = 2.22$
$f = 34$ GHz $w = 0.5$ mm

(From Koster and Jansen [8], reprinted with permission of AEU.)

in the series and shunt inductances of an asymmetric strip in a unilateral fin line as a function of the slot width ratio w_b/w_a. For a fixed value of w_a, as w_b is decreased, the shunt inductance L_p as well as the series inductance L_{s2} decrease. The series inductance L_{s1} of the line of fixed slot width w_a increases and as w_b approaches zero, L_{s1} approaches the end-effect inductance of a shorted fin line.

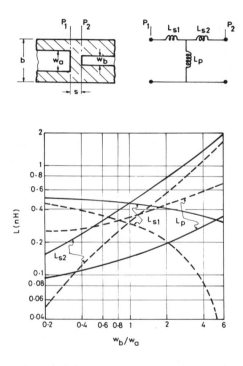

Fig. 8.16 Equivalent T-circuit inductances of asymmetric strip discontinuity in unilateral fin line:

$a = 20.32$ mm	$b = 10.16$ mm
$d = 0.635$ mm	$\epsilon_r = 2.22$
$f = 13$ GHz	$w_a = 0.635$ mm
—— $s = 3.048$ mm	— — — $s = 1.016$ mm

(From Koster and Jansen [8], reprinted with permission of AEU.)

8.4.3 Symmetrical Notch

The performance of notches in unilateral and bilateral fin lines has been characterized by Hennawy and Schunemann [13, 14] by using a rigorous eigenmode calculation and a modal analysis. Figure 8.17 shows equivalent circuit parameters of a symmetrical notch in unilateral fin line as a function of the normalized notch length l/λ_0, where λ_0 is the free-space wavelength [14]. For a notch length less than a half-wavelength, the series element of the π-network is always inductive and the shunt element is capacitive. If the higher order mode coupling between the two steps is neglected, then the equivalent circuit can be considered as a cascade of equivalent circuits of the two steps with a combined transmission-line section of length $2l$. Thus, the series element $(B_{sc} - B_{oc})/2$ is proportional to $n^2/\sin(2\beta l)$, where $\beta(=2\pi/\lambda)$ is the propagation constant of the fundamental mode. The shape of the curve for the series element follows this relation, i.e., for both $l \to 0$ and $l \to \lambda/4$, the inductive susceptance is very large and has a rather flat response for l around $\lambda/8$. The shunt susceptance is capacitive and proportional to $n^2(B + Y_{ob} \tan \beta l)$. Thus, B_{oc} increases with l and reaches a maximum at $l = \lambda/4$. Similar variation has also been reported for a symmetrical notch in bilateral fin line [12]. In both configurations, the higher order mode coupling between the step discontinuities can be neglected for $2l/\lambda_0 > 0.1$, and the error introduced due to neglecting such coupling is less than 10% [13, 14].

8.4.4 Symmetrical Capacitive Strip

A capacitive strip is represented as a T-equivalent network. For a strip length less than a half-wavelength $(l < \lambda_0/4)$, the shunt element is capacitive, but the series element is always inductive. The equivalent circuit parameters of a symmetrically located strip as a function of the normalized strip length is shown in Fig. 8.18(a) for a unilateral fin line, and in Fig. 8.18(b) for a bilateral fin line [13]. As in the case of a notch, the shape of the curve can be explained by means of the simplified equivalent circuit by neglecting the higher order mode coupling between the two steps. The series element X_{sc} is proportional to $1/[(Y_{oa}/n^2)\cot(\beta l) - B]$ and the shunt element $(X_{oc} - X_{sc})/2$ is proportional to

$$-Y_{oa}\left[\left(\frac{Y_{oa}^2}{n^2} - n^2 B^2\right) \sin (2\beta l) + 2B Y_{oa} \cos (2\beta l)\right]$$

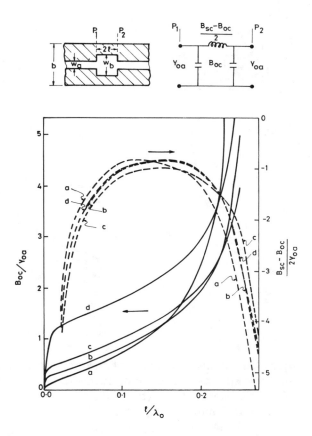

Fig. 8.17 Equivalent π-circuit parameters of a symmetrical notch in unilateral fin line:

    (a) $w_a = 1$ mm $w_b = 2$ mm
    (b) $w_a = 1$ mm $w_b = 3$ mm
    (c) $w_a = 1$ mm $w_b = 3.56$ mm
    (d) $w_a = 0.4$ mm $w_b = 3$ mm

    $a = 7.12$ mm $b = 3.56$ mm
    $d = 0.254$ mm $\epsilon_r = 2.22$
    $f = 30$ GHz

(From Hennawy and Schunemann [14], reprinted with permission of AEU.)

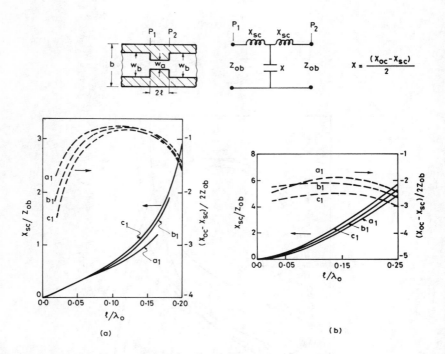

Fig. 8.18   Equivalent circuit parameters of a symmetrically located capacitive strip as a function of normalized strip length: (a) unilateral fin line   (b) bilateral fin line

$a = 15.8$ mm	$b = 7.9$ mm
$d = 0.254$ mm	$\epsilon_r = 2.22$
$f = 15$ GHz	$w_a = 1.5$ mm
$w_b = 3$ mm (curve a_1)	2.5 mm (curve b_1)
2 mm (curve c_1)	

(From Hennawy and Schunemann [13], *IEE Proc.*, Pt. H, 1982, Vol. 129, pp. 342–350, reprinted with permission of IEE.)

The series inductive reactance increases with an increase in the length of the strip, whereas its variation with slot width ratio is small especially for smaller values of l/λ_0. Comparatively, the shunt reactance is a stronger function of the slot width ratio. As a function of strip length, the curve is fairly flat around $l = \lambda_0/8$ with its value increasing as l approaches zero and $\lambda_0/4$. Short capacitive strips of very small length are sometimes introduced as diode mounts in an otherwise uniform fin line. With the slot width narrowed, the beam-lead diodes are directly soldered onto the two metallic fins. The T-equivalent networks of the strip taken parallel to the diode equivalent circuit then enable more accurate design of circuit components.

8.4.5 Bilateral Fin-Line Section Embedded in Unilateral Fin Line

Figure 8.19 shows the equivalent T-network parameters of a bilateral fin-line section embedded in a unilateral fin line as reported by El Hennawy and Schunemann [18]. X_{sc} and X_{oc} denote the input reactances of the T-network when a short circuit and an open circuit, respectively, are placed at the symmetry plane PP'. An interesting feature of this discontinuity is the *parallel resonance* in the *series reactance* for smaller lengths l. The series reactance is *inductive* below resonance and becomes *capacitive* above resonance (for larger lengths). This feature is in contrast to the notch and strip, which always exhibit an inductive series reactance. This type of double transition finds useful application in the design of *pin*-diode switches [18].

8.4.6 Discontinuities in E-plane Circuits

Figures 8.20 and 8.21 show the measured equivalent circuit parameters reported by Konishi [19] for an open-ended ridge guide and for an inductive strip between a ridge guide and a waveguide, respectively. For the open-ended ridge guide, the series reactance increases with an increase in frequency, whereas the shunt susceptance is rather insensitive (Fig. 8.20). In the case of the inductive coupling strip (Fig. 8.21), the series reactance X_1 increases with an increase in both the strip width w as well as the frequency, whereas the series reactance X_2 toward the ridge guide is altered negligibly.

A narrow metallic strip located axially in a rectangular waveguide represents an inductive element. The equivalent circuit parameters for a metallic strip reported by Konishi *et al.* [3] are depicted in Fig. 8.22. As in the case of an inductive strip in fin line, the series reactance increases, and the shunt reactance decreases with an increase in the strip width. For a metallic strip that extends only partially into the waveguide (Fig. 8.23), Chang and Khan [20] have derived the equivalent circuit parameters. It has been shown that the T-equivalent network has a series resonant shunt circuit. The characteristics reported in [20] for a nontouching axial strip in X-band waveguide are depicted in Fig. 8.23. The reactances are normalized with respect to the wave impedance Z of the rectangular guide. From Fig. 8.23(a), it can be seen that for a fixed strip depth $d = 0.3$ inches, the shunt reactance is capacitive at 8 GHz, and for higher frequencies the shunt reactance is inductive for lower values of the strip width

s, becoming capacitive as s increases. The effect of varying the insertion depth d into the guide is shown in Fig. 8.23(b). It can be seen that the series inductive reactance X_s is insensitive to depth, and the shunt reactance is capacitive for smaller depths, becoming increasingly inductive as d is increased.

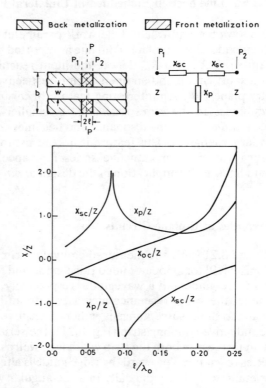

Fig. 8.19 Equivalent T-network parameters of a section of bilateral fin line embedded in a unilateral fin line:
  Z = wave impedance of the unilateral fin line
  $a = 7.112$ mm $b = 3.556$ mm
  $d = 0.254$ mm $\epsilon_r = 2.22$
  $w = 0.4$ mm
  WR-28 waveguide

(From Hennawy and Schunemann [18], Copyright © 1982 IEEE, reprinted with permission.)

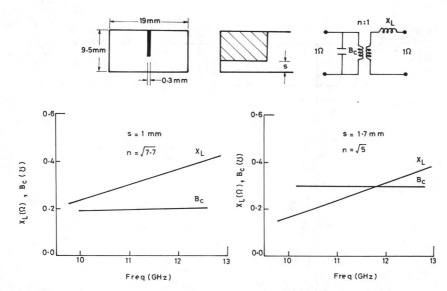

Fig. 8.20   Equivalent circuit parameters of an open end in a ridge
guide.
(From Konishi [19], Copyright © 1978 IEEE, reprinted with permission.)

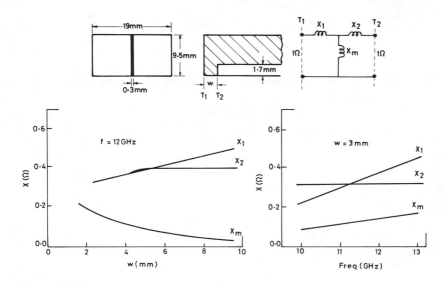

Fig. 8.21   Inductive coupling strip between ridge guide and rectangular
guide and its equivalent circuit parameters.
(From Konishi [19], Copyright © 1978 IEEE, reprinted with permission.)

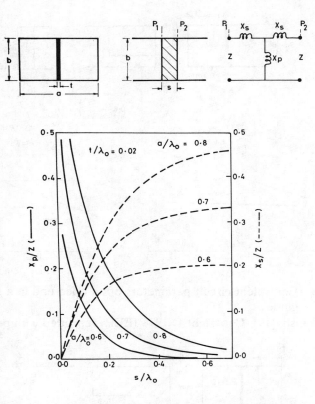

Fig. 8.22 Axial inductive strip in a waveguide and its equivalent circuit
parameters:
λ_0 = free-space wavelength
(From Konishi *et al.* [3], Copyright © 1974 IEEE, reprinted with permission.)

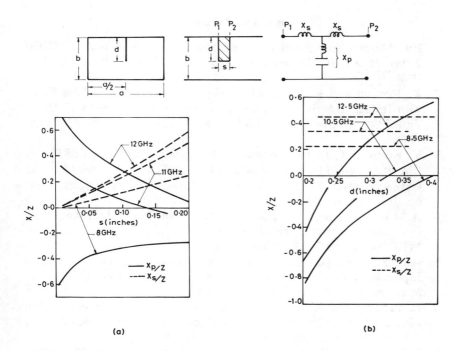

Fig. 8.23   Centered nontouching metallic strip in a rectangular
                waveguide and equivalent circuit parameters as a function of:
                (a) strip width *s* and (b) strip depth *d*
(From Chang and Khan [20], Copyright © 1976 IEEE, reprinted with
permission.)

REFERENCES

1. P.J. Meier, "Integrated Fin Line Millimeter Components," *IEEE Trans. Microwave Theory Tech.*, Vol. MTT-22, pp. 1209–1216, Dec. 1974.

2. Y. Konishi and K. Uenakada, "The Design of a Band Pass Filter with Inductive Strip Planar Circuit Mounted in Waveguide," *IEEE Trans. Microwave Theory Tech.*, Vol. MTT-22, pp. 869–873, Oct. 1974.

3. Y. Konishi, K. Uenakada, and N. Hoshino, "The Design of Planar Circuit Mounted in Waveguide and the Application to Low Noise 12 GHz Converter," *IEEE MTT-S Int. Microwave Symp. Digest,* 1974, pp. 168–170.

4. A.M.K. Saad and K. Schunemann, "A Simple Method for Analyzing Fin Line Structures," *IEEE Trans. Microwave Theory Tech.*, Vol. MTT-26, pp. 1002–1007, Dec. 1978.

5. A.M.K. Saad and K. Schunemann, "A Rectangular Waveguide Equivalent for Bilateral and Unilateral Fin Lines," *Arch. Elek. Ubertragung.*, Vol. 35, pp. 287–292, July-Aug. 1981.

6. E. Pic and W.J.R. Hoefer, "Experimental Characterization of Fin Line Discontinuities Using Resonant Techniques," *IEEE MTT-S Int. Microwave Symp. Digest,* 1981, pp. 108–110.

7. R.H. Jansen, "Hybrid Mode Analysis of End Effects of Planar Microwave and Millimeter Wave Transmission Lines," *IEE Proc.*, Vol. 128, Pt. H, No. 2, pp. 77–86, April 1981.

8. N.H.L. Koster and R.H. Jansen, "Some New Results on the Equivalent Circuit Parameters of the Inductive Strip Discontinuity in Unilateral Fin Lines," *Arch. Elek. Ubertragung.*, Vol. 35, pp. 497–499, Dec. 1981.

9. A. Beyer, "Calculation of Discontinuities in Grounded Fin Lines Taking into Account the Metalization Thickness and the Influence of the Mount-Slits," *12th Eur. Microwave Conf. Proc.*, 1982, pp. 681–686.

10. Y. Konishi and H. Matsumura, "Short End Effect of Ridge Guide with Planar Circuit Mounted in a Waveguide," *IEEE Trans. Microwave Theory Tech.*, Vol. MTT-27, pp. 168–170, Feb. 1979.

11. A. Wexler, "Solution of Waveguide Discontinuities by Modal Analysis," *IEEE Trans. Microwave Theory Tech.*, Vol. MTT-15, pp. 508–517, Sept. 1967.

12. H. El. Hennawy and K. Schunemann, "Analysis of Fin-Line Discontinuities," *9th Eur. Microwave Conf. Proc.*, 1979, pp. 448–452.

13. H. El. Hennawy and K. Schunemann, "Impedance Transformation

in Fin Lines," *IEE Proc.*, Vol. 129, Pt. H, No. 6, pp. 342–350, Dec. 1982.

14. H. El. Hennawy and K. Schunemann, "Computer Aided Design of Fin Line Detectors, Modulators and Switches," *Arch. Elek. Ubertragung.*, Vol. 36, pp. 49–56, Feb. 1982.

15. R. Sorrentino and T. Itoh, "Transverse Resonance Analysis of Fin Line Discontinuities," *IEEE Trans. Microwave Theory Tech.*, Vol. MTT-32, pp. 1633–1638, Dec. 1984.

16. H. Helard, J. Citerne, O. Picon, and V.F. Hanna, "Solution of Fin-Line Discontinuities through the Identification of its First Four Higher Order Modes," *IEEE MTT-S Int. Microwave Symp. Digest,* 1983, pp. 387–389.

17. R.E. Collin, *Field Theory of Guided Waves,* McGraw-Hill, New York, 1960.

18. H. El. Hennawy and K. Schunemann, "New Structures for Impedance Transformation in Fin Lines," *IEEE MTT-S Int. Microwave Symp. Digest,* 1982, pp. 198–200.

19. Y. Konishi, "Planar Circuit Mounted in Waveguide Used as a Down-converter," *IEEE Trans. Microwave Theory Tech.*, Vol. MTT-26, pp. 716–719, Oct. 1978.

20. K. Chang and P.J. Khan, "Equivalent Circuit of a Narrow Axial Strip in Waveguide," *IEEE Trans. Microwave Theory Tech.*, Vol. MTT-24, pp. 611–614, Sept. 1976.

Chapter 9
Applications

9.1 INTRODUCTION

A variety of millimeter-wave integrated circuits can be realized by using fin-line techniques predominantly. These include, in addition to the fin-line circuitry, metal insert circuits and other photolithographically produced circuit patterns, mounted in the E-plane of rectangular waveguides. As discussed in Ch. 1, fin line is the most versatile non-TEM medium that is amenable to integration with quasi-TEM planar transmission lines such as the microstrip, coplanar line, and the suspended stripline. By judiciously combining one or more of these planar transmission lines with fin lines, we can enhance the performance capabilities of many practical fin-line components.

The preceding chapters generally cover nearly all the background material needed for the design of fin-line components. The theory, design, and performance of various fin lines are presented in Ch. 2–5. The design aspects of several basic elements encountered in fin-line circuits—namely, the transitions, resonators, and discontinuities—are discussed in Ch. 6–8. This chapter pertains to integrated components realized by using the various fin-line techniques. Components covered in detail are directional couplers, power dividers, filters, switches, attenuators, detectors, modulators, mixers, and oscillators. Because all these components are well proven in fin-line media at least up to W-band, circuit layouts and configurations of several components published in the literature are included to illustrate the operating principles and salient practical considerations. Nonreciprocal devices, such as the isolators and circulators, which are not well developed in fin-line technology, are briefly reviewed.

9.2 DIRECTIONAL COUPLERS

Directional couplers form an integral part of various millimeter-wave components. In particular, 3 dB couplers are normally incorporated in mixers, phase modulators, monopulse comparators, and phase shifters. Couplers with loose couplings are used for power monitoring. Millimeter-wave couplers suitable for integration in fin-line circuits are discussed in this section. These include the E-plane *printed probe couplers* [1–6], *branch-guide couplers* [7], hybrid *branch-line couplers* [8–11], *parallel-coupled fin-line couplers* [12–14], and *fin-line microstrip couplers* [15].

9.2.1 E-Plane Probes

The printed probe circuit as an E-plane four-port coupling network was proposed by Meier [1–2]. Figure 9.1(a, b) shows the basic structure of the four-port network with a capacitive probe. The coupling element is mounted in the E-plane common to a pair of parallel waveguides. The common broad wall between the two guides is slotted along the E-plane to accept a pair of dielectric substrates. The probe is printed on one of the substrates, and the second substrate is placed so that the probe is insulated from the common wall. The probe is symmetrically located and extends by an equal length into the two guides. As in the case of fin lines, the thickness of each of the two outer broad walls into which the substrates protrude is kept equal to one quarter-wavelength ($\lambda_d/4$) in the dielectric so as to prevent leakage of power. Figure 9.1(c) shows the equivalent circuit of a single probe element in a four-port guiding structure with port 1 excited by a source and ports 2 to 4 that are match-terminated to the wave impedance Z_0 of the dielectric slab-loaded waveguide. The value of Z_0 can be calculated by using the formula [16]:

$$Z_0 = \frac{745b}{a \sqrt{k_e - (\lambda_0/2a)^2}} \tag{9.1}$$

where k_e is the equivalent dielectric constant of the slab-loaded waveguide and λ_0 is the free-space wavelength. The value of k_e can be easily calculated by using the formulas given in Vartanian *et al.* [16]. The element values L and C can then be determined by matching the theoretical coupling values that provide the best fit with the measured values. Basic design data relating the dimensions of the printed probe with the coupling that it can provide may thus be generated.

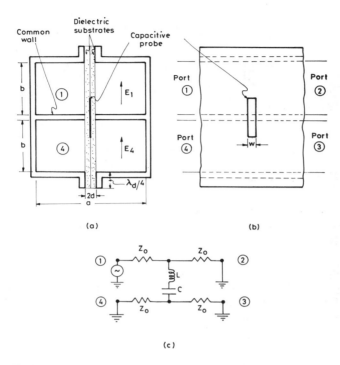

Fig. 9.1 E-plane four-port coupler using a capacitive probe:
    (a) cross-sectional view
    (b) printed probe on the substrate
    (c) equivalent circuit

For a narrow capacitive strip (w small), the inductive reactance is negligible as compared with the capacitive reactance. The coupling due to the capacitive probe, therefore, increases monotonically with frequency.

Unlike the capacitive probe in which the coupling is essentially electric, the printed loop (P_1 in Fig. 9.2) offers both electric and magnetic coupling, each of which can be independently controlled. By adjusting the loop dimensions, it is possible to achieve nearly constant coupling over a wide band. Figure 9.2 also shows several other compensated L-C probes. The series inductance associated with these probes offers a coupling *versus* frequency response which is opposite in trend to that due to the capacitance. The series inductance can be reduced by widening the printed strip at the center of the probe. Thus, by adjusting the series inductance, it is possible to achieve the desired frequency compensation resulting in wideband performance.

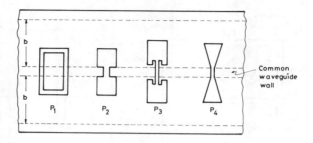

Fig. 9.2 Compensated probes.

The coupling offered by a single probe element is generally weak. For tighter coupling over a desired band, it is necessary to use an array of elements with appropriate coupling coefficients [3, 5, 6, 17].

In the following, we present some practical aspects and measured performance characteristics of isolated coupling elements in the form of a capacitive strip and a compensated L-C probe. The design and characteristics of couplers that use an array of capacitive probes and loops are discussed in the subsequent section.

Capacitive Probe

Figure 9.3 shows the structural features of a four-port printed probe coupler [6]. The housing dimensions correspond to the standard X-band waveguide. The dielectric substrates used are RT-duroid™, having a relative dielectric constant $\epsilon_r = 2.22$ and thickness $d = 0.254$ mm. The two halves of the housing are aligned by means of guiding pins.

Fig. 9.3 Parts of printed probe coupler.

Figures 9.4 and 9.5 depict the measured performance of capacitive probes operating over X band for a normalized probe depth in the range $0.2 < h/b \leq 0.4$ and normalized probe widths in the range $0.05 < w/b \leq 0.2$. It is essential to keep the probe depth and width within such a small range in order to ensure that the input VSWR does not exceed a specified

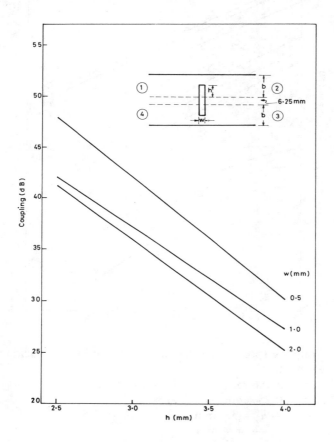

Fig. 9.4 Coupling (port 1 to 3) *versus* probe depth h for a capacitive probe element:
$a = 22.86$ mm
$b = 10.16$ mm
$d = 0.254$ mm
$\epsilon_r = 2.22$
$f = 10$ GHz

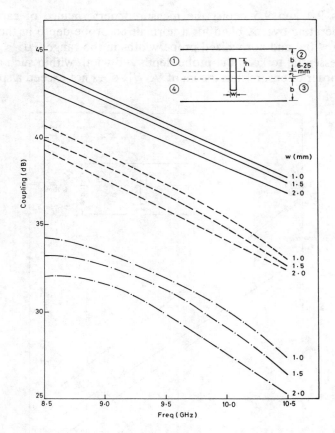

Fig. 9.5 Coupling (port 1 to 3) *versus* frequency for a capacitive probe element:

$a = 22.86$ mm $b = 10.16$ mm
$d = 0.254$ mm $\epsilon_r = 2.22$
——— $h = 3.0$ mm   ————— $h = 3.5$ mm
—·—·— $h = 4$ mm

value of about 1.3. As expected, the coupling (from port 1 to port 3) increases with an increase in the probe depth (Fig. 9.4) and probe width as well as frequency (Fig. 9.5). The parameters L and C of the probe for a measured coupling can be calculated by using the equivalent circuit of Fig. 9.1(c).

Compensated Probe

Figure 9.6 shows a typical *L-C* probe and the inductive compensation effect on the coupling variation. For a fixed set of parameters, *l*, *w*, and *h* with $l > w$, the coupling increases with frequency, reaches a maximum and then decreases at higher frequencies. It can be seen that for a probe with $l = 5$ mm and $h = 2$ mm, increasing the width *w* from 1 mm to 2 mm results in considerable flattening of the coupling response *versus* frequency. The results show that a single probe gives a relatively flat coupling on the order of 36 dB over a frequency range from 8.2 to 10.2 GHz.

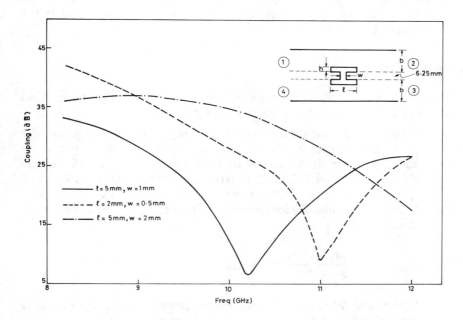

Fig. 9.6   Coupling (port 1 to 3) characteristics of an L-C probe:
$a = 22.86$ mm
$b = 10.16$ mm
$d = 0.254$ mm
$\epsilon_r = 2.22$
$h = 2$ mm

9.2.2 Printed Probe Array Couplers [6]

Chebyshev Capacitive Probe Array

Couplers with tight coupling and broad bandwidth can be realized by using an *array* of printed probes. It is well known that Chebyshev arrays offer optimal performance in filters and couplers [18]. Chebyshev arrays are those in which the relative voltage amplitudes at the various elements in the array are proportional to the coefficients of the Chebyshev polynomial. The performance is optimum in the sense that for a given number of elements and specified bandwidth, this array offers the minimum reflection coefficient, or, for a specified reflection coefficient, it offers the maximum bandwidth.

Design Example

Consider the example of a seven-element Chebyshev array for operation at X band. The salient design steps are as follows:

- Determine the bandwidth ratio $p = \lambda_1/\lambda_2$, where λ_1 and λ_2 are the guide wavelengths in the dielectric slab-loaded guide at the lower and upper ends of the desired frequency band. If we are considering a frequency range 8.2 to 12.4 GHz, then we have $\lambda_1 = 58.2$ mm at $f_1 = 8.2$ GHz and $\lambda_2 = 29.0$ mm at $f_2 = 12.4$ GHz. Thus, $p = 2.007$.
- Calculate the interelement spacing l_s (from center to center) by using the formula:

$$l_s = \frac{\lambda_1 \lambda_2}{2(\lambda_1 + \lambda_2)} = 9.68 \text{ mm}$$

- Let Φ_1 and Φ_2 denote the electrical spacings between the elements corresponding to the lowest and the highest frequencies within the operating band.

$$\Phi_1 = \frac{180°}{1 + p} = 59.86°$$

$$\Phi_2 = \pi - \Phi_1 = 120.14°$$

- Relate the wave amplitude coupled through each element to the Chebyshev response.

First, construct Table 9.1 consisting of seven rows ($n = 1$ to 7) and seven columns (m = 0 to 6) by using the following simple procedure. Calculate x_0 = $1/\cos \Phi_1$ = 1.99. By denoting x_{nm} as the element value, we insert x_{10} = 2 and x_{21} = x_0 = 1.99. Along the diagonal, the element value $x_{n,n-1}$ is given by $(x_0)^{n-1}$. In the first column (m = 0), the values of x_{n0} for n = 3, 5, and 7 are obtained by using x_{n0} = $(2x_0 x_{n-1,1} - x_{n-2,0})$. For entries other than m = 0, x_{nm} = $[(x_{n-1,m-1} + x_{n-1,m+1}) x_0 - x_{n-2,m}]$. The horizontal rows in Table 9.1 thus provide the desired voltage coupling for Chebyshev arrays of two to seven elements for 8.2 to 12.4 GHz range. The relative amplitude coefficients C_is are tabulated in Table 9.2. The numbers indicated within the brackets are the relative couplings expressed in dB. The decibel values are calculated by using the formula:

$$20 \log_{10} \left(\frac{\sum_i C_i}{C_i} \right)$$

Table 9.1

COUPLING COEFFICIENTS IN CHEBYSHEV ARRAYS:
VOLTAGE COUPLING (UP TO SEVEN ELEMENTS)

n \ m	0	1	2	3	4	5	6
1	2.0						
2		1.99					
3	5.92		3.96				
4		17.67		7.88			
5	64.41		46.88		15.68		
6		203.81		116.63		31.21	
7	746.75		590.79		278.52		62.10

Table 9.2

RELATIVE COUPLING COEFFICIENTS
(SEVEN-ELEMENT ARRAY)

Element number	1	2	3	4	5	6	7
Coupling Coefficient dB:	1.0 (32.48)	4.485 (19.43)	9.514 (12.90)	12.025 (10.86)	9.514 (12.90)	4.485 (19.43)	1.0 (32.48)

- The probe dimensions for the seven elements of the array at an operating frequency of 10 GHz are obtained by matching the relative couplings with those measured for the individual elements.

The coupling and isolation characteristics measured for the seven-element capacitive probe array are depicted in Fig. 9.7. The coupler gives a mean coupling of 12.5 dB with a variation of ± 0.5 dB and an isolation better than 32 dB over the frequency range of 8.2 to 10.5 GHz.

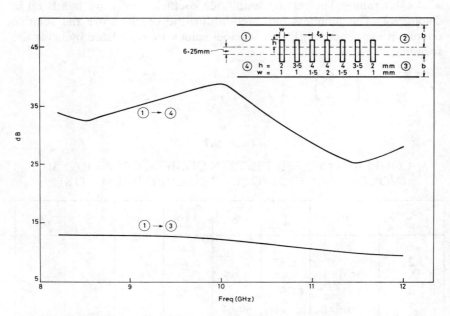

Fig. 9.7   Characteristics of 7-element capacitive probe array coupler:
$a = 22.86$ mm
$b = 10.16$ mm
$d = 0.254$ mm
$\epsilon_r = 2.22$

Printed Loop Array

As in the case of a single capacitive strip, the maximum dimension of the printed loop is governed by the maximum tolerable value of input VSWR. Experiments have shown that for a single loop at X band, the coupling is weak (on the order of 42 dB) for values of h/b less than 0.2, and for h/b greater than 0.25, the VSWR at the input port exceeds 1.3. For l large, the coupling tends to remain reasonably constant over a certain frequency range, and then increases with an increase in frequency. For small lengths ($2w < l < 3w$), the inductive compensation effect is small, and the loop performance approaches that of a capacitive probe.

Figure 9.8 shows the measured characteristics of loop array couplers consisting of 2, 6, and 12 loops. The center-to-center spacing between two adjacent loops is $\lambda_g/4$, where λ_g is the wavelength in the dielectric slab-loaded waveguide at the midband frequency (10 GHz). As many as 12 loops are required to achieve a coupling on the order of 12.5 dB over about 2 GHz bandwidth.

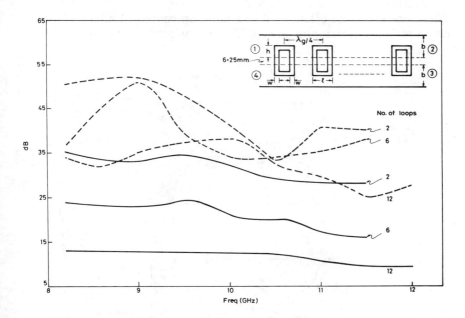

Fig. 9.8   Characteristics of printed loop array couplers:

$a = 22.86$ mm $b = 10.16$ mm
$d = 0.254$ mm $\epsilon_r = 2.22$
$h = 2.5$ mm $w = 2$ mm
$l = 6$ mm   ——— coupling
——— isolation

9.2.3 Branch-Guide Couplers [7]

Branch-guide couplers also make use of split-block waveguide housings as in the printed probe coupler. However, the coupling from the lower guide to the upper guide is via the grooves cut in the common broad wall, instead of by means of E-plane probes. Bates *et al.* [7] have reported this type of coupler, the structural features of which are displayed in Fig. 9.9. Because the coupler does not incorporate any dielectric substrate, the dielectric loss is eliminated. The structure, however, is compatible with fin line and other E-plane circuits. It has been reported that 3 dB couplers designed for Ka band operate over 27 to 36 GHz with a directivity as well as return loss better than 30 dB. Other couplers with couplings from 3 to 10 dB for operation at E band and W band have also been reported [7]. These are known to offer ±1 dB variation in coupling and a typical isolation of 25 dB over approximately 70% bandwidth in the respective waveguide band.

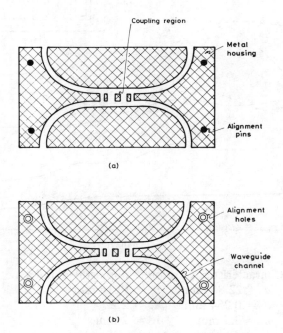

Fig. 9.9 Branch guide 3 dB-coupler (after Bates *et al.* [7]).

9.2.4 Hybrid Branch-line Couplers [9, 10]

Based on De Ronde's hybrid strip-slot coupler [8], wideband hybrid branch-line couplers adaptable to fin-line technology have been reported by Hennawy *et al.* [9] and Callsen and Schmidt [10]. De Ronde's coupler is basically a microstrip four-port hybrid with the strip conductor pattern on the top surface and a slot in the ground plane of the dielectric substrate, as shown in Fig. 9.10(a). The conducting strip connecting the two main microstrip lines acts as a shunt branch, and the slot section acts as a series branch. In an ideal coupler, coupling takes place only in the two hybrid junctions, and the junctions are free of parasitic reactances. The series and shunt branches are decoupled. Furthermore, the two branches have identical quasi-TEM mode phase characteristics and their lengths are equal to one quarter-wavelength at midband. Detailed analysis and design of such an ideal coupler are available in Schiek [11].

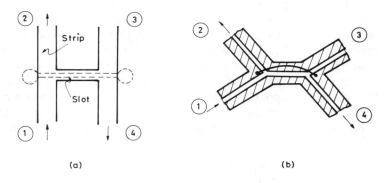

(a)   (b)

Fig. 9.10   (a) De Ronde's hybrid strip-slot coupler.
        (b) Hybrid fin-line coupler.
(Fig. 9.10(a) after De Ronde [8]. Fig. 9.10(b) from Hennawy *et al.* [9], reprinted with permission of AEU.)

The layout of a hybrid fin-line coupler reported by Hennawy *et al.* [9] is shown in Fig. 9.10(b). It may be considered as a complementary version of the De Ronde coupler, in which the microstrip conductor pattern is replaced by the slot pattern of a fin line and the slot is replaced by a wire. In this structure, the wire forms the shunt branch and the slot oriented parallel to it forms the series branch. The shunt branch can also be realized by printing a strip on the backside of the substrate. Hennawy *et al.* [9]

have presented an approximate design theory that takes into account the influence of the parasitic elements of the connecting junctions. In practical couplers, the wire length as well as its distance from the substrate (in the case of a printed strip, its width and length) should be optimized to achieve maximum directivity over the desired frequency range. Furthermore, placing a thin sheet of absorbing material near the narrow wall of the waveguide helps to suppress any spurious resonances. Practical Ka-band couplers for 3 dB and 10 dB couplings have been reported [9], which show an isolation on the order of 20 dB and an insertion loss of about 0.5 dB over nearly an octave band.

Figure 9.11 shows the layout of another hybrid fin-line coupler and its equivalent circuit as reported by Callsen and Schmidt [10]. In this, the strip-slot section is connected to antipodal fin lines via two hybrid junctions. A metal iris is inserted into the waveguide housing at plane AB in order to prevent coupling between the antipodal fin lines as well as to prevent any spurious resonances in the junction cavity. In the equivalent circuit, the two hybrid junctions are represented by hybrid transformers. The strip-slot section between the two junctions is represented by two uncoupled transmission lines. The parameters Z_p and β_p are the characteristic impedance and propagation constant of the transmission line representing the *microstrip mode,* and Z_s and β_s are the corresponding notations for the *slotline mode.* It is apparent from the equivalent circuit that when ports 1 and 2 are excited in even-mode (signals are equal in amplitude and phase), only the parallel-connected microstrip mode is excited, and when they are

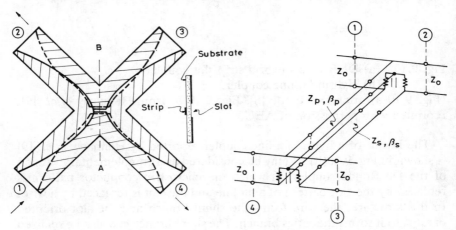

Fig. 9.11 Hybrid fin-line coupler and its equivalent circuit.
(From Callsen and Schmidt [10], *Electronics Letters,* 1982, Vol. 18, pp. 161–163, reprinted with permission of IEE.)

excited in odd-mode (signals are equal in amplitude, but out of phase), only the serially connected slot mode is excited at the hybrid junction. When a signal is fed to one port (let us say, port 1), the even- and odd-mode waves add constructively toward port 2 and destructively toward port 3. Assuming equal phase constants for the even- and odd-modes, the condition for perfect matching and isolation is given by [10]:

$$Z^2 = Z_p Z_s \qquad (9.2)$$

where Z is the characteristic impedance of the antipodal fin line. As in the De Ronde coupler, the strip-slot section is one quarter wavelength long at the center frequency. The coupling coefficient S_{12} is given by

$$S_{12} = \left[\frac{(2Z_p/Z)^2 - 1}{(2Z_p/Z)^2 + 1} \right) \qquad (9.3)$$

The other scattering parameters are given by

$$|S_{13}| = 0, \ |S_{14}|^2 = 1 - |S_{12}|^2 \qquad (9.4)$$

For a specified coupling $|S_{12}|$, the normalized impedance of the slot and the strip can be obtained from (9.2) and (9.3). The slot length l_s and the strip length l_p are given by

$$l_s = \frac{\lambda_s}{4} = \frac{\lambda_0}{4\sqrt{\epsilon_{fs}}} \qquad (9.5a)$$

$$l_p = \frac{\lambda_p}{4} = \frac{\lambda_0}{4\sqrt{\epsilon_{fp}}} \qquad (9.5b)$$

where ϵ_{fs} and ϵ_{fp} are the effective dielectric constants for the slot mode and strip mode, respectively, and λ_0 is the free-space wavelength. These parameters as well as the widths of the slot and strip can be calculated by using the spectral-domain immittance formulas (see Ch. 3).

Callsen and Schmidt [10] have reported the measured performance of an experimentally optimized 3 dB coupler, with a quartz overlay on the slot side of the substrate. The function of the dielectric overlay is to minimize the difference between the even-mode and odd-mode effective dielectric constants, thereby improving the directivity of the coupler. The coupler is reported to give an isolation in the range 20 to 25 dB, an insertion loss of 0.5 dB, and less than 0.5 dB amplitude imbalance over the entire Ka band.

9.2.5 Parallel-Coupled Fin-Line Couplers

Parallel-coupled fin-line couplers can be realized by using the natural coupling between two symmetrically located slots, as shown in Fig. 9.12. The printed pattern on the substrate is complementary to the conventional parallel-coupled microstrip coupler pattern. While microstrip couplers are essentially backward-wave couplers, the parallel-coupled fin-line coupler offers forward-wave coupling. For example, if a signal is fed to port 1, port 3 forms the coupled port and port 4 is the isolated port. The even- and odd-modes propagate with different phase velocities, and the coupling is periodic along the length of the line. In such a distributed coupler, the coupling length L required for complete transfer of power from port 1 to port 3 is given by [19]:

$$L = \frac{\pi}{\beta_{\text{even}} - \beta_{\text{odd}}} \tag{9.6}$$

where β_{even} and β_{odd} are the phase constants for the even-mode and odd-mode, respectively. Because β_{even} and β_{odd} can be determined from the spectral domain solutions of edge-coupled fin lines (Ch. 3), the 0 dB coupling length L can be calculated as a function of frequency for various slot widths w and spacings $2s$. Suitable combinations of w and s that offer minimum variation in L as a function of frequency over the desired band are chosen for the design. Since the coupling is periodic, the length of the coupling region l for any intermediate coupling can be calculated by using the formula [12, 20]:

$$|S_{13}| = \sin\left(\frac{\pi}{2} \cdot \frac{l}{L}\right) \tag{9.7}$$

where $|S_{13}|$ denotes the amplitude of the coupling coefficient between ports 1 and 3. The coupling coefficient $|S_{12}|$ is then given by

$$|S_{12}| = \sqrt{1 - |S_{13}|^2} = \cos\left(\frac{\pi}{2} \cdot \frac{l}{L}\right) \tag{9.8}$$

These formulas do not take into account the coupling in the nonuniformly coupled regions on either side of the uniform coupling length l. The effective length l_{eff} of the coupler is slightly longer than l and is given by [20]

$$l_{\text{eff}} = l + \frac{2L}{\pi} \int_{z1}^{z2} [\beta_{\text{even}}(z) - \beta_{\text{odd}}(z)] \, dz \tag{9.9}$$

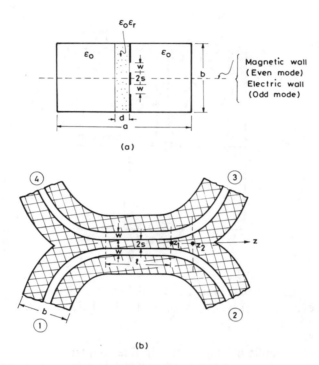

Fig. 9.12 Typical parallel coupled fin-line coupler:
(a) cross-sectional view
(b) slot pattern

where the integration is carried out along the axial (z) direction of the coupler. The points z_1 and z_2 correspond to the two junctions at the two ends of the nonuniformly coupled region. Beyond the junction plane at $z = z_2$, the coupling between the connecting arms is negligible and β_{even} is practically equal to β_{odd}. These junction effects due to the coupling between the coupling arms can be minimized by keeping the bends as short as possible. While designing the bend, however, it is necessary to ensure that the reflection coefficient at the port is within a tolerable limit.

Figure 9.13 shows the layout of a practical parallel-coupled fin-line coupler reported by Beyer *et al.* [13]. The short-circuiting pins shown in the figure serve the function of preventing waveguide resonances in the junction area. The four ports of the coupler are connected to asymmetrical fin lines. The fin taper provided at each of the four ports is for matching to the standard rectangular waveguide. The measured performance reported in [13] for a 3 dB coupler in this configuration shows a return loss as well as directivity better than 20 dB over about 10% bandwidth about an operating frequency of around 32 GHz.

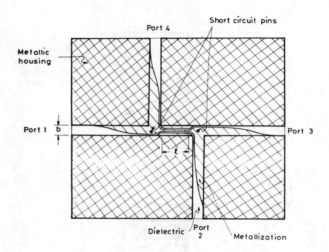

Fig. 9.13 Layout of a practical parallel coupled fin-line coupler.
(From Beyer *et al.* [13], Copyright © 1985 IEEE, reprinted with permission.)

Two other configurations of the fin-line coupler, one which makes use
of nonuniformly coupled slots (Fig. 9.14(a)) and another which uses a
stepped coupling strength distribution (Fig. 9.14(b)), have been reported
by Kpodzo *et al.* [14]. In Fig. 9.14(a), the slot width w is uniform, but the
spacing $2s$ between the adjacent slots is minimum at the center of the
coupling length l, and increases linearly on either side up to the length
$l/2$. With a signal fed to port 1, coupling to port 3 can be increased by
decreasing the spacing $2s_0$ at the center of the coupling region, and increasing the slot width w and the length l. The taper angle θ influences
the directivity as well as the effective coupling length. A 3 dB forward-
wave coupler operating over approximately 25% bandwidth about 15 GHz
with a directivity better than 20 dB and an insertion loss of around 0.3 dB
has been reported in this configuration [14]. By contrast, the stepped
section coupler (Fig. 9.14(b)) is reported to offer smaller bandwidth (approximately 7%), but with a lesser insertion loss in the range 0.1 to 0.2
dB.

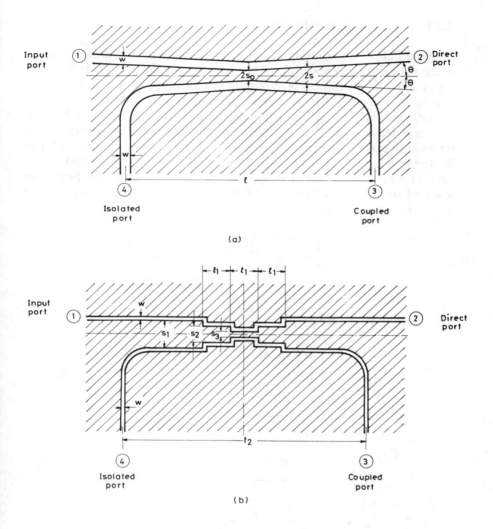

Fig. 9.14   (a) Nonuniform fin-line coupler.

(b) Stepped section fin-line coupler.

(From Kpodzo *et al.* [14], Copyright © 1980 IEEE, reprinted with permission.)

9.2.6 Fin-Line Microstrip Coupler

A fin-line microstrip directional coupler based on the ultra flat strip-slot coupler of De Ronde [8], but constructed to suit a unilateral fin-line input and a microstrip coupled output, is shown in Fig. 9.15. In this configuration, the microstrip is oriented at an angle θ with respect to the slot of the unilateral fin line and is printed on the back side of the substrate. A signal fed to port 1 of the unilateral fin line becomes constructively coupled to the microstrip conductor in the forward direction (toward port 3). In the reverse direction along the strip toward port 4, there is destructive interference. The two microstrip outputs are taken from the broadside walls of the housing by means of OSM connectors. Port 4 is terminated in an external matched load.

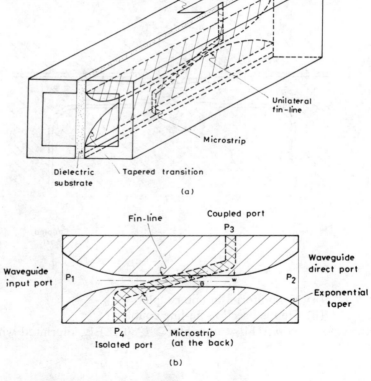

(a)

(b)

Fig. 9.15 Fin-line microstrip coupler:
(a) assembled view
(b) pattern on the substrate

Typical measured performance characteristics of a coupler at X band with the microstrip width corresponding to 50 Ω and for different slot widths (w) and angles of inclination (θ) are reported in [15]. The results show that the coupler with a 1 mm slot width gives the best performance in terms of broadband coupling as well as isolation, with the coupling becoming tighter as θ is increased from 2.5° to 10°. Figure 9.16 demonstrates the typical measured characteristics for $\theta = 4°$. The results show moderately good directivity (>15 dB) and tight coupling on the order of 2.5 dB($\pm$ 0.5 dB) over the entire X band.

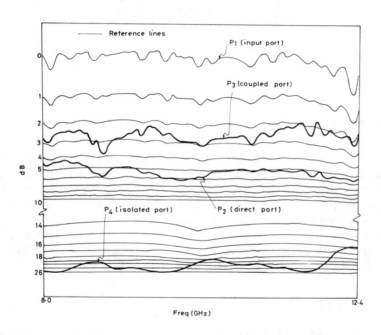

Fig. 9.16   Measured performance of fin-line microstrip coupler:
$a = 22.86$ mm $b = 10.16$ mm
$d = 0.5$ mm $\epsilon_r = 2.2$
$w = 1$ mm $\theta = 4°$

9.3   POWER DIVIDERS

The various types of hybrid fin-line couplers described in Sec. 9.2 can also work as *power division networks*. In addition, broadband power dividers have been realized by using series connections of two fin lines as shown in Fig. 9.17. For example, a 1:1 power divider that uses a 300 Ω

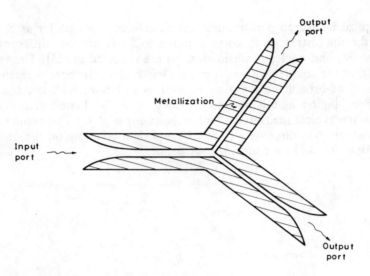

Fig. 9.17 Typical slot pattern of fin-line power divider.

input line and two 150 Ω output lines is reported to give a return loss of about 20 dB and a power division of 3.4 ± 0.2 dB at each output arm over the entire Ka band [21]. Broadband power dividers having unequal power divisions can be designed by choosing different ratios of slot widths, corresponding to different line impedances.

It is important to note that such power division networks are reactive dividers and these are not matched four-port networks. Thus, they do not have isolation as does a generally accepted power divider.

9.4 FILTERS

9.4.1 Types of Slot Patterns

Typical slot patterns used in practical fin-line filters are illustrated in Fig. 9.18. *Low-pass filters* can be built in asymmetrical fin-line configuration by etching a series of narrow notches at periodic intervals along the length of the slot, as shown in Fig. 9.18(a) [22, 23].

Bandpass filters are generally realized by cascading half-wave rectangular resonators [24–41]. The coupling between adjacent resonators can be achieved by means of an inductive strip (Fig. 9.18(b, c)), a post (Fig. 9.18(d)), or a notch (Fig. 9.18(e)). Among these types, the inductive coupled resonator filter, in which the slot width equals the waveguide

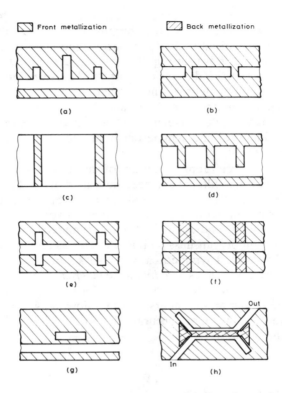

Fig. 9.18 Typical slot patterns of low-pass (a), bandpass (b–f), and
bandstop (g–h) fin-line filters.

height (Fig. 9.18(c)), is of special importance because of its high-Q performance. With an increase in the slot width of the resonators, the conductor loss due to the grounded fins reduces and the Q-factor increases.
The optimal value of Q is achieved when the slot width reaches the waveguide height. Further improvement in the Q-factor is possible by eliminating the dielectric backing altogether and inserting pure metallic sheets
bearing the slot patterns [25, 26, 33–39].

A different configuration of the bandpass filter, which does not make
use of half-wave resonators, is shown in Fig. 9.18(f). This configuration
consists of a bilateral section embedded into a unilateral fin line [41]. If
the length of the bilateral section is made equal to a half-wavelength, then
the structure offers a *bandstop filter* characteristic.

Figure 9.18(g) shows a typical bandstop filter, consisting of a half-wave
resonating slot coupled to the main slot of the fin line [40, 41]. An entirely

different type of bandstop filter is shown in Fig. 9.18(h) [40]. This is a planar hybrid with two of its ports terminated in short circuits. Such a configuration is specifically suited for narrowband operation.

The slot patterns shown in Fig. 9.18(a–e, g) can be realized on either one or both sides of the dielectric substrate. *Pure-metal-insert filters* can also be constructed by defining the slot pattern on a thin metal sheet by means of chemical milling or etching, and then inserting the sheet in the E-plane of the rectangular waveguide. *Double-planar bandpass filters* consisting of two identical and symmetrically placed metal inserts have also been reported [37–39].

The equivalent circuit representations of various types of discontinuities encountered in fin-line filters have been described in Ch. 8. Almost all the discontinuities, except those used in the planar hybrid filter (Fig. 9.18(h)) can be represented either as a T-network or π-network. It has been shown by Matthaei, Young, and Jones [42] that a symmetrical T-network connected to a section of transmission line operates as an *impedance inverter* (Fig. 9.19). Similarly, a symmetrical π-network connected to a section of transmission line operates as an *admittance inverter* (Fig. 9.20). With these equivalences, the well known filter design formulas [42] can be directly utilized for designing fin-line filters. In the following, we shall discuss this method as well as other more accurate design techniques that have been reported in the literature.

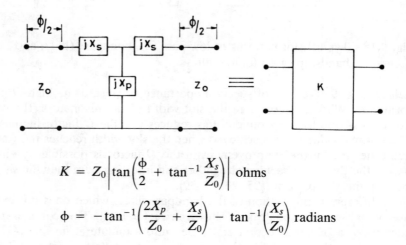

$$K = Z_0 \left| \tan\left(\frac{\phi}{2} + \tan^{-1}\frac{X_s}{Z_0}\right)\right| \text{ ohms}$$

$$\phi = -\tan^{-1}\left(\frac{2X_p}{Z_0} + \frac{X_s}{Z_0}\right) - \tan^{-1}\left(\frac{X_s}{Z_0}\right) \text{ radians}$$

Fig. 9.19 Equivalence between T-network and impedance K-inverter.

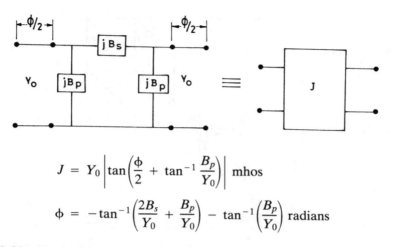

$$J = Y_0 \left| \tan\left(\frac{\phi}{2} + \tan^{-1} \frac{B_p}{Y_0} \right) \right| \text{ mhos}$$

$$\phi = -\tan^{-1}\left(\frac{2B_s}{Y_0} + \frac{B_p}{Y_0} \right) - \tan^{-1}\left(\frac{B_p}{Y_0} \right) \text{ radians}$$

Fig. 9.20 Equivalence between π-network and admittance J-inverter.

9.4.2 Low-Pass Filters

Low-pass filters consisting of a sequence of notches cut along the slot edge of an asymmetric fin line have been reported [22, 23]. The geometrical features of such a filter are depicted in Fig. 9.21(a). The filter equivalent circuit shown in Fig. 9.21(b) is made up of alternating π-networks (representing the notches) and uniform transmission line sections. The electrical length of the jth section is $\theta_j = 2\pi l_j/\lambda_g$, where λ_g is the guide wavelength of an asymmetric fin line at the cut-off frequency of the filter. The characteristic admittance of all the transmission line sections is Y_0, which is the same as that of the asymmetric fin line of slot width w. By using the equivalence given in Fig. 9.20, the filter network is transformed to another equivalent network, consisting of admittance J inverters, as shown in Fig. 9.21(c). The filter design equations can now be written in the form [42]:

$$J_{j-1,j} = Y_0 \left| \tan\left(\frac{\Phi_j}{2} + \tan^{-1} \frac{B_{pj}}{Y_0} \right) \right| \qquad (9.10a)$$

$$\Phi_j = -\left[\tan^{-1}\left(\frac{2B_{sj}}{Y_0} + \frac{B_{pj}}{Y_0} \right) + \tan^{-1} \frac{B_{pj}}{Y_0} \right] \qquad (9.10b)$$

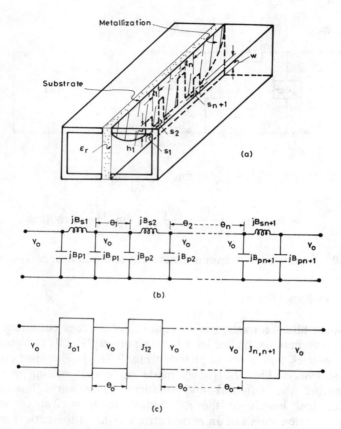

Fig. 9.21 (a) Fin-line low-pass filter.
  (b) Filter network using π-equivalent for notch.
  (c) Equivalent network using admittance inverters.

The electrical length θ_j between notches j and $j + 1$ is given by

$$\theta_j = \theta_0 + \frac{1}{2}(\Phi_j + \Phi_{j+1}) \tag{9.11}$$

where $\theta_0 = \pi/2$ at the cut-off frequency of the filter.

Procedures for characterizing the notch discontinuities have been described in Ch. 8. From the susceptance parameters B_{sj} and B_{pj} ($j = 1$, . . . , $n + 1$) of the π-networks, the electrical separation $\theta_j(j = 1$, . . . , n) between consecutive notches can be calculated by using (9.10b) and (9.11). The response of the filter can then be evaluated from the $ABCD$ matrix representation of the network. It may be noted that this design does not take into account the evanescent-mode interaction between the irises.

Filters of the type considered above are known to offer broadband performance with very sharp cut-off [22].

9.4.3 Bandpass Filters

The most popular bandpass filter configuration consists of alternating inductive strips and half-wave slot resonators. For low-loss performance, these filters invariably adopt either large-gap fin lines [27–32] or pure-metal-insert E-plane configurations [25–27, 33–39]. Figures 9.22 and 9.23 illustrate a class of such large-gap fin lines and pure-metal-insert E-plane

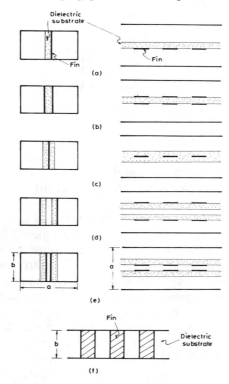

Fig. 9.22 Class of large gap fin-line filters:
  (a) unilateral septum
  (b) bilateral septum
  (c) insulated septum
  (d, e) broadside-coupled septum
  (f) printed pattern for (a)–(e)

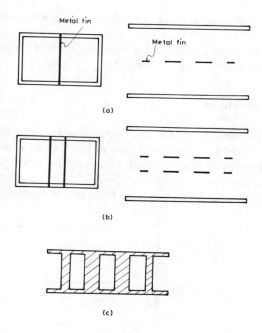

Fig. 9.23 E-plane metal-insert filters:
    (a) single metal insert
    (b) double metal insert
    (c) resonator pattern for (a) and (b)

filters, respectively. With the slot width equal to the waveguide height, both configurations eliminate the need for a tapered fin transition from the waveguide to the E-plane filter. Pure-metal-insert filters, in particular, combine the advantages of low-cost production through batch-processing techniques and low-loss performance of conventional waveguide circuits. With a relatively thick metallic sheet, these filters can offer Q-factors of about 1700 at 30 GHz as compared with a value of about 700–800 for the dielectric counterpart [43]. However, it may be noted that the dimensional tolerance of these filters is as stringent as in a pure metal waveguide filter. The large-gap fin-line filter alleviates this problem to some extent by concentrating the energy within the dielectric substrate. The fin-line configuration is also convenient for integrating the filter with other circuits on a single substrate.

Bandpass filter designs have been treated extensively in the literature. These include the simple approximate theories based on experimental data [23, 24], equivalent circuit models [25–26, 36], and the equivalent waveguide approach [27]. Accurate theories that take into account the higher order mode interaction between the discontinuities as well as the finite thickness of dielectric substrates, fins, and metal inserts have also been reported [29–35, 37, 38]. In the following, we discuss some of the more useful design techniques.

Metal-Insert E-plane Filters—Approximate Design Using Impedance Inverter Equivalent Networks

The design of shunt-inductance coupled waveguide filters using low-pass to bandpass transformation and equivalent impedance inverter networks is available in Matthaei, Young, and Jones [42]. Based on this approach, bandpass filter designs have been reported [25, 26, 36] for pure-metal-insert E-plane configurations of the type shown in Fig. 9.24(a). It is assumed that the metal thickness is negligible. Following the design method

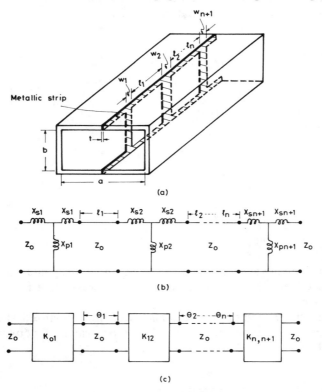

Fig. 9.24 (a) Bandpass filter with inductive strips.
(b) Equivalent circuit using T-equivalent for strip.
(c) Equivalent circuit using impedance inverters.

provided in [42], we will outline the design steps for the filter shown in Fig. 9.24:

- Specify the center frequency (f_0), bandwidth (Δf), passband insertion loss, and skirt selectivity for the bandpass filter.
- By using the low-pass to bandpass mapping, choose the number of sections (n) and the low-pass prototype element values (g_1, g_2, ..., g_n).
- Calculate the guide wavelength λ_{g0} for the rectangular waveguide at the center frequency f_0:

$$\lambda_{g0} = \frac{\lambda_0}{\sqrt{1 - (\lambda_0/2a)^2}} \tag{9.12}$$

where λ_0 is the free-space wavelength at f_0.
- Calculate the K-inverter parameters $K_{j,j+1}$.

$$\frac{K_{01}}{Z_0} = \sqrt{\frac{\pi}{2} \cdot \frac{\omega_a}{g_0 g_1}} \tag{9.13a}$$

$$\frac{K_{j,j+1}}{Z_0} = \frac{\pi \omega_a}{2} \cdot \frac{1}{\sqrt{g_j g_{j+1}}}, \quad j = 1, \ldots, n-1 \tag{9.13b}$$

$$\frac{K_{n,n+1}}{Z_0} = \sqrt{\frac{\pi}{2} \cdot \frac{\omega_a}{g_n g_{n+1}}} \tag{9.13c}$$

where

$$\omega_a = \left(\frac{\lambda_{g0}}{\lambda_0}\right)^2 \cdot \frac{\Delta f}{f_0} \tag{9.13d}$$

The element values g_0 and g_{n+1} correspond to the generator and load, respectively. For a filter matched to the waveguide impedance Z_0, $g_0 = g_{n+1} = 1$.
- From the K-inverter values, calculate the normalized shunt reactances X_p/Z_0. If we set $X_s = 0$ in the equivalent T-network of Fig. 9.19, then

$$\frac{X_{pj}}{Z_0} = \frac{K_{j-1,j}/Z_0}{\left[1 - \left(\frac{K_{j-1,j}}{Z_0}\right)^2\right]} \tag{9.14}$$

Up to here, the design steps are the same as those given in [42] for shunt-inductance coupled waveguide filters.

● Consider now the general T-network representation of inductive strips, as shown in Fig. 9.24(b). From the design curves of normalized shunt reactance X_p/Z_0 and normalized series reactance X_s/Z_0 of an inductive strip as a function of frequency for various strip widths, find the strip width that yields the value of X_p/Z_0 as calculated above at f_0, and also find the corresponding value of X_s/Z_0. Thus, all the strip widths $w_j(j = 1, 2, \ldots, n + 1)$ are determined.

● From the general model of the inverter, while taking into account the normalized series reactance X_s/Z_0 (Fig. 9.24(c)), determine the spacing between the adjacent strips (resonator lengths l_j) by using

$$\left(\frac{2\pi}{\lambda_{g0}}\right)l_j = \theta_j' + \frac{1}{2}(\Phi_j + \Phi_{j+1}) \tag{9.15a}$$

$$\Phi_j = -\tan^{-1}\left(\frac{2X_{pj}}{Z_0} + \frac{X_{sj}}{Z_0}\right) - \tan^{-1}\left(\frac{X_{sj}}{Z_0}\right) \tag{9.15b}$$

where $\theta_j' = \pi, j = 1, 2, \ldots, n$ at the center frequency f_0.

It may be noted that the above design formulas do not take into account the higher order mode interaction between the discontinuities. The influence of higher order mode coupling, however, is small in the case of pure metal insert filters as compared with their dielectric backed fin-line counterpart. This is because, in the fin-line case, a metallic strip appears as a larger discontinuity due to the higher concentration of field in the slot. As a consequence of this, the higher order modes are excited much more strongly than in a waveguide without dielectric loading. The simple design technique given above can be applied to pure-metal-insert filters when the thickness of the septa is negligible in comparison with the wavelength. It has been shown by Konishi and Uenakada [26] that the measured insertion loss at X band of a two-section E-plane metal insert filter having 0.3 mm thick inductive strips matches very well with the theoretical design based on their equivalent circuit approach (using zero-thickness approximation). For the same septa thickness and filter parameters, the exact insertion loss calculations of Vahldieck et al. [33] are also found to match well with the theoretical curve published in [26]. It may be noted that a septa thickness of 0.3 mm at X band corresponds to about one percent of the wavelength.

In the following, we discuss some exact analytical techniques, which take into account the higher order mode interaction as well as finite thicknesses of the dielectric substrate, fins, and metal inserts. The filter parameters are generally optimized through an optimization routine to yield the desired characteristic. In such cases, the equivalent circuit approach helps us to arrive quickly at initial guess values of filter parameters, thus resulting in savings of computational time.

The equivalent circuit method requires *a priori* knowledge of equivalent T-network parameters for inductive strips. These can be evaluated either through experiments or from scattering parameter calculations. The values of the normalized series reactance $j\overline{X}_s$ and the shunt reactance $j\overline{X}_p$ of the T-network can be easily calculated from the scattering parameters of the inductive strip. The normalized impedance matrix $\overline{Z}$ is given by

$$[\overline{Z}] = \begin{bmatrix} j(\overline{X}_s + \overline{X}_p) & j\overline{X}_p \\ j\overline{X}_p & j(\overline{X}_s + \overline{X}_p) \end{bmatrix} \tag{9.16}$$

In terms of the scattering matrix $[S]$, we have

$$[\overline{Z}] = [I + S] \; [I - S]^{-1} \tag{9.17}$$

where I is the identity matrix. By equating the elements of the two matrices in (9.16) and (9.17), we get

$$j\overline{X}_p = \frac{2S_{12}}{(1 - S_{11})^2 - S_{12}^2} \tag{9.18a}$$

$$j\overline{X}_s = \frac{1 - S_{12} + S_{11}}{1 - S_{11} + S_{12}} \tag{9.18b}$$

Large-Gap Fin-Line and Metal-Insert Filters—Exact Analysis Based on Field Theory Treatment

Figure 9.22 shows a class of large-gap fin-line filters having low insertion loss potential. Among the first three basic configurations, the insulated fin line is known to possess much lower Q-factor than the bilateral fin line [43]. Shih *et al.* [32] have observed experimentally that the insertion loss of large-gap fin-line filters with unilateral septum is always greater than that of filters with bilateral septum for the same design specifications. One possible explanation put forward in [32] is that there is greater dielectric loss in a filter with unilateral septum, while the conductor loss is about the same in both cases. Shih *et al.* have reasoned that little energy penetrates into the narrow dielectric space between the two strips in a filter with bilateral septum, whereas with unilateral septum the energy is coupled

more or less evenly through the air region and the dielectric-filled region
on either side of the septum. Thus, comparatively less dielectric loss is
encountered in the bilateral case. Furthermore, with little energy in the
dielectric substrate, the current flow on the inner surfaces of the two strips
is negligible in the bilateral case. The conductor loss is essentially due to
the current flow on the two outer surfaces, which is identical to a single
strip carrying current on both sides, as in the unilateral case. Apart from
the advantage of offering very low insertion loss, the bilateral construction
is reported to be less sensitive to mechanical tolerances than the unilateral
construction [31]. Filters with bilateral septums are therefore preferred
over those with unilateral or insulated septa.

The low-insertion-loss bilateral fin-line bandpass filter (Fig. 9.25) has
been studied by Arndt *et al.* [29–31]. The design is based on the exact field
theory treatment and takes into account the effects of higher order mode
propagation as well as the finite thicknesses of the substrate and the metal
fins. The same technique has also been applied to pure-metal-insert E-
plane filters with septa of finite thickness [33, 37–39]. In the following, we
shall outline the salient features of this method by considering the example
of a bilateral fin-line filter.

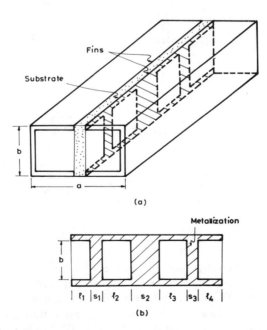

Fig. 9.25 (a) Low insertion loss bandpass filter with bilateral septum.
(b) Printed pattern on both sides of the substrate.

The fin line is regarded as consisting of alternating waveguide structures of two different types, as illustrated in Fig. 9.26(a); one is a dielectric slab-loaded waveguide and the second consists of three parallel waveguides with the middle guide being filled with a dielectric of relative dielectric constant ϵ_r. The analysis involves determination of scattering matrices for these two types of waveguide sections by embedding each section in a

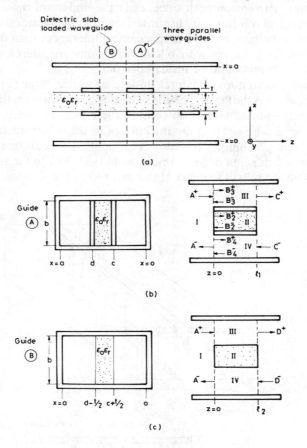

Fig. 9.26   Filter configuration of Fig. 9.25 for field theory treatment:

        (a) top view showing alternating waveguide structures

        (b) three parallel waveguide section within the waveguide

        (c) dielectric slab-loaded section within the waveguide

standard waveguide, as illustrated in Fig. 9.26(b, c). The scattering parameters of the complete fin-line filter are obtained by suitably combining the scattering matrices of the various sections.

Assuming the dominant TE_{10} type of wave to be incident from the rectangular waveguide, the fields excited in the filter can be classified as the TE_{m0} type because there are no structural variations in the y-direction. The only nonzero field components are E_y, H_x, and H_z. These can be obtained from the x-component of the magnetic Hertzian vector potential π^h, which, in turn, is a solution of the vector Helmholtz equation [44]:

$$\nabla^2 \pi^h + k^2 \pi^h = 0, \quad k^2 = \omega^2 \mu \epsilon \tag{9.19}$$

Let us consider the three-parallel-waveguide structure (Fig. 9.26(b)), where the x-component of π^h is first expressed as a sum of suitable eigenmodes for each of the subregions $R = $ I, II, III, and IV. Thus,

$$\pi_x^{h(R)} = \sum_{m=1}^{\infty} A_m^{R\pm} \sin\left(\frac{m\pi \cdot f^R}{p^R}\right) \cdot \exp(\mp j \, k_{zm}^R \cdot z) \tag{9.20}$$

The E_y component is given by

$$E_y^R = -j\omega\mu \, \frac{\partial}{\partial z} \, \pi_x^{h(R)} \tag{9.21a}$$

The magnetic field components H_x and H_z are then obtained by using

$$H_x^R = \frac{1}{j\omega\mu} \cdot \frac{\partial E_y^R}{\partial z} \tag{9.21b}$$

$$H_z^R = -\frac{1}{j\omega\mu} \cdot \frac{\partial E_y^R}{\partial x} \tag{9.21c}$$

The abbreviations f^R, p^R, and k_{zm}^R denote the following [31]:

$$\begin{bmatrix} f^I \\ f^{II} \\ f^{III} \\ f^{IV} \end{bmatrix} = \begin{bmatrix} x \\ d - \dfrac{t}{2} - x \\ a - x \\ x \end{bmatrix} \tag{9.22a}$$

$$
\begin{bmatrix} p^{\mathrm{I}} \\ p^{\mathrm{II}} \\ p^{\mathrm{III}} \\ p^{\mathrm{IV}} \end{bmatrix} = \begin{bmatrix} a \\ d - c - t \\ a - \left(d + \dfrac{t}{2} \right) \\ c - \dfrac{t}{2} \end{bmatrix} \tag{9.22b}
$$

$$
\begin{bmatrix} (k_{zm}^{\mathrm{I}})^2 \\ (k_{zm}^{\mathrm{II}})^2 \\ (k_{zm}^{\mathrm{III}})^2 \\ (k_{zm}^{\mathrm{IV}})^2 \end{bmatrix} = \begin{bmatrix} k_0^2 - \left(\dfrac{m\pi}{a} \right)^2 \\ k_0^2 \epsilon_r - \left(\dfrac{m\pi}{p^{\mathrm{II}}} \right)^2 \\ k_0^2 - \left(\dfrac{m\pi}{p^{\mathrm{III}}} \right)^2 \\ k_0^2 - \left(\dfrac{m\pi}{p^{\mathrm{IV}}} \right)^2 \end{bmatrix} \tag{9.22c}
$$

The tangential field components are matched at the corresponding interfaces of the adjacent subregions at $z = 0$, and the coefficients $A_m^{R\pm}$ are determined by using the orthogonality of eigenmodes. This yields a four-port scattering matrix $[S]$ for the junction $z = 0$. By referring to Fig. 9.26(b), we can write

$$
\begin{bmatrix} A^- \\ B_2^+ \\ B_3^+ \\ B_4^+ \end{bmatrix} = [S] \begin{bmatrix} A^+ \\ B_2^- \\ B_3^- \\ B_4^- \end{bmatrix} \tag{9.23}
$$

The scattering matrix for the step discontinuity at $z = l_1$ is determined similarly. The two-port scattering matrix of the three-parallel-waveguide section of length l_1 embedded in a waveguide is obtained as

$$
\begin{bmatrix} A^- \\ C^+ \end{bmatrix} = \begin{bmatrix} [S_{11}] & [S_{12}] \\ [S_{21}] & [S_{22}] \end{bmatrix} \begin{bmatrix} A^+ \\ C^- \end{bmatrix} \tag{9.24}
$$

The scattering matrix of the dielectric slab-loaded section of length l_2 embedded in a waveguide (Fig. 9.26(c)) is determined in a similar manner. By referring to Fig. 9.26(c), we can write

$$\begin{bmatrix} A^- \\ D^+ \end{bmatrix} = \begin{bmatrix} [S_{11}]' & [S_{12}]' \\ [S_{21}]' & [S_{22}]' \end{bmatrix} \begin{bmatrix} A^+ \\ D^- \end{bmatrix} \qquad (9.25)$$

To determine the common propagation constant k_{zm} in regions II, III, and IV of the dielectric slab-loaded guide, the tangential field components E_y and H_z are matched at the dielectric interfaces at $x = c + t/2$ and $d - t/2$. This leads to a transcendental equation, the root of which is numerically evaluated to yield k_{zm}. The scattering matrix of the complete fin-line filter is obtained by suitably combining the scattering matrices of individual sections as described in [45].

If the thickness of the dielectric substrate is reduced to a negligibly small value, the design approaches that of a metal-insert filter. Pure-metal-insert filters with septa of finite thickness have also been directly analyzed by using the same technique [30, 33]. The filter is regarded as alternating sections of rectangular waveguide and bifurcated waveguide (Fig. 9.27(a)). The scattering matrix of the bifurcated waveguide section is determined by embedding it in an empty waveguide (Fig. 9.27(b)). If A^+ and A^- denote the forward- and backward-wave amplitudes, respectively, in the input guide, and C^+ and C^- denote the corresponding quantities for the output guide, then the scattering matrix of the section of length l is given by the same relation as in (9.24). The scattering matrix of the complete filter is obtained by suitably combining the matrices of cascaded sections. The filter dimensions are then determined by applying an optimization technique [30]. The procedure involves optimizing the slot-resonator lengths l_i and septum widths s_i (see Fig. 9.25) for a prescribed maximum passband attenuation L_{pmax} and a minimum stopband attenuation L_{smin}. For this, an error function $F(\bar{x})$, which is to be minimized, is defined as

$$F(\bar{x}) = \sum_{i=1}^{N_s} \left[\frac{L_{smin}}{a_{21}(f_i)} \right]^2 + \sum_{i=1}^{N_p} \left[\frac{a_{21}(f_i)}{L_{pmax}} \right]^2 \qquad (9.26)$$

where f_i are the frequency sample points, N_s and N_p are the number of sample points in the stopband and passband, respectively, and $a_{21}(f_i) = 20 \log [1/|S_{21}(f_i)|]$ is the calculated value of filter attenuation at f_i. In practical designs, about 20 to 30 frequency sample points are found to be adequate. For a fixed number of resonators, the resonator lengths and septum widths denoted by $\bar{x} = (l_1, l_2, \ldots ; s_1, s_2, \ldots)$ are varied to minimize $F(\bar{x})$. Details of the analysis and optimization techniques are available in [29–31, 33]. These publications also include the calculated and

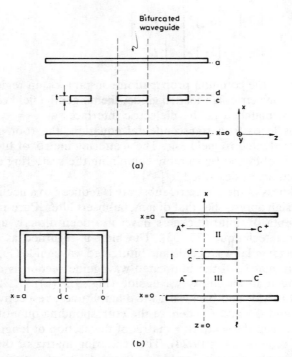

Fig. 9.27   E-plane metal insert filter (Fig. 9.24(a)) for field theory
treatment:
   (a) top view
   (b) bifurcated waveguide section within a standard
   waveguide

measured insertion loss characteristics of three- to five-resonator bandpass
filters in the X to W bands. Measured passband insertion losses for the
fin-line filters are typically 0.3, 0.7, and 1.5 dB at midband frequencies of
12, 34, and 75 GHz, respectively, and for the metal-insert filters they are
0.1, 0.6, and 0.7 dB at midband frequencies of 12, 33, and 76 GHz,
respectively [30].

   Figures 9.28 and 9.29 show the insertion loss characteristics reported
in [30] for a three-resonator bilateral fin-line filter and a three-resonator
E-plane metal-insert filter, respectively. Comparison between the two
graphs shows that the metal insert filter, as well as offering a slightly lower
insertion loss, also improves the skirt selectivity at the higher end of the
passband.

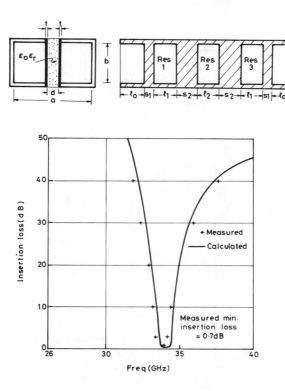

Fig. 9.28   Calculated and measured insertion loss of 3-resonator bilateral fin-line filter at Ka band:

$a = 7.112$ mm	$b = 3.556$ mm
$\epsilon_r = 2.22$	$d = 0.254$ mm
$l_0 = 19.77$ mm	$s_1 = 0.705$ mm
$l_1 = l_2 = 3.75$ mm	$s_2 = 3.9$ mm
substrate = RT-duroid™ 5880	Copper cladding thickness $t = 17.5$ μm

(From Bornemann *et al.* [30], reprinted with permission of IERE.)

General E-plane Filters—Exact Analysis Using Computer-Aided Design Algorithm

A computer-aided design (CAD) algorithm, based on the *residue-calculus technique* [46] and a generalized scattering parameter method [47], has been described by Shih *et al.* [32]. The treatment is general and ap-

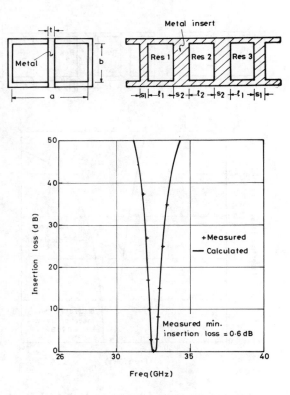

Fig. 9.29 Calculated and measured insertion loss of 3-resonator E-plane metal insert filter at Ka band:

$a = 7.112$ mm $b = 3.556$ mm
$t = 0.51$ mm $s_1 = 1.009$ mm
$l_1 = 4.778$ mm $s_2 = 3.87$ mm
$l_2 = 4.796$ mm

(From Bornemann *et al.* [30], reprinted with permission of IERE.)

plicable to a class of E-plane filters, illustrated in Figs. 9.22 and 9.23, under the assumption that the thickness of fins or metal inserts is negligibly small. The CAD algorithm consists of an analysis routine and an optimization routine. The salient steps in this method are given below [32]:

1.   First, a single junction created by a semi-infinite septum in a waveguide is considered. For example, the geometry for characterizing a single junction for a bilateral fin-line filter (Fig. 9.25(a)) is shown in Fig. 9.30. Only one-half of the structure with the symmetry plane

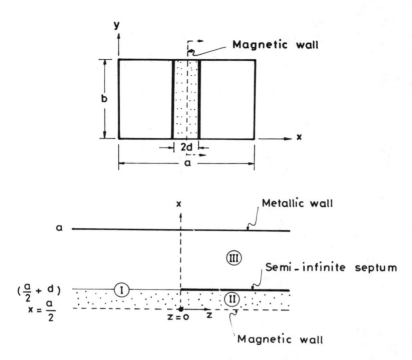

Fig. 9.30   Geometry for characterization of semi-infinite septum for bilateral fin-line filter (after Shih *et al.* [32]).

replaced by a magnetic wall is adequate for the analysis. The total fields (TE_{m0} type) in each of the three regions marked I, II, and III are expanded in terms of eigenmodes. Then, matching the tangential field components at the junction $z = 0$ and using the orthogonality of eigenmodes results in an infinite set of equations. The scattering matrix of the junction is obtained by applying the residue-calculus technique [46]. This matrix contains all the information regarding the dominant mode as well as the higher order modes.

2.   A septum of finite length s is considered next (Fig. 9.31). If $[S_1]$ denotes the scattering matrix of junction 1 as calculated in step 1, then the scattering matrix $[S_2]$ of junction 2 is given by

$$[S_2] = [S_1]^T \qquad\qquad (9.27)$$

The concept of the generalized scattering matrix [47] is then applied. This takes into account the multiple reflections between the two

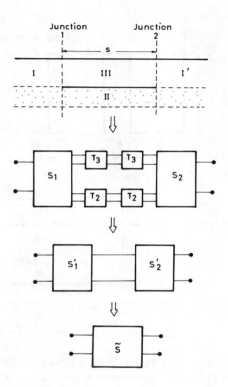

Fig. 9.31 S-parameter derivation for a single septum.
(From Shih *et al.* [32], Copyright © 1983 IEEE, reprinted with permission.)

junctions. Let $[T_2]$ and $[T_3]$ denote the matrices due to the propagating modes as well as the evanescent modes for a distance $s/2$ in the guided regions II and III, respectively. Then, a transmission matrix T is defined as

$$[T] = \begin{bmatrix} [I] & [0] & [0] \\ [0] & [T_2] & [0] \\ [0] & [0] & [T_3] \end{bmatrix} \tag{9.28}$$

where [I] and [0] are the identity matrix and the zero matrix, respectively. The matrices $[S_1']$ and $[S_2']$ in Fig. 9.31 are given by

$$[S_1'] = [T][S_1][T] \tag{9.29a}$$

$$[S_2'] = [T][S_2][T] \tag{9.29b}$$

The scattering matrix $[\tilde{S}]$ for the septum of length s is obtained by combining $[S_1']$ and $[S_2']$.

3. The scattering parameters of the complete filter are obtained by suitably combining the scattering matrices of the various septums and the alternating dielectric-loaded waveguide sections.

4. An optimization routine is used in which an error function $F(\bar{x})$ as defined in (9.26) is minimized. Filter parameters are optimized to yield the desired filter performance.

The effect of finite thicknesses of fins and metal inserts has been taken into account in a modified analysis [34]. Details of this analysis are available in [32, 34].

Figure 9.32 illustrates the effect of metal-insert thickness on the filter's performance [34]. The resonator and septum lengths given in the figure

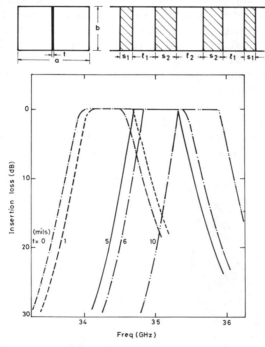

Fig. 9.32 Effect of septum thickness on E-plane metal insert bandpass filter performance:

$a = 7.112$ mm $\quad b = 3.556$ mm
$s_1 = 1.6641$ mm $\quad s_2 = 4.8211$ mm
$l_1 = 3.6178$ mm $\quad l_2 = 3.6108$ mm

(From Shih and Itoh [34], Copyright © 1983 IEEE, reprinted with permission.)

426 DESIGN & ANALYSIS OF FIN LINES

are the optimized values for a 5-mil septum thickness. The graph shows a clear upward shift in the center frequency as the thickness is increased. It has been pointed out [34] that increasing the strip thickness effectively shortens the equivalent length of the resonators, and as a consequence the resonant frequency shifts to a higher value. Other predicted effects are the reduction in bandwidth and an increase in the passband ripple.

Double-Planar Metal-Insert Filters and Other Special Filters for Improved Stopband Attenuation

Single metal-insert filters in standard waveguide offer good performance when the passband is situated in the middle of the waveguide band. The filter subregions between the septa and the waveguide side walls are below cut-off and coupling between the resonators takes place via the evanescent fields along the strips. For filters designed to operate near the higher end of the waveguide band, the stopband frequencies on the higher side exceed the waveguide band. For frequencies exceeding the cut-off frequency of the subregions between the septa and the waveguide side walls, waves are no longer evanescent, and power is increasingly transported by the propagating waves along the strips. The inductive coupling between the resonators is destroyed, resulting in a lowering of the stopband attenuation. This problem is alleviated in the double-planar metal-insert filter (Fig. 9.33) by virtue of preserving the evanescent fields in the strip region over an extended frequency range at the higher end.

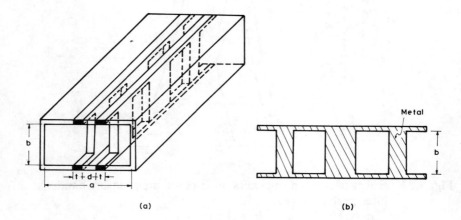

(a)   (b)

Fig. 9.33 (a) Double-planar metal insert filter.
(b) Metal double insert.

The double-planar metal-insert filter with septa of finite thickness has been analyzed [37, 38] by using the same method [29–31] as outlined above with regard to the exact method for large-gap and metal-insert fin lines. Bornemann *et al.* [37] have stated that field expansion into nine eigenmodes at each discontinuity is adequate for computer optimization of double-planar metal-insert filters. Figure 9.34 shows the insertion loss characteristic for a four-resonator filter reported in [37]. The graph clearly illustrates

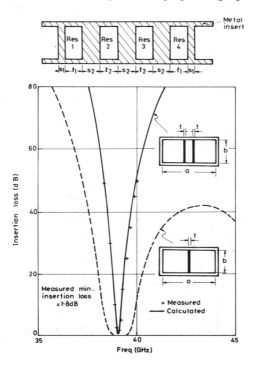

Fig. 9.34 Calculated and measured insertion loss for a 4-resonator double-planar metal insert filter :
––––– single planar metal insert filter for comparison
$a = 7.112$ mm $b = 3.556$ mm
$s_1 = 0.403$ mm $l_1 = 3.637$ mm
$s_2 = 2.448$ mm $l_2 = 3.689$ mm
$s_3 = 3.646$ mm $t = 150$ μm
$d = 1.8$ mm
(From Bornemann *et al.* [37], first presented at the 13th European Microwave Conference, reprinted with permission.)

the fact that significantly higher stopband attenuation above the passband is achievable in the case of a twin metal-insert filter as compared with a single one.

Another way to enhance the stopband attenuation at higher frequencies is to reduce the distance between the side walls of the waveguide in the filter section, which is then matched to a standard waveguide with a taper at each end [38]. Vahldieck and Hoefer [39] have suggested using a more convenient construction in which the filter section is directly connected to a standard waveguide, thus forming an abrupt step junction at either end. The step junctions are then included in the analysis of the filter. Figure 9.35 shows the geometry as well as a comparison of the insertion loss characteristic of a four-resonator single metal-insert filter in a reduced-section guide with that of a filter in standard waveguide [39]. The filter in a reduced-section guide shows considerably higher stopband attenuation in addition to an upward shift in the spurious second passband as compared with its conventional counterpart. A similar feature has also been reported for fin-line filters realized in narrow waveguides.

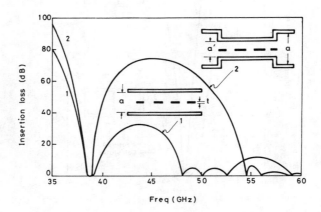

Fig. 9.35 Four-resonator single metal insert filter:
           waveguide height b = 3.556 mm
           t = 50 μm
           Filter 1: a = 7.112 mm
           Filter 2: a = 7.112 mm a' = 5.689 mm
(From Vahldieck and Hoefer [39], Copyright © 1985 IEEE, reprinted with permission.)

The same design principle has also been applied to realize filters that are required to operate at the lower end of the waveguide band [39]. In this case, the filter section is housed in a wider waveguide with standard waveguides connected at each end. This arrangement, in addition to improving the stopband attenuation, shortens the filter length and pushes the spurious second passband upward in frequency. The use of twin metal inserts in place of a single one can further improve the stopband attenuation and spurious response.

Double-Dielectric Fin-Line Filters

The advantage of double-dielectric fin-line filters (Fig. 9.22(d, e)) over the twin metal-insert filter is that the former is amenable to circuit integration on a common substrate, as are other fin-line circuits. This advantage, however, is at the expense of increased loss due to the dielectric substrates. Of the two versions shown in Fig. 9.22, the configuration with fins facing the side walls is less lossy because most of the energy appears in the air regions between the fins and the adjacent side walls. Typical measured insertion-loss characteristic for a three-resonator filter at X band with fins facing each other is shown in Fig. 9.36 and that of a filter at Ka band with fins facing the side walls is shown in Fig. 9.37.

9.4.4 Bandstop Filters

Slot patterns sketched in Fig. 9.18(f–h) can offer bandstop filter characteristics. In the first case (Fig. 9.18(f)), a bandstop filter is realized by embedding half-wave sections of bilateral fin line into a unilateral fin line [41]. With a suitable choice of the slot width, the cut-off frequency of the first higher order mode (HE_{20}) of the bilateral fin line can be arranged to fall within the normal waveguide band. The reaction cavity of a bandstop filter is thus realized at the half-wave resonance of this mode. In the second case (Fig. 9.18(g)), the reaction cavity is composed of a half-wave slot resonator coupled to the main slot of the normal fin line [40, 41]. The coupling level depends on the slot widths as well as the spacing between the slots. Practical bandstop filters adopt a cascade of several such resonators arranged parallel to the main line. The spacing between the resonator elements is a quarter-wavelength (or an odd multiple of a quarter-wavelength) in a single-slot fin line. The design of filters with a cascade of several resonators can be carried out using the equivalent circuit approach described under Sec. 9.4.3. A K-inverter network is extracted from

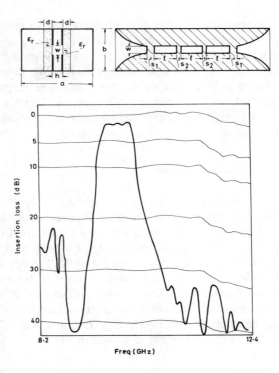

Fig. 9.36 Measured insertion loss characteristic of a 3-resonator
double-dielectric fin-line filter (fins facing each other):
X-band waveguide: $a = 22.86$ mm $b = 10.16$ mm
polystyrene substrates: $\epsilon_r = 2.2$ $d = 0.5$ mm
$h = 0.5$ mm $w = 8$ mm
$l = 13$ mm $s_1 = 2$ mm
$s_2 = 8$ mm

the equivalent circuit of the coupling section and cascaded with the reaction
type of cavity. As pointed out in the preceding section, this design neglects
higher order mode coupling. For more accurate design, the reaction cavity
and the coupling junction can be characterized by its scattering matrix, as
described in Sec. 9.4.3. Good initial values for computer optimization can
be obtained from the equivalent circuit approach.

The filter pattern shown in Fig. 9.18(h) is of a different type. The circuit
makes use of a planar hybrid with two ports terminated in a short circuit.
The design of the hybrid is described in [9] and the filter design procedure
is available in [42]. A narrowband filter of this type is reported to give an
attenuation of about 40 dB [40].

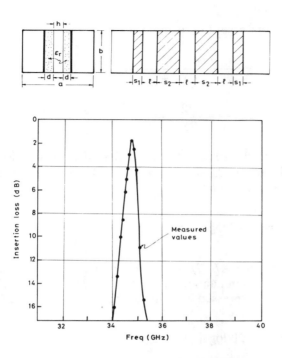

Fig. 9.37   Measured insertion loss characteristic of a 3-resonator
double-dielectric fin-line filter (fins facing side walls):
Ka-band waveguide: $a = 7.112$ mm $b = 3.556$ mm
RT-duroid™ substrate: $\epsilon_r = 2.22$ $d = 0.127$ mm
$h = 0.127$ mm $w = b$
$l = 3.72$ mm $s_1 = 0.73$ mm
$s_2 = 4.13$ mm

9.5   PIN-DIODE ATTENUATORS AND SWITCHES

9.5.1   Basic Series and Shunt Type Circuits

Positive-intrinsic-negative (*pin*) diode switches and attenuators can be
realized by adopting either a series type of circuit, wherein the diode is
mounted in series with a transmission line (Fig. 9.38(a)), or a shunt type
of circuit, wherein the diode is shunt mounted across the transmission line
(Fig. 9.38(b)). The input reflection coefficient S_{11} and the voltage transmission coefficient S_{21} for such networks can be obtained directly from
their *ABCD* parameters. For symmetrical, reciprocal two-port networks,

as in the present case, the relations are

$$S_{11} = S_{22} = \frac{BY_0 - CZ_0}{2A + BY_0 + CZ_0} \tag{9.30a}$$

$$S_{21} = S_{12} = \frac{2}{2A + BY_0 + CZ_0} \tag{9.30b}$$

where Z_0 is the characteristic impedance of the transmission line in which the diode is mounted, and $Y_0 = 1/Z_0$. The attenuation α through the network is then given by

$$\alpha(\text{dB}) = -20 \log_{10} \left| \frac{1}{S_{21}} \right| \tag{9.31}$$

By substituting the $ABCD$ parameters of a series element in (9.30b) and using (9.31), the attenuation through the series type of basic circuit (Fig. 9.38(a)) can be expressed in terms of the diode impedance Z_d:

$$\alpha(\text{dB}) = -20 \log_{10} \left| 1 + \frac{Z_d}{2Z_0} \right| \tag{9.32}$$

Similarly, the attenuation through the shunt type of basic circuit (Fig. 9.38(b)) is obtained as

$$\alpha(\text{dB}) = -20 \log_{10} \left| 1 + \frac{Y_d}{2Y_0} \right|, \; Y_d = \frac{1}{Z_d} \tag{9.33}$$

The impedance Z_d of the diode can be represented in terms of a general equivalent circuit, as shown in Fig. 9.38(c), where R_j, C_j, R_s, L_s, and C_p represent the junction resistance, junction capacitance, bulk semiconductor and contact resistance, parasitic series inductance, and package capacitance, respectively. For a chip diode, the elements L_s and C_p may be omitted. R_j has a large value on the order of several kΩ under zero bias, and decreases rapidly with an increase in the forward bias current. It is this property which is utilized for achieving variable attenuation through the network. Values of C_j are generally in the range 10–100 fF, and R_s is on the order of an ohm. The actual values depend on the manufacturing process of the diode.

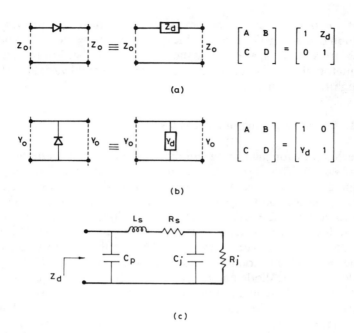

Fig. 9.38 (a) Series mounted diode.
(b) Shunt mounted diode ($Y_d = 1/Z_d$, $Y_0 = 1/Z_0$).
(c) General equivalent circuit of *pin* diode.

For operation as an on-off switch, the *pin* diode is switched between two fixed bias states. For an ideal switch, the diode should present a perfect short circuit when forward biased (*on* state) and a perfect open circuit when reverse biased (*off* state). In practice, owing to the small series resistance and lead inductance under forward bias, the diode presents a near short circuit. Similarly, under reverse bias, the small junction capacitance gives rise to a large impedance.

In the case of the series type of switch (Fig. 9.38(a)), transmission takes place when the diode is on and the attenuation through the network, as calculated from (9.32), is termed as *insertion loss*. When the diode parameters corresponding to the off state are substituted in (9.32), the attenuation is termed as *isolation*. These definitions are interchanged for the shunt type of switch shown in Fig. 9.38(b); that is, when the diode is on, the attenuation refers to isolation, and when the diode is off, it refers to insertion loss. The design criterion for a switch is to achieve the minimum insertion loss and the maximum isolation. Improved insertion loss and isolation characteristics can be achieved by mounting more than one diode, which are suitably spaced along the transmission line. For operation as an attenuator, the forward bias current is varied to yield variable attenuation through the network.

9.5.2 Characterization of *pin* Diodes

Techniques for measuring *pin*-diode parameters in general have been described by White [48]. The *pin*-diode attenuators and switches used in fin-line configuration commonly employ beam-lead diodes. It is helpful to characterize the diode by mounting it in a fin line, wherein the circuit is later to be built. Experimental characterization of *pin* diodes mounted in fin line has been reported by several investigators [24, 49, 50]. One way is to determine the parameters by measuring the small-signal impedance of the diode shunt mounted across the slot of a fin line [50]. By varying the dc bias to the diode and tuning out the diode reactance part by means of a variable short at the output end, the input reflection coefficient is reduced to zero. This condition arises when the real part of the diode admittance becomes equal to the characteristic admittance Y_0 of the fin line. If we neglect C_p and R_s in the equivalent circuit (Fig. 9.38(c)), we can write

$$Y_0 = \text{Re}(Y_d) \approx \frac{G_j}{(1 - \omega^2 L_s C_j)^2} \qquad (9.34)$$

The small-signal conductance G_j is determined by the dc characteristic of the diode. The series inductance can be extracted from measurement of the transmission coefficient S_{21} with the diode in the on state $(G_j \rightarrow \infty)$. The expression is given by

$$L_s = \frac{|S_{21}|}{2\omega Y_0} \qquad (9.35)$$

The characteristic admittance Y_0 of the fin line is computed accurately from the spectral domain formulas. The value of L_S calculated from (9.35) is then substituted in (9.34) to determine C_j.

9.5.3 Shunt Circuits

Conventional unilateral fin lines with narrow slots that are compatible with the beam-lead diodes offer impedances in the range of 150 to 200 Ω.

Comparatively, the inductive reactance of the on-state diode is generally a few ohms and the capacitive reactance of the off-state diode is several hundred ohms. The ratio of these two reactances governs the dynamic range of the attenuator by using a single diode.

In order to reduce the insertion loss and increase the isolation level, two or more diodes are incorporated in the circuit. Attenuators and switches using two to four diodes in a shunt or series type of configuration have been reported. [1, 2, 21, 23, 28, 51–56]. Such circuits can be analyzed by multiplying the $ABCD$ matrices of the various cascaded circuit elements. With the knowledge of the equivalent circuit parameters of the diodes, the various discontinuity elements, and the transmission line sections, the transmission and reflection coefficients can be evaluated.

Shunt attenuators and switches are known for their broadband performance. Figure 9.39(a) shows a basic layout of an attenuator with three shunt-mounted beam-lead diodes [21]. The diodes are spaced by one quarter-wavelength in a unilateral fin line at midband. As an example of its performance, the attenuation characteristic of a Ka-band attenuator, as reported in [21], is shown in Fig. 9.39(b). The graph shows variable

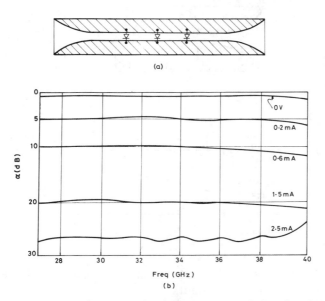

Fig. 9.39 Typical measured attenuation characteristic of a shunt type attenuator using three diodes (diodes: ai 6-6474-30, quartz substrate).

(From Hofmann *et al.* [21], Copyright © 1978 IEEE, reprinted with permission.)

attenuation from about 0.4 dB up to about 28 dB and broadband performance over practically the entire Ka band. This is a reflection type of
attenuator. Matched attenuators can be realized in bilateral fin-line configuration with one diode mounted across the slot on one side of the
substrate, and a second diode mounted across the slot on the opposite side
[21]. The two diodes are biased separately in such a way that one diode
reflects and thus produces the attenuation and the second diode provides
for the matching. Attenuation can be increased by adding more diodes.
The maximum achievable attenuation in this bilateral configuration, however, is limited (to about 20 dB) because part of the energy appears at
the fins on the opposite side, and hence cannot be coupled to the diodes
[21].

A broadband switch in unilateral fin line that uses two sections of bilateral fin line with shunt-mounted diodes is illustrated in Fig. 9.40a [52].
In the equivalent circuit (Fig. 9.40(b)), the bilateral fin-line section is
represented by its equivalent T-network, and the diode is modeled as an

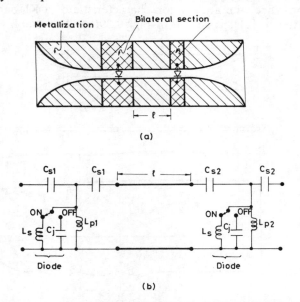

Fig. 9.40   (a) Shunt type *pin*-diode switch using bilateral fin-line
section for diode mount.
(b) Equivalent circuit: ON—forward bias, OFF—reverse
bias.
(From Hennawy and Schunemann [52], Copyright © 1982 IEEE, reprinted
with permission.)

inductance in the on state and a capacitance in the off state. The capacitive reactance of the bilateral section is utilized for series tuning of the shunt inductive susceptance when the diodes are in the on state. The two bilateral sections are of different lengths so as to stagger the two series resonant frequencies in relation to the midband frequency. This helps to enhance the isolation bandwidth. Details of the stagger-tuning technique employed in switches are available in [48]. The distance between the two bilateral sections is determined from the condition for maximum transmission when the diodes are in the off state. Alternatively, bandpass filter design techniques can be applied for maximally flat response.

Shunt attenuators and switches have been realized in various millimeter-wave bands for frequencies up to 145 GHz. For example, a two-diode attenuator has been reported by Callsen [53] which yields a maximum insertion loss of 2 dB and a minimum isolation of 25 dB over a frequency range from 130 to 145 GHz.

9.5.4 Series Circuits

Series attenuators can be realized by mounting *pin* diodes across series stubs [51, 55] or across notches [54, 57] in a fin line (Fig. 9.41). A narrow slit cut in one of the fins acts as a series stub. In a simple equivalent circuit

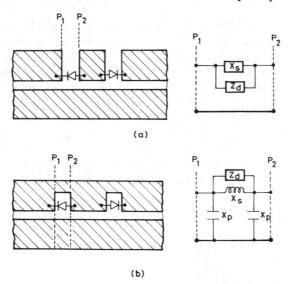

(a)

(b)

Fig. 9.41 Layout of series type *pin*-diode attenuators using:
      (a) narrow series stub
      (b) notches

(Fig. 9.41(a)), a series stub is replaced by a reactance X_s parallel to the diode impedance Z_d. The dimensions of the series stub are chosen such that the series stub tunes out the parasitic inductive reactance of the diode when the diode is on. High attenuation is achieved due to this parallel resonance. For transmission, the diode is in the off state, so that the stub presents a very low impedance in series with the line, resulting in low insertion loss. Owing to the parallel resonance, this type of attenuator yields large attenuation over a narrow bandwidth. For example, a 90 GHz series type of two-diode attenuator, reported in [55], shows about 40 dB attenuation over a bandwidth of approximately 750 MHz.

In the second type shown in Fig. 9.41(b), the notch is represented by an equivalent π-network. According to the design given in [54, 57], Z_d of the diode in the off state is tuned out by the series reactance X_s of the notch to provide high isolation. This determines the notch width. The capacitive shunt elements X_p must be incorporated into the circuit so that the effective length of the transmission line section between the notches is equal to one quarter-wavelength in the fin line. For the on-state diode, the diode admittance must be much larger than the characteristic admittance of the fin line so as to offer minimum insertion loss.

9.5.5 Y-Junction SPDT Switches

Single-pole double-throw (SPDT) switches have been built using a series Y-junction in fin line [21, 55, 58]. A basic layout of such a switch and its equivalent circuit are shown in Fig. 9.42. The Y-junction is represented by an equivalent circuit identical to that of an E-plane junction in a rectangular waveguide. $Y_d(ON)$ and $Y_d(OFF)$ refer to the admittance of the diode in the on state and off state, respectively. Koh $et\ al.$ [58] have analyzed the switch performance under the assumption that the on-state diode approximates a short circuit and the off-state diode approximates an open circuit. If λ and Y_0 represent the guide wavelength and the characteristic admittance of the fin line, then the parameters B_a and B_b of the Y-junction can be calculated (approximately) by using [58]:

$$\frac{B_a}{Y_0} = 0.6455 \, \frac{2b}{\lambda} \tag{9.36a}$$

$$\frac{B_b}{Y_0} = \frac{2\sqrt{3}}{\pi} \cdot \frac{\lambda}{b} \tag{9.36b}$$

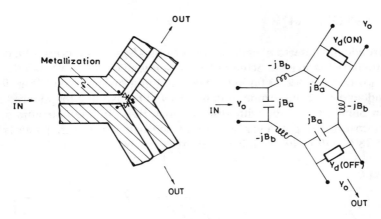

Fig. 9.42 Layout of SPDT switch and its equivalent circuit.

These formulas, along with the expression for the input impedance of a short circuited section of transmission line, namely,

$$Z_{sc} = j\, Z_0 \tan \beta l \tag{9.37}$$

are used to determine the correct position of the on-state diode.

In practical circuits, diodes are mounted as close to the junction as possible in order not to limit the bandwidth of the circuit. Additional diodes can be mounted at suitable spacings away from the first diode. An SPDT switch with two diodes in each of the two output arms is reported to give a maximum insertion loss of 1.75 dB and a minimum isolation of 23 dB over the entire Ka band [58]. They have also demonstrated that with three diodes in each arm, the maximum insertion loss increases to 2 dB, whereas the minimum isolation improves to 30 dB. SPDT switches of this type have been realized for various waveguide bands up to 100 GHz. They serve as Dicke switches in radiometers and as transmitting-receiving switches for radar applications [59].

The switching time of *pin*-diode switches depends on the manufacturing of the diodes. Switching time as low as a few nanoseconds have been realized. A switching time lower than one nanosecond is possible with the use of Schottky-barrier diodes, but at the expense of increased insertion loss [50].

9.6   DETECTORS

Broadband detectors make use of zero-bias Schottky diodes. In a design reported by Meinel and Schmidt [60], beam-lead diodes are bonded across the slot of a unilateral fin line terminated in a matched load (Fig. 9.43). Broadband matched termination is achieved by painting the tapered transition behind the diode with absorber material. Fin-line detectors of this type, covering one or even two waveguide bands in the frequency range from 18 to 170 GHz, have been reported [59, 60].

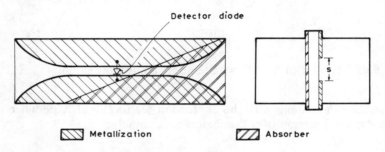

Fig. 9.43   Configuration of a fin-line detector.
(From Meinel and Schmidt [60], reprinted with permission of Plenum Publishing Corporation.)

The design of a different type of matched detector circuit by using a computer-aided design technique has been described by Hennawy and Schunemann [57, 61]. The layout of the circuit is illustrated in Fig. 9.44. The stub at the back of the diode is used for tuning out the imaginary part of the diode impedance and the three-section transformer in front is used for matching the real part. The inherent bandwidth of the circuit is limited because of the stub. In the equivalent circuit, Z_d generally includes the impedance of the diode and the stub, and Z_0 represents the characteristic impedance of the input fin line. These parameters and the number of notches are specified in the design. Then, using the equivalent circuit approach and with the knowledge of the equivalent T-network parameters of the notches, we can calculate the dimensions of the notches and the distances between them. An iterative procedure may be adopted to achieve the realizable dimensions.

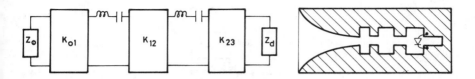

Fig. 9.44 Layout of a detector circuit and its equivalent circuit. (From Hennawy and Schunemann [61], Copyright © 1981 IEEE, reprinted with permission.)

9.7 MODULATORS

Phase-shift keying (PSK) modulators are commonly used in communication equipment and phased array systems. Digital modulators of the reflection type as well as the transmission type have been realized in finline configuration [14, 57, 61–66]. In the reflection type of modulator, the input reflection coefficients corresponding to the two steady-state impedances in the on and off states of the diode have equal magnitude, but they differ in phase by a specified value. It is essentially a two-state switching network, which also performs the desired transformation.

The layout of a reflection type of phase modulator described by Kpodzo *et al.* [14] for achieving 180° and 90° phase shifts is shown in Fig. 9.45. The impedance-matching networks consist of a short-circuited stub behind the *pin* diode and a short notch for introducing series inductance in front of the diode. The short is realized by metalizing the opposite side of the substrate. The circuit also integrates a microstrip low-pass filter to serve as a biasing network. The design of the matching circuit makes use of the fact that for a given phase change $\Delta\Phi$, the impedance to be matched is uniquely related to the impedances of the diode in the two switched states [14, 67]. For a 180° phase modulator, this corresponds to the *hyperbolic middle-point impedance,* as defined in [67]. This impedance is given by [14]:

$$Z_m = R_m + jX_m \tag{9.38}$$

$$R_m = \left\{ R_1 R_2 \left[1 + \left(\frac{X_1 - X_2}{R_1 + R_2} \right)^2 \right] \right\}^{1/2} \tag{9.39a}$$

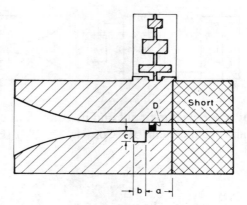

Fig. 9.45 Slot pattern of a reflection phase modulator with *pin*-diode D
        HPND-4050 Hewlett Packard:
              180° phase shift: $a = 3.85$ mm, $b = 0.2$ mm, $c = 1.0$ mm
               90° phase shift: $a = 2.9$ mm, $b = 0.2$ mm, $c = 1.5$ mm
(From Kpodzo *et al.* [14], Copyright © 1980 IEEE, reprinted with permission.)

$$X_m = \frac{R_1 X_2 + R_2 X_1}{R_1 + R_2} \tag{9.39b}$$

where $Z_1 = R_1 + jX_1$ and $Z_2 = R_2 + jX_2$ are the diode impedances
corresponding to the two switching states. It has been shown that for a
90° phase modulator, the hyperbolic middle-point impedance must be
transformed to a well defined mismatch impedance [14, 62]. In a practical
circuit, the slot width of the main fin line is chosen to be compatible with
the diode dimensions and its characteristic impedance is as close to R_m as
possible to facilitate easy matching. Then, with the knowledge of the
equivalent circuit parameters of short notches and the end correction in a
shorted fin, we determine the dimensions *a, b,* and *c* marked in Fig. 9.45.
The dimensions noted in Fig. 9.45 are for 180° and 90° phase modulators
realized in unilateral fin line at Ku band [14]. The waveguide (WR-62)
cross section is 15.8 mm × 7.9 mm and the substrate is RT-duroid® having
a thickness of 0.25 mm and $\epsilon_r = 2.22$. The fin-line slot width is 0.25 mm.
These modulators are reported to give more than 26% bandwidth and less
than 0.5 dB insertion loss. Two such modulators have been combined to
realize a quadriphase modulator with 0, 90°, 180°, and 270° phase shifts
[14]. The insertion loss of this modulator is 1.7 dB at 15 GHz.

In a different scheme proposed by Schieblich *et al.* [63], a capacitor is placed in series with the *pin* diode. Figure 9.46 shows the layout of the 180° reflection phase modulator that adopts this scheme. The main fin-line slot is situated on one side of the substrate. On the opposite side, the diode is connected between a grounded fin and a rectangular metal patch, which serves as a capacitor. The diode is biased via a narrow strip connected to the metal patch. Simple formulas have been provided for calculating the values of the capacitance C and the electrical length θ of the short-circuited fin-line section for a prescribed phase difference $\Delta\Phi$ between the two reflection coefficients. The diode is considered as an ideal switch, and the dispersion characteristics of the circuit in the two switching states are equalized by setting the derivative $d/df(\Delta\Phi)$ equal to zero. The formulas are [63]:

$$\sin\theta \cdot \sin\left(\theta + \frac{\Delta\Phi + \epsilon}{2}\right) + \theta\sin\left(2\theta + \frac{\Delta\Phi + \epsilon}{2}\right) = 0 \qquad (9.40)$$

$$C = \frac{\sin\left(\dfrac{\Delta\Phi + \epsilon}{2}\right)}{\sin\theta \cdot \sin\left(\theta + \dfrac{\Delta\Phi + \epsilon}{2}\right)} \qquad (9.41)$$

where all parameters refer to the center frequency f_0 and ϵ is the phase error. The measured performance of a Ku-band 180° phase modulator reported in [63] shows a phase error below 4°, amplitude imbalance of less than 0.5 dB, and an insertion loss of about 0.5 dB over a frequency range from 13.5 to 18 GHz.

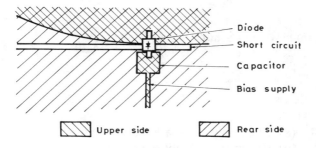

Fig. 9.46 Fin-line slot pattern of a 15 GHz 180° phase modulator. (From Schieblich *et al.* [63], Copyright © 1983 IEEE, reprinted with permission.)

Figure 9.47 shows the circuit layout and operating principle of a biphase PSK modulator reported by Thorpe [64] for Ka-band operation. It is a balanced circuit that incorporates equal-length switched paths. Two beam-lead diodes are mounted at the slotline T-junction across the slots of the two side arms of the "*tee*." The double-ended quarter-wave transformer inside the annular ring splits the ring symmetrically so that the diodes can be biased separately while maintaining good RF continuity. The diodes are biased such that when one diode is in the on state (short circuit), the second one is in the off state (open circuit). The input signal is thus routed through one of the two arms. Figure 9.47(b) illustrates the electric field orientations in the slot, resulting in 180° phase change between the two switching combinations of the diodes. This modulator is reported to offer 3 dB insertion loss across 7% bandwidth and a switching speed of 100 Mbit/s [64].

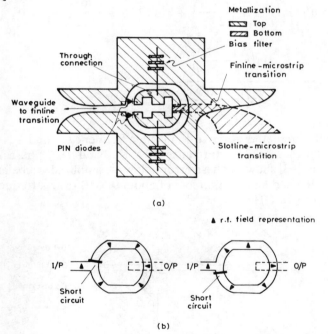

Fig. 9.47   (a) Circuit layout of a PSK modulator.
            (b) Principle of circuit operation.
(From Thorpe [64], Copyright © 1983 IEEE, reprinted with permission.)

9.8 MIXERS

The mixer is a commonly used component in almost all radar and communication receivers. Mixers with broad bandwidth capabilities at both RF and IF are particularly suited for electronic warfare (EW) applications. Both narrow- and broadband mixers have been realized by using fin-line techniques. In the following, we shall describe fin-line mixers under the following categories: *single-ended, balanced, double-balanced,* and *subharmonically pumped* mixers.

9.8.1 Single-Ended Mixers

A single-ended mixer is the simplest of all types and can be realized in fin line by directly adapting the well known waveguide technique. Such fin-line mixers were first realized by Meier [68, 69] for Ka band. The beam-lead mixer diode is connected across the fin-line slot. The RF and local oscillator (LO) signals are fed from the two end ports via integrated E-plane filters. The IF is then extracted from the broadside wall by means of a coaxial connection. A single-ended mixer has also been realized in pure-metal-insert configuration, but at X band, by Konishi [70, 71]. The equivalent network approach used in this design can be applied to mixers at higher frequencies.

9.8.2 Balanced Mixers

A major advantage of the balanced mixer over the single-ended mixer is the suppression of local oscillator noise. It is a two-diode circuit in which the signal and LO are isolated from each other without the use of filters. A balanced mixer can be constructed by combining two single-ended mixers on a single substrate with a 90° or 180° hybrid. For example, balanced mixers have been reported to incorporate printed probe couplers [2, 72] and 3 dB hybrid couplers [73].

The first balanced mixer to be realized for operation over the entire Ka band was by Gysel [74]. The main feature of this mixer is the broadband 180° hybrid junction formed by combining a fin line and a coplanar line, as shown in Fig. 9.48(a). The mixer diodes (matched pair) are mounted at the junction such that they appear in series from the RF port and in parallel from the LO port. The diodes are oriented antiparallel. Thus, the RF signal fed from the symmetrical fin-line port is in phase at the two diodes, and the LO signal fed from the coplanar side is 180° out of phase.

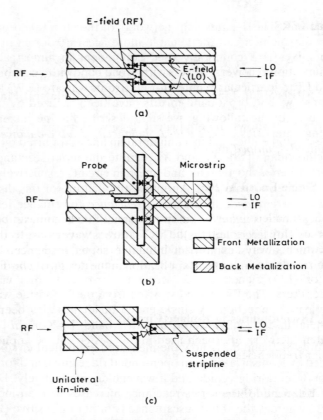

Fig. 9.48 Types of planar hybrids for fin-line mixers:
  (a) fin line to coplanar-line junction (after Gysel [74])
  (b) probe type transition (after Mehran *et al.* [84])
  (c) fin line to suspended stripline junction (after Bui and
  Ball [81])

This arrangement also provides inherent isolation between the RF and LO
signals. The IF output is extracted via a low-pass filter. Balanced mixers
using this type of hybrid have been realized for frequencies up to 140 GHz
[51, 59, 75–77]. Several other mixer circuits with changes incorporated in
the coupling arrangement between the RF port and the LO port, as well
as in the diplexing circuits for LO and IF, have also been reported [3, 23,
54, 56, 77–87]. Two typical examples of hybrids are illustrated in Fig.
9.48(b, c). In Fig. 9.48(b), the fin line to microstrip junction functions as

a magic-*tee*, and the conducting strip protruding from the microstrip acts as a probe. As in the case of the junction shown in Fig. 9.48(a), the cross arms are in series with the fin-line input (RF) and in parallel with the microstrip input (LO) from the right. The impedance levels of the microstrip, cross arms and the fin line must be in the ratio 1:2:4. A suitable choice of impedance levels in practical circuits is 50 Ω for the microstrip, 100 Ω for each of the cross arms, and 200 Ω for the fin line [78, 84]. The diodes are mounted antiparallel but symmetrically in the two cross arms. A short-circuited section of the slot beyond the diode helps to tune out the capacitive susceptance of the diode. The probe length is adjusted so as to match the microstrip input. In another example of a broadband 180° planar hybrid (Fig. 9.48(c)), the diodes are mounted directly across the junction between a fin line (for RF) and a suspended substrate stripline [81, 86]. In this arrangement as well, the RF and LO ports are isolated from each other because the electric field lines in the fin line and suspended stripline are perpendicular to each other.

Figure 9.49 shows the layout of a balanced mixer using the type of hybrid illustrated in Fig. 9.48(a). As discussed above, if the impedance of the fin line is 200 Ω, then the impedance of the coplanar line and the asymmetrical fin line is 100 Ω. The LO signal is fed through the asymmetrical fin line at port 2, and port 3 is terminated in a variable short to permit tuning of the LO input impedance. The lumped-element low-pass filter connected to the coplanar line is designed for an input impedance of 50 Ω. The number of elements and the element values of the low-pass filter can be obtained from the well known design formulas [42], and their

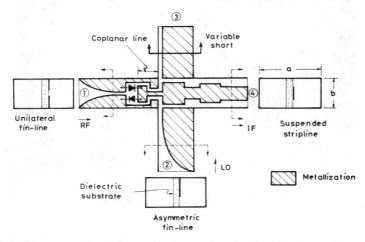

Fig. 9.49 Layout of a balanced mixer using fin-line–coplanar-line hybrid.

translation in suspended stripline configuration can be carried out by using the formulas provided in [88], for example. In a practical design, each of the parts—namely, the fin-line taper, low-pass filter, and the coplanar junction—can be first tested individually before realizing the entire pattern on a single substrate. It is also necessary to characterize the mixer diodes and provide for suitable impedance matching. Figure 9.50 illustrates the fabricational details of a practical mixer. In the example shown, the low-pass filter consists of two sections.

As an example of a broadband balanced mixer, the circuit layout of a W-band mixer reported by Tahim *et al.* [86] is shown in Fig. 9.51. The fin line to suspended stripline hybrid junction operates on the same principle as that shown in Fig. 9.48(c). The LO power is fed to the mixer diodes via an antipodal fin line to suspended stripline transition and a bandpass filter. The LO bandpass filter and the IF low-pass filter are built in suspended stripline. The bandpass filter helps to isolate the RF from LO. The fin-line taper and the slot width on the RF side can be adjusted to provide good impedance matching to the mixer diodes. A W-band balanced mixer in this configuration is reported to offer a conversion loss of 8 to 12 dB over a 32 GHz instantaneous IF bandwidth when the RF is varied from 76 to 108 GHz [86].

Fig. 9.50 Photograph of Ka-band fin-line balanced mixer.

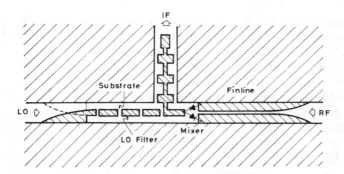

Fig. 9.51   Circuit layout of a broadband balanced mixer using fin line
             to suspended stripline transition.
(From Tahim *et al.* [86], Copyright © 1983 IEEE, reprinted with permission.)

9.8.3   Double-Balanced Mixers

The double-balanced mixers have advantages over the single-balanced
mixers in terms of reduced filtering requirements and improved dynamic
range. Simple fin-line mixer designs having more than an octave bandwidth
were first reported by Knochel and Schlegel [89]. One example is illustrated
in Fig. 9.52. In this design, two pairs of diodes are mounted across a gap
created between a bilateral fin-line and an antipodal fin line. In another

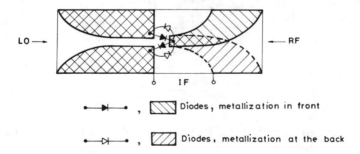

Fig. 9.52   Layout of double-balanced fin-line mixer.
(From Knochel and Schlegel [89], first presented at the 10th European
Microwave Conference, reprinted with permission.)

arrangement (Fig. 9.53(a)), the diode pairs are connected across a junction between two bilateral fin lines [89]. On either side of the bilateral section is connected one diode pair with no crossover. The IF output is extracted by means of the wires connected to the fins.

Figure 9.53(b) shows a different diode-mounting arrangement suggested by Blaisdell *et al.* [90]. In this, the junction between a bilateral fin line and an antipodal fin line consists of a broadside-edge coupled stripline with conductor strips arranged in the form of a circular arc. The E-field lines at the cross-sectional planes of the broadside-edge coupled stripline on the LO side and on the RF side are shown separately in the figure. The two fields are perpendicular to each other, thus providing isolation between the RF and LO. The diodes are connected to an annular ring to form a star configuration. The inner rings on either side of the substrate are connected together by means of a plated through-hole and the IF output is coupled from this junction.

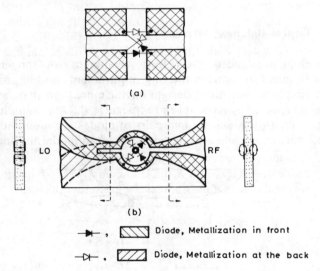

Fig. 9.53 Arrangement for mounting diode pairs for double-balanced fin-line mixers:
(a) junction between two bilateral fin lines
(b) junction between a bilateral fin line and an antipodal fin line

(Fig. 9.53(a) From Knochel and Schlegel [89], first presented at the 10th European Microwave Conference, reprinted with permission. Fig. 9.53(b) From Blaisdell *et al.* [90], Copyright © 1982 IEEE, reprinted with permission.)

9.8.4 Subharmonically Pumped Mixers

In all the mixers considered above, the RF and LO frequencies differ by the intermediate frequency. Subharmonically pumped mixers have been reported [91, 92] in which the LO frequency is nearly half the RF. The IF, therefore, is given by $f_{IF} = f_{RF} - 2f_{LO}$. Because of this large frequency difference between the RF and LO signals, the filtering and diplexing circuits are simplified in these mixers. For example, in a X-band mixer described by Begemann [91], the RF input waveguide itself acts as a high-pass filter. Its cut-off frequency is higher than the IF and LO frequencies, thus preventing IF and LO from entering the RF port. Another example is the wideband subharmonic mixer presented by Meier [92] for W-band operation. The mixer is built in asymmetrical fin-line configuration. Its key elements are the simple fin-line filters incorporated as LO and RF diplexing circuits and a low capacitance diode mount. The mixer is reported to give an instantaneous bandwidth of 12 GHz in the vicinity of 94 GHz.

9.9 OSCILLATORS

Millimeter-wave oscillators using *Gunn* or *IMPATT* diodes are more commonly built by using waveguide cavities (e.g., [93, 94]) or in coaxial configurations (e.g., [95, 96]). For millimeter-wave frequencies up to about 100 GHz, oscillators have also been realized in fin-line media [2, 4, 21, 97–101]. Waveguide oscillators score over fin-line versions mainly because of their much higher Q-factors, while both are compatible for integration with other fin-line circuits. Fin-line oscillators, however, have the advantage in terms of better reproducibility of printed circuits. Practical fin-line oscillators have mostly used Gunn diodes as active elements. The difficulties with the use of IMPATT diodes are that they require a lower impedance level than the Gunn diodes and also need much more precise tuning facilities.

Figure 9.54 shows schematic representations of some fin-line oscillator circuits [97–101]. In all of these, the Gunn diode is mounted in the bottom ground wall of the waveguide housing, with its cap soldered to the lower end of the fin. The waveguide wall serves as a heat sink. For better heat dissipation, a copper heat sink can be threaded to the waveguide wall beneath the diode. Bias reaches the diode through the metallic fin. The fin is insulated from the metal housing by a thin dielectric (e.g., Teflon™) foil. When a varactor diode is incorporated for electronic tuning, a dc block in the form of a vertical slit is provided to separate its bias line from that of the Gunn diode (Fig. 9.54(c, d)). The circuits are shown with noncontacting shorting plungers for mechanical tuning.

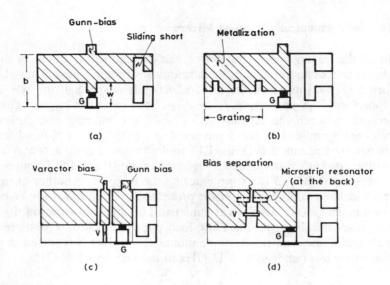

Fig. 9.54 Schematic representations of some types of fin-line oscillator
circuits due to:
      (a) Knochel [97]
      (b) Hofmann [98]
      (c) Cohen [99]
      (d) Solbach [101]

Figure 9.54(a) shows a basic oscillator circuit due to Knochel [97]. In
this circuit, the portion of the fin line to the right of the diode forms a
resonant cavity. The slot width w of the resonating section affects the
tuning range and the circuit efficiency in a complementary manner. Specifically, choosing a small value for w provides for wider tuning range, but
at the expense of degradation in the Q-factor, and hence lower efficiency.
For best circuit efficiency, the Q-factor of the cavity is maximized by setting
w equal to the full height of the waveguide. The conducting strip bridging
the diode to the fin provides for the impedance transformation of the active
element. The dimensions of the strip, therefore, depend rather critically
on the reactive part of the diode impedance.

A different operating principle is involved in the grating oscillator design
of Hofmann [98] (Fig. 9.54(b)). In this oscillator, the frequency of oscil-
lation is determined mainly by the stopband frequency of the periodic
structure, which, in turn, depends on the distance between the stubs. The

impedance transformation ratio is essentially determined by the length and number of stubs. The design, however, requires a fairly long grating structure for achieving optimal circuit efficiency.

A fin-line oscillator incorporating wideband mechanical tuning, and also varactor tuning for FM capability, has been presented by Cohen [99]. The main features are sketched in Fig. 9.54(c). The circuit shows two dc blocks in the form of vertical slits in the fin. They are spaced by about a quarter-wavelength. The variable short behind the diode provides the necessary reactive termination. Oscillator circuits of this type operating up to 100 GHz have been demonstrated [99]. Above 80 GHz, the oscillators use an additional resonant cap between the fin and the top of the Gunn diode package. A different configuration of a varactor-tuned Gunn oscillator due to Solbach *et al.* [100, 101] is sketched in Fig. 9.54(d). The circuit incorporates a single short-circuited stub loaded with a varactor. A microstrip resonator printed on the back of the substrate provides the short-circuit termination. A narrow slit in the fin above the stub serves as a dc block. The equivalent circuit of Fig. 9.54(d) is shown in Fig. 9.55. The portion of the circuit between the diode and the short-circuit stub behaves like a half-wavelength resonator. The stub, along with the section of line of length l_1, provides the necessary impedance transformation to match the source element to the output guide. With this type of circuit, varactor tuning ranges of 700 MHz at 35 GHz and 400 MHz at 60 GHz have been reported [100].

For frequencies above about 70 GHz, Gunn oscillators operating in the second harmonic mode have been found to be more efficient and cost effective [93, 94]. Such oscillators require a reactive termination for the fundamental mode. In addition, a high impedance transformation ratio is needed to match the extremely low source impedance of the harmonic oscillator.

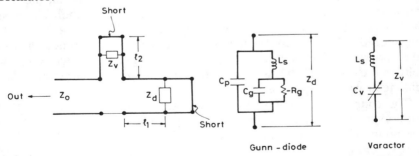

Fig. 9.55 Equivalent circuit representation of Gunn oscillator shown in Fig. 9.54(d) (after Solbach *et al.* [100]).

A fin-line oscillator using a FET device has been reported by Meinel [102]. The device is mounted at a fin-line T-junction, as shown in Fig. 9.56. Beam-lead FETs are particularly suitable for such circuits. The oscillator, in its harmonic mode of operation, is reported to deliver an output of 3 mW at 30 GHz with 4% efficiency.

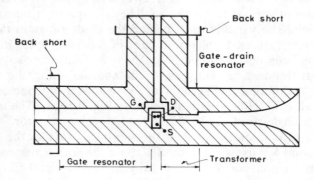

Fig. 9.56 Fin-line FET oscillator ·
(From Meinel [102], first presented at the 11th European Microwave Conference, reprinted with permission.)

9.10 ISOLATORS

Isolators and circulators are the two most useful nonreciprocal components required for integration in transmitters and receivers. A ferrite field-displacement isolator compatible with unilateral fin line was first introduced by Beyer and Solbach [103]. The structure is similar to the standard waveguide isolator, except that in a fin-line version, the magnetized ferrite slab is kept closer to the center of the waveguide, rather than near the waveguide wall. This is because in a unilateral fin-line the circularly magnetized field shifts to a plane nearer the center of the guide than in an empty waveguide. Such isolators, however, require a very high magnetic field on the order of 1800 A/cm at Ka band [104], and even larger at higher millimeter-wave frequencies.

The coupled-slot fin-line isolator proposed by Sillars and Davis [105] requires much lower dc magnetic fields, typically 160 A/cm for Ka-band operation. The basic guiding structure consists of an edge-coupled fin line loaded with a ferrite slab, as shown in Fig. 9.57. The slots are excited in the odd-mode, for which the x-axis represents an electric wall. The ferrite is magnetized parallel to the direction of propagation. This causes displacement of the field from one slot to the other. If a resistive card is placed on one slot, then, for the magnetic field applied in one direction,

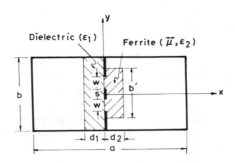

Fig. 9.57 Ferrite-loaded coupled-slot fin line.
(From Davis and Sillars [106], Copyright © 1985 IEEE, reprinted with permission.)

the wave is shifted to the slot covered with resistive card, thus offering high isolation; for the reverse orientation of the magnetic field, the wave is transmitted through the second slot without attenuation. In a practical device (Fig. 9.58), two ferrite slabs are placed on the coupled slots separated by a piece of resistive card covering only one slot. The two ferrite slabs are magnetized antiparallel by placing a bar magnet along each slab. The odd-mode is launched by feeding the coupled slots from a single slot by using a transition as shown in the figure. With this arrangement, the device exhibits a nonreciprocal behavior. The taper in the ferrite slabs and the resistive card are essentially used to provide better matching and reduce the losses. It has been pointed out that a small magnetic field produced by each magnet is adequate to saturate the ferrite slabs. A Ka-band isolator in this configuration is reported to give a maximum isolation of 41.5 dB with a 20 dB isolation bandwidth of 6.75 GHz [106].

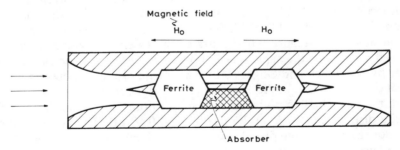

Fig. 9.58 Twin ferrite coupled-slot fin-line isolator.
(From Davis and Sillars [106], Copyright © 1985 IEEE, reprinted with permission.)

9.11 CIRCULATORS

A circulator using a fin-line Y-junction was first demonstrated by Meier [69]. The device is reported to give an isolation of 21 dB with an insertion loss of 0.5 dB at 70 GHz. Other versions of fin-line Y-junction circulators were subsequently reported [104, 107, 108]. Beyer and Wolff [104] made use of an antipodal fin-line Y-junction with three impedance transformers and a magnetized sphere at the center. An antipodal fin line with tapered fins can offer impedance transformation over a large range, typically from about 500 Ω for large slot widths to about 10 Ω for overlapping fins (Ch. 5). Furthermore, the main direction of the electric field near the slot gradually changes along the line. This property is utilized in the circulator.

E-plane circulators using unilateral and bilateral fin-line Y-junctions have been demonstrated by Braas and Schieblich [107]. In this type of circulator, a ferrite resonator disk is centered at the junction with a dc magnetic field applied perpendicular to the surface of the disk. Figure 9.59 shows the mounting arrangement along with the field patterns in the ferrite resonator. The TM_{11} mode of the resonator is coupled to the fin lines by means of their longitudinal magnetic field components. The ferrite resonator coupled to the bilateral fin-line slots is illustrated in Fig. 9.59(b, c) and to the unilateral fin-line slots in Fig. 9.59(d). The unilateral fin-line slots open at the resonator surface. With the use of quarter-wave transformers and optimization of the distance to the ferrite resonator, a 20 dB isolation bandwidth of about 10% with an insertion loss of 0.5 dB has been achieved at X band for this type of circulator [107]. One practical difficulty with such fin-line Y-junction circulators is that they are extremely sensitive to any asymmetries in the Y-junction and in the positioning of the ferrite disk. For symmetric operation of the circulator, the disk is required to be centered with a tolerance of about 10^{-3} with respect to a wavelength.

Improved bandwidth performance in Y-junction circulators has been realized by Goebel and Schieblich [109] using H-plane geometry near the ferrite resonator. Figure 9.60 illustrates the essential features of an improved version of the same quasi-H-plane fin-line circulator as reported later by Schieblich and Unger [110]. The ferrite disk is centered at the Y-junction by means of a dielectric ring. The slots entering the Y-junction from the three fin-line ports are bent so as to run nearly tangential to the ferrite disk, but away from the ferrite (Fig. 9.60(a)). The act of keeping the slots away from the disk that is close to the edge of the junction helps to reduce the tolerance problems. The electric field lines within the Y-junction bend out of the slots and become vertically aligned in the narrow space between the upper wall and the metalized layer of the substrate. Accordingly, the magnetic field lines become nearly parallel to the substrate. Thus, a gradual transition takes place from an E-plane to a H-plane

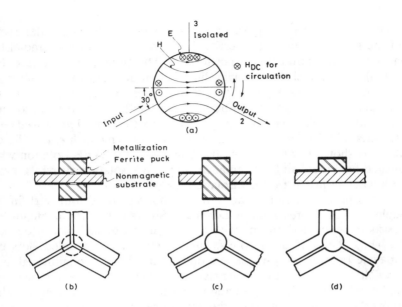

Fig. 9.59 Schematic diagram of field patterns in the ferrite resonator
(a), some configurations for mounting the resonator disk in
bilateral (b, c), and unilateral fin line (d).
(From Braas and Schieblich [107], *Electronics Letters*, 1981, Vol. 17, pp.
701–702, reprinted with permission of IEE.)

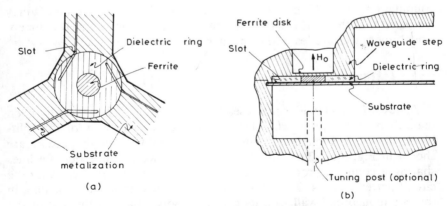

Fig. 9.60 Configuration of the quasi-H-plane fin-line circulator:
(a) top view of the Y-junction showing tangential slots;
(b) cross-sectional view of the Y-junction.
(Private communication with C. Schieblich and U. Goebel, reproduced
with permission.)

structure. The waveguide junction behaves essentially like a circular cavity, and the section between the ferrite disk and the slots forms a radial line that acts as a quarter-wave transformer. The tuning plunger (see Fig. 9.60(b)) acts as a shorted coaxial line section and helps to establish the resonance condition. By adjusting the plunger and the slot shape, the performance of the device can be optimized, either with respect to large bandwidth or high isolation. Figure 9.61 shows the typical measured characteristics of a K-band fin-line circulator due to Schieblich *et al.* The circulator is shown to offer about 30% bandwidth for 24 dB isolation when adjusted for broadband performance, and 30 dB isolation over 15% bandwidth when adjusted for high isolation.

A four-port circulator in the form of a nonreciprocal four-port fin-line coupler has been presented by Davis and Sillars [106]. The configuration consists of a coupled fin line with a piece of ferrite slab placed on both slots (Fig. 9.62). If the ferrite is unmagnetized, the coupled slots can propagate both the even-mode and odd-mode. When a longitudinal magnetic field is applied to the ferrite slab, the device acts like a nonreciprocal coupler. The nonreciprocal isolation can be improved by placing a dielectric overlay on the ferrite slab, thereby concentrating the field inside the ferrite. The direction of circulation can be reversed by reversing the direction of the applied magnetic field. The performance of a Ka-band circulator shows a 20 dB isolation bandwidth of 3.6 GHz at the coupling ports (S_{12}, S_{34}) with an insertion loss in the range from 2.5 to 3.5 dB at the transmission ports (S_{14}, S_{32}) [106]. The various parameters of this device are slot width = 0.2 mm, slot spacing = 1 mm, ferrite length = 30 mm, coupling length = 35 mm, and dc magnetic field H_0 = 160 A/cm. It may be noted that the ferrite slab is several wavelengths long and the dimensional tolerances are less stringent than for the fin-line circuit.

9.12 AMPLIFIER

A novel FET amplifier that uses fin-line technology has recently been realized by L'Ecuyer *et al.* [111]. The cross-sectional view of the split-block double-waveguide housing and the amplifier circuit pattern are shown in Fig. 9.63. The circuit makes use of two asymmetrical fin lines sharing a common broad wall, through which the substrate carrying the circuit pattern passes. The FET device is installed in a small opening in the common broad wall with its gate lead bonded across the slot of the lower asymmetrical fin line and its drain lead bonded across the slot of the upper asymmetrical fin line. The source pad is bonded to the printed circuit board. The fins in the lower and upper guides, which are located on opposite sides of the FET device, are gradually tapered to form tran-

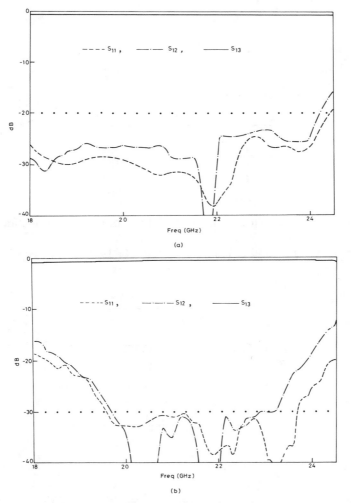

Fig. 9.61 Measured reflection (S_{11}), isolation (S_{12}), and transmission (S_{13}) characteristics of a K-band fin-line circulator (Fig. 9.60) adjusted for:

(a) broadband performance;

(b) high isolation;

ferrite disk material: Trans-Tech TT2-101

diameter = 3 mm, height = 1 mm

saturation magnetization = 0.3 T

surrounding dielectric material: Teflon®

(Private communication with C. Schieblich and U. Goebel, reproduced with permission.)

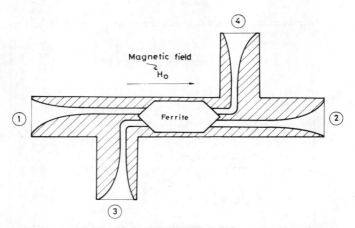

Fig. 9.62   Ferrite-loaded four-port fin-line coupler (cross-sectional view
              as in Fig. 9.57).
(From Davis and Sillars [106], Copyright © 1985 IEEE, reprinted with
permission.)

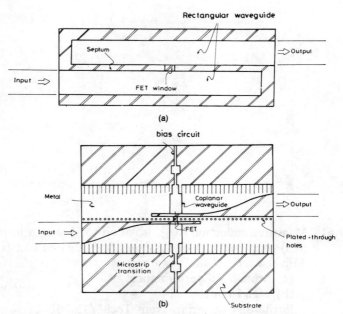

Fig. 9.63   (a) Split-block type of double-waveguide housing.
              (b) Amplifier circuit pattern.
(From Jean L'Ecuyer *et al.* [111], Copyright © 1986 IEEE, reprinted with
permission.)

sitions to input and output rectangular waveguides, respectively. The second port of each of the two asymmetrical fin lines is short-circuited at a distance of one quarter-wavelength beyond the FET terminals, so as to present an open circuit to the FET.

The bias circuit consists of a coplanar waveguide section running from the edge of the main slot to the outer broad wall of the guide, which then makes a transition to a microstrip line. The length of the coplanar section is half a wavelength at RF so as to reflect a short in series with the fin-line slot. The substrate incorporates a series of plated through-holes at the common broad wall junction. This prevents any RF coupling between the two waveguides through the substrate.

By using an NE67300 FET device and 0.01 inch thick RT-duroid™ substrate ($\epsilon_r = 2.22$), L'Ecuyer *et al.* [111] have reported a 17 GHz amplifier with a gain of 6 dB over a bandwidth of 1 GHz.

9.13 ANTENNAS

After the demonstration of the first fin-line antenna in 1978 by Meier [2], several theoretical and experimental investigations have been reported on similar antennas [112–115]. The configuration of a typical fin-line antenna is shown in Fig. 9.64. The protruding portion of the dielectric substrate with tapered fins forms the antenna. It is basically an end-fire traveling-wave antenna [112]. At the abrupt junction where the fin line ends, some energy is radiated from the waveguide aperture. This can cause distortion in the main lobe, and also raise the sidelobe levels of the radiation pattern. Reducing the slot width of the fin-line feeding point helps to reduce this stray radiation by concentrating the fields nearer the slot. The gain of the antenna and the bandwidth are influenced mainly by the length and contour of the taper.

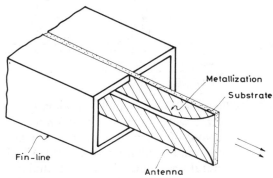

Fig. 9.64 Fin-line antenna.

By using tapers that are several wavelengths long, antenna gains in the range 10 to 15 dBi have been achieved [112, 113]. A linear taper with a flare angle of about 10° is reported to offer optimum results over nearly one octave bandwidth [112]. Even wider bandwidths can be achieved by using an exponential type of taper [114].

In order to obtain better sidelobe suppression, Beyer and Wolff [115] have presented a *Vivaldi antenna* using fin-line technology. The layout of the antenna for Ka band is shown in Fig. 9.65, along with its radiation patterns in unilateral as well as bilateral fin line. The fins are tapered such that the slot width at the end of the taper is larger than half a wavelength. The radiation patterns in the unilateral case are asymmetrical (Fig. 9.65(b)), whereas the patterns in the bilateral case are symmetrical (Fig. 9.65(c)). This is to be expected because the unilateral fin line is basically an asymmetrical structure, whereas the bilateral fin-line is a symmetrical structure.

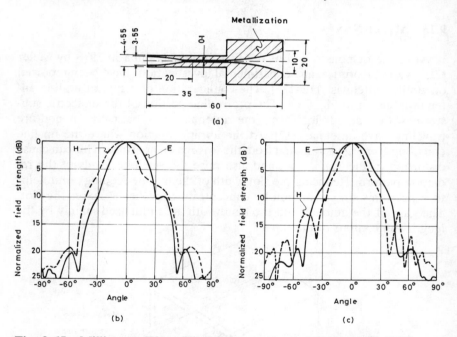

Fig. 9.65 Millimeter Wave Vivaldi—antenna on RT-duroid™ 5880 substrate with a thickness of 0.5 mm (f = 32 GHz):
  (a) layout of a Vivaldi antenna, dimensions in mm
  (b, c) radiation characteristics of a Vivaldi antenna in unilateral and bilateral fin-line technique, respectively.

(From Beyer and Wolff [115], Copyright © 1985 IEEE, reprinted with permission.)

It may be noted that the unilateral fin-line antenna shows better sidelobe suppression (about 20 dB) than is available in the bilateral case. The E- and H-plane beamwidths, however, are slightly larger than in the bilateral fin-line antenna.

REFERENCES

Directional Couplers
1. P.J. Meier, "Planar Multiport Millimeter Integrated Circuits," *IEEE MTT-S Int. Microwave Symp. Digest,* June 1977, pp. 385–388.
2. P.J. Meier, "Millimeter Integrated Circuits Suspended in the E-Plane of Rectangular Waveguide," *IEEE Trans. Microwave Theory Tech.,* Vol. MTT-26, pp. 726–733, Oct. 1978.
3. P.J. Meier, "E-Plane W-Band Printed Circuit Balanced Mixer," *IEEE Trans. Microwave Theory Tech.,* Vol. MTT-31, pp. 227–230, Feb. 1983.
4. L.D. Cohen and P.J. Meier, "Advances in E-Plane Printed Milli-meter-Wave Circuits," *IEEE MTT-S Int. Microwave Symp. Digest,* June 1978, pp. 27–29.
5. F. Arndt, J. Bornemann, D. Grauerholz, and R. Vahldieck, "Material and Circuit Evaluation for Millimeter-Wave Applications: 3 dB Fin-Line Printed Probe Coupler for 31 GHz," *ESA Journal,* Vol. 5, pp. 243–247, 1981.
6. N.P. Sharma, "Studies on Integrated Fin-Line Discontinuities and Printed Probe Coupler," Master's of Technology Thesis, Department of Electrical Engineering, Indian Institute of Technology, New Delhi, July 1983.
7. R.N. Bates, S.J. Nightingale, and P.M. Ballard, Millimeter-Wave E-Plane Components and Subsystems, *The Radio and Electronic Engineer,* Vol. 52, pp. 506–512, Nov.-Dec. 1982.
8. F.C. De Ronde, A New Class of Microstrip Directional Couplers, *IEEE MTT-S Int. Microwave Symp. Digest,* May 1970, pp. 184–186.
9. H. El. Hennawy, R. Knochel, and K. Schunemann, "Wideband Branchline Couplers in Fin-Line Technology," *Arch. Elek. Ubertragung.,* Vol. 37, pp. 40–46, Jan.-Feb. 1983.
10. H. Callsen and L.P. Schmidt, "Quasiplanar 3 dB Hybrid for Millimeter-Wave Integrated Circuits," *Electron. Lett.,* Vol. 18, No. 4, pp. 161–163, Feb. 1982.
11. B. Schiek, "Hybrid Branchline Couplers—A Useful New Class of Directional Couplers," *IEEE Trans. Microwave Theory Tech.,* Vol. MTT-22, pp. 864–869, Oct. 1974.

12. H. Callsen, L.P. Schmidt, and K. Solbach, "Breitbandige Finlei-tungs-Richtkoppler," *Wiss. Ber. AEG Telefunken,* No. 54, pp. 241–250, 1981.

13. A. Beyer, D. Kother, and I. Wolff, "Development of a Coupler in Fin-Line Technique," *IEEE MTT-S Int. Microwave Symp. Digest,* June 1985, pp. 139–142.

14. E. Kpodzo, K. Schunemann, and G. Begemann, "A Quadriphase Fin-Line Modulator," *IEEE Trans. Microwave Theory Tech.,* Vol. MTT-28, pp. 747–752, July 1980.

15. P. Nagpal, "Analysis of Double-Dielectric Fin-Line and Develop-ment of Fin-Line Filters and Couplers," Master's of Technology The-sis, Department of Electrical Engineering, Indian Institute of Technology, New Delhi, July 1983.

16. P.H. Vartanian *et al.,* "Propagation in Dielectric Slab-Loaded Rec-tangular Waveguide," *IRE Trans. Microwave Theory Tech.,* Vol. MTT-6, pp. 215–222, April 1958.

17. E.S. Hensperger, "The Design of Multi-hole Coupling Arrays," *Mi-crowave Journal,* Vol. 2, pp. 38–42, Aug. 1959.

18. R.E. Collin, *Foundations of Microwave Engineering,* McGraw-Hill, New York, 1966.

19. K. Kurokawa, *An Introduction to the Theory of Microwave Circuits,* Academic Press, New York, 1969.

20. R. Rudokas and T. Itoh, "Passive Millimeter-Wave IC Components Made of Inverted Strip Dielectric Waveguides," *IEEE Trans. Mi-crowave Theory Tech.,* Vol. MTT-24, pp. 978–981, Dec. 1976.

Power Dividers

21. H. Hofmann, H. Meinel, and B. Adelseck, "New Integrated mm-wave Components Using Fin-Lines," *IEEE MTT-S Int. Microwave Symp. Digest,* June 1978, pp. 21–23.

Filters

22. C. Nguyen and K. Chang, "Millimeter-Wave Low Loss Fin-Line Low-Pass Filters," *Electron. Lett.,* Vol. 20, No. 24, pp. 1010–1011, Nov. 1984.

23. J. Reindel, "Printed WG Circuits Trim Component Costs," *Micro-waves,* pp. 60–63, Oct. 1980.

24. P.J. Meier, "Integrated Fin-Line Millimeter Components," *IEEE Trans. Microwave Theory Tech.,* Vol. MTT-22, pp. 1209–1216, Dec. 1974.

25. Y. Tajima and Y. Sawayama, "Design and Analysis of a Waveguide-Sandwich Microwave Filter," *IEEE Trans. Microwave Theory Tech.,* Vol. MTT-22, pp. 839–841, Sept. 1974.

26. Y. Konishi and K. Uenakada, "The Design of a Band-Pass Filter with Inductive Strip-Planar Circuit Mounted in Waveguide," *IEEE Trans. Microwave Theory Tech.*, Vol. MTT-22, pp. 869–873, Oct. 1974.

27. A.M.K. Saad and K. Schunemann, "Design and Performance of Fin-Line Band-Pass Filters," *9th Eur. Microwave Conf. Digest*, Sept. 1979, pp. 397–401.

28. K. Solbach, "The Status of Printed mm-wave E-Plane Circuits," *IEEE Trans. Microwave Theory Tech.*, Vol. MTT-31, pp. 107–121, Feb. 1983.

29. F. Arndt, J. Bornemann, D. Grauerholz, and R. Vahldieck, "Material and Circuit Evaluation for Millimeter-Wave Applications: High-Q Fin-Line Filters for Millimeter Waves," *ESA Journal*, Vol. 5, pp. 33–42, 1981.

30. J. Bornemann, R. Vahldieck, F. Arndt, and D. Grauerholz, "Optimized Low Insertion Loss Millimeter-Wave Fin-Line and Metal Insert Filters," *The Radio and Electronic Engineer*, Vol. 52, pp. 513–521, Nov.-Dec. 1982.

31. F. Arndt, J. Bornemann, D. Grauerholz, and R. Vahldieck, "Theory and Design of Low Insertion Loss Fin-Line Filters," *IEEE Trans. Microwave Theory Tech.*, Vol. MTT-30, pp. 155–163, Feb. 1982.

32. Y.C. Shih, T. Itoh, and L.Q. Bui, "Computer-Aided Design of Millimeter-Wave E-Plane Filters," *IEEE Trans. Microwave Theory Tech.*, Vol. MTT-31, pp. 135–142, Feb. 1983.

33. R. Vahldieck, J. Bornemann, F. Arndt, and D. Grauerholz, "Optimized Waveguide E-Plane Metal Insert Filters for Millimeter Wave Applications," *IEEE Trans. Microwave Theory Tech.*, Vol. MTT-31, pp. 65–69, Jan. 1983.

34. Y.C. Shih and T. Itoh, "E-Plane Filters with Finite-Thickness Septa," *IEEE Trans. Microwave Theory Tech.*, Vol. MTT-31, pp. 1009–1013, Dec. 1983.

35. Y.C. Shih, "Design of Waveguide E-Plane Filters with All-Metal Inserts," *IEEE Trans. Microwave Theory Tech.*, Vol. MTT-32, pp. 695–704, July 1984.

36. D.W. Ball and L.Q. Bui, "E-Plane Filters Designed for Millimeter Use," *Microwave Systems Design Handbook*, 1983, pp. 290–291.

37. J. Bornemann, F. Arndt, R. Vahldieck, and D. Grauerholz, "Double Planar Integrated Millimeter-Wave Filter," *13th Eur. Microwave Conf. Proc.*, 1983, pp. 168–173.

38. F. Arndt, J. Bornemann, R. Vahldieck, and D. Grauerholz, "E-Plane Integrated Circuit Filters with Improved Stopband Attenuation," *IEEE Trans. Microwave Theory Tech.*, Vol. MTT-32, pp.

1391–1394, Oct. 1984. *See also* correction in *IEEE Trans. Microwave Theory Tech.,* Vol. MTT-33, p. 437, May 1985.

39. R. Vahldieck and W.J.R. Hoefer, "A New Class of Optimized Fin-Line and E-Plane Metal Insert Filters with Improved Characteristics," *IEEE MTT-S Int. Microwave Symp. Digest,* June 1985, pp. 182–184.

40. A.S. Omar and K. Schunemann, "Realizations and Design of Band-Stop Filters," *13th Eur. Microwave Conf. Digest,* 1983, pp. 157–162.

41. A.S. Omar, H. El. Hennawy, and K. Schunemann, "Filter Realizations with Fin-Lines," *IEEE MTT-S Int. Microwave Symp. Digest,* June 1983, pp. 160–162.

42. G.L. Matthaei, L. Young, and E.M.T. Jones, *Microwave Filters, Impedance-Matching Networks, and Coupling Structures,* Artech House, Dedham, MA, 1980.

43. P.J. Meier, "Equivalent Relative Permittivity and Unloaded Q-Factor of Integrated Fin-Line," *Electron. Lett.,* Vol. 9, No. 7, pp. 162–163, April 1973.

44. R.E. Collin, *Field Theory of Guided Waves,* McGraw-Hill, New York, 1960.

45. H. Patzelt and F. Arndt, "Double-Plane Steps in Rectangular Waveguides and their Application for Transformers, Irises, and Filters," *IEEE Trans. Microwave Theory Tech.,* Vol. MTT-30, pp. 771–777, May 1982.

46. R. Mittra and S.W. Lee, *Analytical Techniques in the Theory of Guided Waves,* Macmillan, London, 1971.

47. C.F. Vanblaricum, Jr., and R. Mittra, "A Modified Residue-Calculus Technique for Solving a Class of Boundary Value Problems—Part II: Waveguide Phased Arrays, Modulated Surfaces, and Diffraction Gratings," *IEEE Trans. Microwave Theory Tech.,* Vol. MTT-17, pp. 310–319, June 1969.

Attenuators and Switches

48. J.F. White, *Microwave Semiconductor Engineering,* Van Nostrand Reinhold, New York, 1982.

49. P.J. Meier, "Integrated Fin-Line Millimeter Components," *IEEE MTT-S Int. Microwave Symp. Digest,* 1977, pp. 195–196.

50. H. Meinel and B. Rembold, "New Millimeter-Wave Fin-Line Attenuators and Switches," *IEEE MTT-S Int. Microwave Symp. Digest,* 1979, pp. 249–252.

51. W. Menzel and H. Callsen, "Integrated Fin-Line Components and Subsystems at 60 and 94 GHZ," *IEEE Trans. Microwave Theory Tech.,* Vol. MTT-31, pp. 142–146, Feb. 1983.

52. H. El. Hennawy and K. Schunemann, "New Structures for Imped-
    ance Transformation in Fin-Lines," *IEEE MTT-S Int. Microwave
    Symp. Digest*, 1982, pp. 198–200.
53. H. Callsen, "Fin-Line PIN-Diode Attenuator and Switch for the 140
    GHz Range," *8th Int. Conf. on Infrared and Millimeter Waves Digest*,
    Dec. 1983, pp. F 3.4/1–2.
54. H. Meinel, B. Adelseck, and H. Callsen, "A Survey of Planar In-
    tegrated mm-wave Components," *Military Microwaves Conf. Digest*,
    1980, pp. 82–87.
55. H. Meinel and H. Callsen, "Fin-Line PIN-Diode Attenuators and
    Switches for the 94 GHz Range," *Electron. Lett.*, Vol. 18, No. 13,
    pp. 541–542, June 1982.
56. B. Adelseck *et al.*, "A Survey of Planar Integrated Millimeter-Wave
    Components," *The Radio and Electronic Engineer*, Vol. 52, No. 1,
    pp. 46–50, 1982.
57. H. El. Hennawy and K. Schunemann, "Computer-Aided Design of
    Fin-Line Detectors, Modulators and Switches," *Arch. Elek. Uber-
    tragung.*, Vol. 36, pp. 49–56, Feb. 1982.
58. L.W. Koh, I.M.H. Williamson, M.L. Nyss, O. Gadoury, and D.E.
    Wheeler, "Ka-band Fin-Line SPDT Switch," *Microwave Journal*,
    Vol. 26, pp. 105–107, June 1983.
59. W. Menzel, H. Meinel, B. Rembold, and L.P. Schmidt, "Planar
    Integrated Components Perform up to 110 GHz," *Microwave System
    News*, pp. 92–100, Nov. 1982.

Detectors
60. H. Meinel and L.P. Schmidt, "High Sensitivity Millimeter-Wave De-
    tectors Using Fin-Line Technology," *5th Int. Conf. on Infrared and
    Millimeter Waves Digest*, 1980, pp. 133–135.
61. H. El. Hennawy and K. Schunemann, "Computer-Aided Design of
    Semiconductor Mounts in Fin-Line Technology," *IEEE MTT-S Int.
    Microwave Symp. Digest*, 1981, pp. 307–309.

Modulators
62. E. Kpodzo, K. Schunemann, and H. El. Hennawy, "A Quadriphase
    Modulator in Fin-Line Technique," *IEEE MTT-S Int. Microwave
    Symp. Digest*, 1979, pp. 119–121.
63. C. Schieblich, U. Goebel, and V. Beres, "Broadband Reflection Type
    Phase Modulators," *IEEE MTT-S Int. Microwave Symp. Digest*,
    1983, pp. 510–512.
64. W. Thorpe, "An E-Plane Broadband Bi-phase Balanced Modulator
    for Ka-band," *IEEE MTT-S Int. Microwave Symp. Digest*, 1983, pp.
    513–515.

65. W. Thorpe and J.D. Gilliland, "29 GHz E-plane Bi-phase Modulator," *Electron. Lett.,* Vol. 19, No. 3, pp. 107–109, Feb. 1983.

66. R. Mehran, L. Ludewig, and L. Szabo, "Integrated Ka-band Fin-Line Mixer/Modulator," *Electron. Lett.,* Vol. 20, No. 22, pp. 934–935, Oct. 1984.

67. T.A. Dorschner, "Characterization of Reflection Phase Modulators Using Hyperbolic Geometry," *3rd Eur. Microwave Conf. Proc.,* 1973, pp. A.9.1–A.9.4.

Mixers

68. P.J. Meier, "New Developments with Integrated Fin-Line and Related Printed Millimeter Circuits," *IEEE MTT-S Int. Microwave Symp. Digest,* 1975, pp. 143–145.

69. P.J. Meier, "Integrated Fin-Line—A Versatile and Proven Millimeter Transmission Line," *Microwave Journal,* Vol. 19, pp. 24–25, Nov. 1976.

70. Y. Konishi, "Planar Circuit Mounted in Waveguide Used as a Downconverter," *IEEE Trans. Microwave Theory Tech.,* Vol. MTT-26, pp. 716–719, Oct. 1978.

71. Y. Konishi, K. Uenakada, N. Yazawa, N. Hoshino, and T. Takahashi, "Simplified 12-GHz Low-Noise Converter with Mounted Planar Circuit in Waveguide," *IEEE Trans. Microwave Theory Tech.,* Vol. MTT-22, pp. 451–454, April 1974.

72. P.J. Meier, "E-Plane Components for a 94 GHz Printed-Circuit Balanced Mixer," *IEEE MTT-S Int. Microwave Symp. Digest,* 1980, pp. 267–269.

73. J.S. Wong and K.I. Chung, "A Ka-band Orthogonal Hybrid Fin-Line Mixer," *IEEE MTT-S Int. Microwave Symp. Digest,* 1982, pp. 379–381.

74. U.H. Gysel, "A 26.5 to 40 GHz Planar Balanced Mixer," *5th Eur. Microwave Conf. Proc.,* 1975, pp. 491–495.

75. R.N. Bates and M.D. Coleman, "Millimeter-Wave Fin-Line Balanced Mixers," *9th Eur. Microwave Conf. Proc.,* 1979, pp. 721–725.

76. W. Menzel, "A 140 GHz Balanced Mixer for Fin-Line Integrated Circuits," *13th Eur. Microwave Conf. Proc.,* 1983, pp. 179–182.

77. W. Menzel and H. Callsen, "94 GHz Balanced Fin-Line Mixer," *Electron. Lett.,* Vol. 18, No. 1, pp. 5–6, Jan. 1982.

78. G. Begemann, "An X-band Balanced Fin-Line Mixer," *IEEE Trans. Microwave Theory Tech.,* Vol. MTT-26, pp. 1007–1011, Dec. 1978.

79. P.J. Meier, "4 and 5 mm-band Printed Circuit Balanced Mixers," *Microwave Journal,* Vol. 22, pp. 66–68, Aug. 1979.

80. P.M. Ballard, "Waveguide-Bandwidth Millimetric Mixer with IF to 18 GHz," *Electron. Lett.,* Vol. 19, No. 2, pp. 46–47, Jan. 1983.

81. L. Bui and D. Ball, "Broadband Planar Balanced Mixers for Milli-meter-Wave Applications," *IEEE MTT-S Int. Microwave Symp. Digest,* 1982, pp. 204–205.

82. R.N. Bates, M.D. Coleman, S.J. Nightingale, and R. Davies, "E-Planes Drop Millimeter Costs," *Microwave System News,* Vol. 10, pp. 74–80, Dec. 1980.

83. R.N. Bates, R.K. Surridge, J.G. Summers, and J.M. Woodcock, "Millimeter-Wave Low Noise E-Plane Balanced Mixers Incorporating Planar MBE GaAs Mixer Diodes," *IEEE MTT-S Int. Microwave Symp. Digest,* 1982, pp. 13–15.

84. R. Mehran, J. Ludewig, and L. Szabo, "Integrated Ka-band Fin-Line Mixer/Modulator," *Electron. Lett.,* Vol. 20, No. 22, pp. 934–935, Oct. 1984.

85. D.W. Ball and L.Q. Bui, "Wideband mm-wave Mixers for EW Applications," *Microwave Journal,* Vol. 25, pp. 65–76, June 1982.

86. R.S. Tahim, G.M. Hayashibara, and K. Chang, "Design and Performance of W-band Broadband Integrated Circuit Mixers," *IEEE Trans. Microwave Theory Tech.,* Vol. MTT-31, pp. 277–283, March 1983.

87. R.S. Tahim, G.M. Hayashibara, and K. Chang, "W-band Broadband Integrated Circuit Mixers," *Electron. Lett.,* Vol. 18, No. 11, pp. 471–473, May 1982.

88. B. Bhat and S.K. Koul, "Unified Approach to Solve a Class of Strip- and Microstrip-like Transmission Lines," *IEEE Trans. Microwave Theory Tech.,* Vol. MTT-30, pp. 679–686, May 1982. *See also* correction in Vol. MTT-30, p. 2067, Nov. 1982.

89. R. Knochel and A. Schlegel, "Octave-band Double-Balanced Integrated Fin-Line Mixers at mm-wavelengths," *10th Eur. Microwave Conf. Digest,* 1980, pp. 722–726.

90. A. Blaisdell, R. Geoffroy, and H. Howe, "A Novel Broadband Double-Balanced Mixer for the 18–40 GHz Range," *IEEE MTT-S Int. Microwave Symp. Digest,* 1982, pp. 33–35.

91. G. Begemann, "A Subharmonically Pumped Fin-Line Mixer for Satellite TV Receiver Applications," *IEEE MTT-S Int. Microwave Symp. Digest,* 1981, pp. 454–456.

92. P.J. Meier, "Wideband Subharmonically Pumped W-band Mixer," *IEEE MTT-S Int. Microwave Symp. Digest,* 1982, pp. 201–203.

Oscillators
93. H. Barth, "141 GHz Generation by a GaAs Gunn Oscillator Upconverter Chain," *IEEE MTT-S Int. Microwave Symp. Digest,* 1982, pp. 364–366.

94. K. Solbach, F. Sicking, and H. Barth, "Harmonic Gunn Oscillators Allow Frequency Growth," *Microwaves and RF,* Vol. 22, pp. 75–80, 127, April 1983.

95. T.G. Ruttan, "Gunn Oscillator at 95 GHz," *Electron. Lett.,* Vol. 11, No. 13, pp. 293–294, July 1975.

96. J.E. Carlstrom, R.L. Plambeck, and D.D. Thornton, "A Continuously Tunable 65–115 GHz Gunn Oscillator," *IEEE Trans. Microwave Theory Tech.,* Vol. MTT-33, pp. 610–619, July 1985.

97. R. Knochel, "Design and Performance of Microwave Oscillators in Integrated Fin-Line Technique," *Microwaves, Optics and Acoustics,* Vol. 3, No. 3, pp. 115–120, May 1979.

98. H. Hofmann, "mm-wave Gunn Oscillator with Distributed Feedback Fin-Line Circuit," *IEEE MTT-S Int. Microwave Symp. Digest,* 1980, pp. 59–61.

99. L.D. Cohen, "Advances in Printed Millimeter-Wave Oscillator Circuits," *IEEE MTT-S Int. Microwave Symp. Digest,* 1980, pp. 264–266.

100. K. Solbach, B. Adelseck, and F. Sicking, "Fin-Line Varactor-Tuned Gunn Oscillators for 35 and 90 GHz," *Mikrowellen Magazin,* Vol. 9, No. 1, pp. 64–66, 1983.

101. K. Solbach, "35 GHz Varactor-Tuned Fin-Line Gunn Oscillator," *12th Eur. Microwave Conf. Digest,* 1982, pp. 697–701.

102. H. Meinel, "A 30 GHz FET Oscillator Using Fin-Line Circuitry," *11th Eur. Microwave Conf. Digest,* 1981, pp. 297–300.

Isolators

103. A. Beyer and K. Solbach, "A New Fin-Line Ferrite Isolator for Integrated Millimeter-Wave Circuits," *IEEE Trans. Microwave Theory Tech.,* Vol. MTT-29, pp. 1344–1348, Dec. 1981.

104. A. Beyer and I. Wolff, "A Fin-Line Isolator and Circulator for the R-band," *11th Eur. Microwave Conf. Digest,* 1981, pp. 321–326.

105. D.B. Sillars and L.E. Davis, "Coupled Slot Fin-Line Isolators," *Electron. Lett.,* Vol. 21, No. 3, pp. 97–98, Jan. 1985.

106. L.E. Davis and D.B. Sillars, "Millimetric Non-reciprocal Coupled-Slot Fin-Line Components," *IEEE MTT-S Int. Microwave Symp. Digest,* 1985, pp. 238–238.

Circulators

107. M. Braas and C. Schieblich, "E-type Circulator for Fin-Lines," *Electron. Lett.,* Vol. 17, No. 19, pp. 701–702, Sept. 1981.

108. U. Goebel and C. Schieblich, "Broadband Fin-Line Circulators," *IEEE MTT-S Int. Microwave Symp. Digest,* 1982, pp. 249–251.

109. U. Goebel and C. Schieblich, "Broadband Fin Line Circulators," *IEEE MTT-S Int. Microwave Symp. Digest,* pp. 249–251, 1982

110. C. Schieblich and H.G. Unger, "Fin Line Ferrite Devices," *Microcoll Conf. Digest* (Budapest), pp. 215–218, 1986.

Amplifier

111. Jean L'Ecuyer, G.B. Gajda, and W.J.R. Hoefer, "A FET Amplifier in Fin-Line Technique," *IEEE MTT-S Int. Microwave Symp. Digest,* 1986, pp. 287–288.

Antennas

112. T. Thungren, E.L. Kollberg, and K.S. Yngvesson, "Vivaldi Antennas for Single Beam Integrated Receivers," *12th Eur. Microwave Conf. Digest,* 1982, pp. 361–366.

113. A. Beyer, "Millimeter-Wave Antenna in Fin-Line Technique," *3rd Int. Conf. on Antennas and Propagation (ICAP) Digest,* 1983, pp. 44–46.

114. P.J. Gibson, "The Vivaldi-Aerial," *9th Eur. Microwave Conf. Digest,* 1979, pp. 101–105.

115. A. Beyer and I. Wolff, "Investigations on Millimeter-Wave Antennas in Fin-Line Technique," *Proc. Int. Symp. on Antennas and Propagation,* 1985, pp. 65–68.

Index